THE SCIENCE OF MOVEMENT

Also by R. A. R. Tricker

THE ASSESSMENT OF SCIENTIFIC SPECULATION
BORES, BREAKERS, WAVES, AND WAKES

THE SCIENCE
OF MOVEMENT

R. A. R. Tricker
B. J. K. Tricker

AMERICAN ELSEVIER PUBLISHING COMPANY, INC.
NEW YORK 1967

© *R. A. R. Tricker*
© *B. J. K. Tricker*
AMERICAN ELSEVIER PUBLISHING COMPANY, INC.
52 Vanderbilt Avenue
New York 10017 New York

LIBRARY OF CONGRESS CATALOG CARD NUMBER 67–14270

Made and printed in Great Britain

Science appears to us with a very different aspect after we have found out that it is not in lecture-rooms only, and by means of the electric light projected on a screen, that we may witness physical phenomena, but that we may find illustrations of the highest doctrines of science in games and gymnastics, in travelling by land and by water, in storms of the air and of the sea, and wherever there is matter in motion.

James Clerk Maxwell

Inaugural lecture as
Cavendish Professor of Physics
University of Cambridge

Contents

List of Plates

Preface

T HE aim which the authors had before them in writing this book was to produce a study of mechanics that would be of greater interest and appeal than some which is commonly undertaken. As its title implies, the book deals with the science of movement and, though mathematics is not avoided, the emphasis is always on the science of the subject. Many of the topics included, such as rotational dynamics, would ordinarily be looked upon as suitable only for advanced students. By adopting an experimental approach, however, it has been possible to make the study suitable for a first reading. The book is written, nevertheless, for serious students, and it is hoped that it will prove useful to any wishing to understand something of the principles of the science of movement. It is hoped, too, that the approach adopted will illustrate the importance of this science in phenomena met with in everyday life. One of the reasons that more abstract courses sometimes make little appeal is that they seem to have no obvious relevance to decisions which the reader feels he is ever likely to be called upon to make.

The science of movement is drawn largely from physics and biology, but the book is not divided into separate sections since the two sciences interlock at so many points. There is also an important area of common ground with athletics to which a good deal of attention is paid; the two fields illuminate each other. Without an adequate knowledge of the mechanics of his art, the athlete is unlikely to excel. On the contrary, he is in fact very liable to be led astray by old wives' tales and unscientific attitudes. The scientist also gains by seeing the principles of his subject in operation. The authors have tried on the one hand to provide the athlete and games player with enough of the science of mechanics to enable them to make intelligent attempts to improve their performances, and on the other to allow the ordinary student of mechanics to understand the wide applications and the importance of his subject.

Except where it is stated to be otherwise, all the experiments described have been performed by the authors specially for the book, and the ciné films and still photographs have been taken by one or other of them for the purpose. The athletes whose performances have been recorded were students at school or college. All were competent performers, able to demonstrate the particular points it was desired to discuss. The thanks of the authors are especially due to the Principal, Staff, and Students of the Lady Mabel College of Physical Education who gave very generously of their time to provide demonstrations for photography. Help was also given by Saint Luke's College, Exeter. Many of the athletic performances were by pupils of one of the authors, and they also co-operated in many of the experiments. Some parts of the book have formed the basis for a series of broadcasts by ATV.

The authors' thanks are due to Mr J. Armstrong, of University College,

London, for permission to publish Plate IV (vii); to Dr E. G. Gray for Plate IV (viii); to Dr D. Harrison for Plate V (ii) (A); to Professor R. Miledi for Plate V (ii) (B); to Professor D. Smith for Plate V (ii) (C); to Dr H. E. Huxley, F.R.S., for Plate V (ii) (D); and to the Gernsheim Collection and the Hulton Picture Library for Plate XV (ii).

The authors would also like to express their appreciation of the assistance of Mr F. Barlow for the loan of the specimen for Plate IV (i) (B); of Miss B. Rodgers, of Long Close Stables, Eton Wick, for help with Plate IX (iv) and Fig. XI (1); of Mr H. E. Aubrey Fletcher for the apparatus producing Plates X (ii–vi); of Mr R. Edmead, owner of the tawny owls used for Plate XII (i); of Mr M. E. Howard for photographing the dissection in Plate XVI (i); of Mr J. S. Carter in connection with Plates XIX (iii–vii); and of Mr A. Goodier for help with Fig. V (4).

B.J.K.T.
R.A.R.T.
Cropston, Leicestershire

CHAPTER I

The Problems of Movement

H o w to explain movement and change was a problem which attracted the attention of men from the time of the Ancient Greeks onwards, and the ideas which the Greeks put forward dominated the stage for some 2,000 years. The explanations adopted in the Middle Ages were largely based upon the writings of Aristotle, who lived from 384 to 322 B.C. His doctrines were available partly as the result of tradition, more or less continuous from the time of the Roman Empire, and partly as the result of the rediscovery of the classics which led up to the Renaissance in Europe in the fourteenth to the sixteenth centuries. Though some of Aristotle's views had been questioned earlier, it was not until the sixteenth and seventeenth centuries that the problems of movement came to be seen from the modern point of view. Many were involved in the preliminary discussions leading to this development, but the two most outstanding figures in what came to be a scientific revolution were Galileo Galilei (1564–1642) in Italy, and Sir Isaac Newton (1642–1727) in England. It was the great change in the theory of movement, initiated by these men, which has since formed the basis for the modern scientific age, to which it, indeed, gave birth.

Two factors account for the very long period of gestation undergone by the theory of movement prior to this, quite apart from the difficulties introduced by the gradual dissolution of the Roman Empire through barbarian invasions and the consequent destruction of libraries and schools. The first of these reasons is that Aristotle produced not only a theory of movement but a complete synthesis accounting for the working of the entire universe, which appeared so satisfactory that it seemed impossible that it could be wrong, except perhaps in a few, more or less unimportant details. His account seemed so generally satisfactory that it was written into the doctrines of the Church, largely on the initiative of St Thomas Aquinas (c. 1225–74). Into this great theory of the universe Aristotle's theory of movement was dovetailed, so that to change the theory of movement meant, in effect, abandoning Aristotle's complete scheme of things. It was as though, today, we were asked to abandon our picture of the universe of the fixed stars, the solar system, the atomic theory of matter, and the whole scientific picture of the world which we now inherit from infancy, in order to improve one aspect in what could not have appeared to be anything more than a minor area of the whole. It is thus, perhaps, not altogether surprising that it was 2,000 years before this reformulation was achieved.

The second factor which contributed a good deal to the difficulty experienced by those living in ancient and medieval times in arriving at a better theory of movement was that their own experience of movement was so very limited. Today we are accustomed to being started and stopped in buses and trains, whisked away in sports cars or aeroplanes possessing accelerations fit to break one's back, cornered at high speed so that we are thrown violently to the side, or carried aloft in express lifts, all of which experiences bring us into direct and obvious contact with the laws of motion. We can feel what it is like to be accelerated or to be made to traverse a curved path, but these experiences were largely denied to the ancient and medieval worlds and indeed it was not until very modern times that they became available. The laws of motion had to be arrived at by close study without any immediate or forceful experience to point the way. Statements which to us may appear to be almost a matter of common sense could only be made as the result of careful observation, and it was by no means clear what had to be looked for. The most violent motions to which men of the ancient and medieval worlds were subjected were those arising from horse riding, and these were not sufficiently violent to render the important considerations obvious. In retracing the arguments today it is possible to call upon direct experience to help to elucidate the problem.

Aristotle divided motion into two classes. There were things which were heavy and which, by their nature, tried to find a place as near to the centre of the earth as possible. Things were thought to possess desires, as human beings, and strove to attain their ends. The centre of the earth was the centre of the universe. It was stationary and was the place which all heavy things sought to attain. They displayed the natural characteristic of gravity, or heaviness. There were other things, such as air and fire, which displayed the opposite property, levity. Their natural place was on high and this they likewise strove to reach. Man was the centre of the whole creation which existed for his benefit. All things were composed of four elements: earth, water, air, and fire in varying proportions. If pure, earth would form a sphere round the centre of the universe; round this would form a sphere of water, round which, in turn, would be a sphere of air and, above all, one of fire. The habitable dry earth existed above the waters on account of the fact that it was impure and consisted of a mixture containing a certain amount of air and fire. Upwards and downwards motion, arising from the striving of objects to find their natural resting place where they could remain at peace, was termed 'natural motion'. All other motion was forced. When a heavy body was lifted, for example, a force was required; the movement was forced, not natural. On the earth natural motion was either straight up or straight down. In the heavens things were different. All things on earth, below the level of the moon, were subject to change and decay. The heavens beyond the moon were perfect and unchanging. Natural motion in the heavens was circular, not linear. Circular motion was looked upon as perfect and could go on indefinitely without starting or stopping. These views were held, with more or less modification, throughout the Middle Ages. The stars were attached to a crystalline sphere which rotated once a day. The planets were also thought of as being attached to other crystalline spheres which rolled between still other spheres to account for the variable motion which they displayed. Although natural motion could take place without the intervention of a mover, by the time of Dante the crystalline spheres came to be looked upon as being maintained in motion by

Intelligences. The sphere of the moon was moved by Angels, that of Mercury was moved by Archangels. Venus was moved by Principalities and the sun by Powers. There was a whole hierarchy of them and many of the names which occur in the old hymns date from this period. The necessity for an unmoved mover to give all these operators a purchase, to enable them to exert their moving forces, was one of the arguments put forward by St Thomas Aquinas for the existence of God, an argument which he had adopted from Aristotle himself.

As opposed to natural motion, forced motion, as its name implied, could only take place through the intervention of a mover. As soon as the mover ceased to act the movement stopped. The world of the ancients was dominated by friction and this fact contributed much to the character of their theory of movement. The problems in which they were interested were those which occur in the movement of stones and building materials, and in pulling the stiff carts and chariots with which they were familiar. Most of the carts would be pulled by oxen and would move very slowly. As soon as the ox ceased to pull, the cart would stop. This would have been the experience of the men too as they pulled the carts to fasten them to the yokes to harness the animals. The theory of forced motion, therefore, came to be enshrined in the principle that nothing moves unless there is a mover. Rest was the natural state of all objects. It needed no explanation. It was movement which had to be explained. To do this it was thought that a given force was required to generate a given velocity in a body. Motion could not be thought of as taking place in a vacuum, which was considered impossible. All movement took place in some medium and against some resistance. If the force acting on the body increased, the velocity of the body would be increased. If the force decreased, the velocity decreased, and if the force ceased to exist the velocity vanished.

It must not be thought that these views were in any way unconvincing or far-fetched. On the contrary, they proved capable of embracing all the phenomena with which the ancient world was familiar. It was true that there were one or two difficult cases which required some further consideration, just as there always are with any theory. There are always some cases which do not appear to fit into the picture immediately and for which some further hypotheses have to be put forward if they are to be accommodated satisfactorily within the scheme. There were one or two cases of this kind, but nothing to disturb the general confidence which was felt in Aristotle's picture as a whole. One of these difficulties arose from the flight of an arrow, which continued to move after it had left the bowstring. Where was the mover to be found in this case? The difficulty was got over by attributing the movement to the action of the air. The bowstring was thought to be capable of communicating its ability to move the arrow to the air, which came round in a kind of eddy from the front and pushed the arrow from behind. The same sort of explanation would apply to the continued motion of a boat after the oars had ceased to be plied, except that it would be the water in this case which would be responsible for the movement. Some such movement in the water would, indeed, be visible, so that the explanation would not appear in the least strained, however it may seem to us today.

Part of Aristotle's theory, namely that a body in a state of rest will continue at rest unless it is acted on by a force, was taken over by Newton and incorporated into his theory of movement. This part we shall make use of ourselves in our study of motion and it will furnish all that is necessary to provide an understanding of a number of problems, such as some of those which occur, for example, in the maintenance of balance. Other problems of balance, however, are quite beyond the scope of Aristotelian ideas and to understand these it will be necessary to go much further into the study of dynamics. It is possible to understand a great deal of this, however, without having recourse to very complicated mathematics.

In following our study of movement it will not be necessary to trace out the historical development of the subject completely. The tremendous confidence which came to be placed in the Newtonian theory of dynamics was largely the result of highly mathematical researches into the movements of the solar system, carried out in the eighteenth century by men like Laplace. Newton's theory of the solar system was thereby confirmed in the minutest detail and it remained in unchallenged supremacy for over 200 years. Indeed, apart from the smallest exceptions it remains so today. To consider Laplace's *Celestial Mechanics* even in outline, however, would take us far beyond the limits of this book. In this volume we shall be engaged in applying Newtonian mechanics to the ordinary situations met with in everyday life, and for this purpose it will suffice if we derive the principles on which it is founded on the basis of simple observations without attempting to follow the historical developments as they occurred before and after the publication of Newton's *Principia* in 1687. We shall, in doing this, in fact be following the method which Newton himself professed to follow. What he claimed to do was to arrive at certain principles from observation of the phenomena (actually he claimed to deduce them from the phenomena) and then 'render them general by induction'. By this phrase he meant testing his principles by applying them to other cases.

It will be profitable to us to discuss some of the difficulties encountered in an earlier phase of the development of the theory of movement, difficulties which had to be overcome by Galileo and his predecessors before further progress became possible. Such a discussion will not detain us for long and it will enable us to clarify the meaning to be attached to some of the terms it will be necessary continually to employ, such as velocity and acceleration, the clearing up of which was the first step in the development of the subject itself.

Falling bodies attracted attention from the earliest days in the study of movement. Observation had shown that as a body falls it travels faster and faster, at least up to a certain point, although the observation of such a simple fact as this is by no means as easy as it might appear, unless one is guided by a good theory to indicate what to look for, and it may become very difficult indeed if the theory with which one is working either does not predict such accelerated motion or, what is worse, indicates something different. We tend to notice those things for which we are on the look-out and not to see others which we are not expecting. However, though the Aristotelian theory of motion can hardly be said to have predicted it, it accounted for this increase in velocity by the greater jubilation with which a body would move as it approached its appointed place in the universe. Just how this increase in velocity occurred remained obscure. Indeed no one was clear about the meaning to be attached to the terms velocity or speed when the speed of the body was changing. Today we are accustomed to having our instantaneous speed indicated to us by a speedometer, but at the time it was by no means certain what was to be the interpretation of such a term as instantaneous velocity, quite apart from how it should be measured.

It was also not clear how the velocity of a falling body altered as it fell. Did it increase uniformly with the distance or with the time for which the body had been falling, or, indeed, did it alter uniformly with either of these quantities? More handicapping still, it was not always realised that there existed any difference at all between these two possibilities.

These difficulties were still current at the time of Galileo, and one of his important contributions to science was to help to resolve them. At first he did not succeed. For the reason that it appeared to be the added height from which a body fell that gave it its greater velocity when compared with that of a body which had fallen through a smaller distance, the hypothesis that the velocity of a body increased uniformly with the distance through which it had fallen, was the one that was generally accepted. Galileo himself adopted it at first. At the same time he also made a mistake in his early calculations which neutralised the error in this assumption, and he thus arrived at the correct result that the distance that a body would fall in a given time would be proportional to the square of the time—that is to say it would fall four times as far in two seconds as it would if it fell for only one second. This was a result that could be tested by experiment, for example, by rolling a ball down an inclined plane as Galileo did himself. He later saw the error in his early calculation and was able to correct it and develop the theory on a correct basis.

These, and similar difficulties, were removed by Newton with his 'method of fluxions'—the differential calculus as we know it today. The instantaneous velocity of a body at a certain time, according to Newton, is to be found by dividing the very short distance it traverses in a very short interval of time about the instant in question, by the time it takes to do so. During such a very short interval of time it is sufficient to regard the velocity as constant, since it could only change by a very small fraction in such a short time. For example, the instantaneous speed of an accelerating motor-car would be 30 miles per hour (44 feet per second) if it travelled 4·4 feet in $\frac{1}{10}$ second at the time in question—or better if it travelled 2·2 feet in $\frac{1}{20}$ second, etc. In the $\frac{1}{10}$ second during which the measurement was being made, the velocity of the motor-car could not change appreciably. If reliable measurements could be made in $\frac{1}{20}$ second these would give the better approximation to the speed at the particular instant in question, since the possibility of change in the vehicle's velocity would be correspondingly reduced. The ratio of the distance traversed to the time taken as both become very small is the meaning to be attached to the term instantaneous speed. This, in fact, is the interpretation to be placed upon the readings given by a speedometer.

Contrary to the view adopted earlier by Galileo and many of his contemporaries and predecessors, the velocity of a falling body does not increase uniformly with the distance through which the fall has taken place. A body which has a velocity of 1 mile per hour after falling a certain distance will not possess a velocity of 2 miles per hour when it has fallen twice the distance altogether. It will not, in fact, acquire the velocity of 2 miles per hour until it has fallen through four times the distance in all. It was part of Galileo's contribution to dynamics to show that the velocity of a falling body increases uniformly with the time of the fall and not with the distance through which it has fallen. The body which has a velocity of 1 mile per hour after falling for a certain time will possess a velocity of 2 miles per hour after it has been falling for twice that time, but in that double interval of time it would have fallen through four times the distance altogether that it covered in the first period.

The timing of a body falling was too difficult an operation for Galileo to do directly, since he possessed only very crude means of measuring short intervals of time. His 'stop watch' in fact was a vessel containing water, with a hole in the bottom closed by his finger. Short intervals of time were measured by weighing the water which flowed through the hole when the finger was removed. With such meagre equipment Galileo had to resort to some means of 'diluting' gravity. He did this by using a ball rolling down an inclined plane, the motion of which he assumed would be similar to that of a body falling freely.

Today, using a simple ciné camera, it is a comparatively easy matter to study directly the motion of a body falling freely under gravity. With an 8-mm. camera working at 64 frames per second a freely falling billiard ball, for example, can be photographed through distances of 7 or 8 feet or more. The pictures can be projected on to a translucent screen and photographed again, superimposed on a single plate in a still camera. Plate I (i) is the result of doing this, and Galileo's results can be obtained by measuring the resulting photograph. The actual results obtained from Plate I will be given a little later, but the increasing distances travelled in the short intervals of time between each exposure are clearly visible. In preparing the still photograph it is desirable to mask off most of the background by means of a piece of paper with a hole in it, to avoid fogging the plate unduly by the repeated exposures. This accounts for the appearance of frames round the earlier positions of the ball in the photograph.

Galileo thus cleared up the meaning that it is desirable to attach to the term acceleration. The acceleration of a body is the rate at which its velocity is increasing. A motor-car which accelerates steadily from 5 miles per hour to 45 miles per hour in 10 seconds would thus possess an acceleration of 4 miles per hour per second. Galileo's experiments showed that falling bodies, or to be exact, a ball rolling down an incline, possess a constant acceleration. In air this is only true of heavy bodies in the first few seconds of their fall, before they are travelling fast enough for wind resistance to become important. It is obviously not true for a light body like a feather which can be blown about by the slightest puff of air. It seems doubtful whether the story is true that Galileo dropped two cannon balls of different sizes from the Leaning Tower of Pisa, to demonstrate that the acceleration of all bodies falling under gravity

PLATE I (i). *Free fall under gravity. Superimposed pictures, taken at 64 frames per second, of a billiard ball falling freely.*

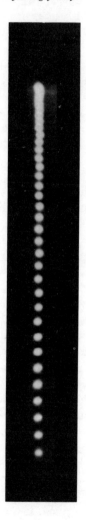

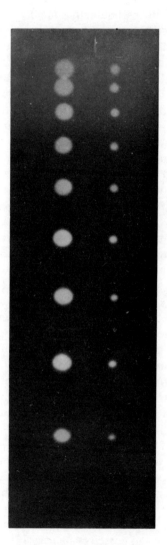

PLATE I (ii). *Free fall under gravity. A croquet ball and a billiard ball were released simultaneously. Every fourth frame is printed superimposed.*

is the same. One such story credits him with climbing the Leaning Tower carrying a cannon ball weighing a hundredweight under one arm and one of a pound under the other. Galileo does not refer to the experiment himself and it is not mentioned as having been seen by any witness. In his early writings Galileo said that in his experience a block of lead soon left a block of wood behind. The question of the effect of the resistance of the air was not cleared up until after the invention of the air pump. It was then found that a feather would fall as rapidly as a piece of metal (traditionally a guinea piece) once the air, or most of it, has been removed.

The ciné camera can also be used to perform Galileo's reputed experiment from the Leaning Tower of Pisa. Plate I (ii) shows the fall of a large croquet ball and a small billiard ball dropped from the same height at the same time by releasing a simple catch. Both are seen to fall together. Although the photographs are taken at the rate of 64 frames per second to secure the best definition possible, only every fourth frame is rephotographed in the super-imposed picture. The importance of the results demonstrated by these photographs for the theory of movement will be discussed in a later chapter.

The subject in which calculations are made about the distances which bodies possessing given accelerations would travel, is known as kinematics. It is a piece of pure mathematics and it deals with hypothetical cases only and involves no scientific knowledge, such as that provided by the experiments of Galileo. The latter is required when it is desired to know whether, in fact, the accelerations which have been assumed in the mathematics are possessed by any actual body. Until this is known the results of the mathematics can never be applied to particular cases. The relationship between the distance which a body moving with a constant acceleration traverses, the time during which the motion has taken place, the initial velocity with which it started and the acceleration is very easy to work out. Three simple kinematical equations connect the quantities involved, and elementary textbooks on mechanics commonly devote a good deal of space to examples of the application of these formulae. For the purposes of the present study, which will be more connected with the science than the mathematics of moving bodies, we shall not make much use of these equations, however, and we shall refrain from considering them further here.

The graphical representation of velocity, acceleration, and distance traversed, however, is worthy of some further consideration since we shall make use of it later. If the velocity of a body which possesses a constant acceleration is plotted against time, a straight line is obtained. The greater the acceleration, the greater is the slope of the line to the axis of time. In Fig. I (1) the line OA represents the velocity of a body which starts at rest at the time $t = 0$ and possesses an acceleration of 1 centimetre per second per second. The line OB gives the velocity of a body similarly starting from rest, but with an acceleration of 2 centimetres per second per second, OC that of one with an acceleration of 3 centimetres per second per second, and OD one with an acceleration of 4. Should the body possess an initial velocity u centimetres per second, instead of starting from rest, the straight line representing its velocity is displaced upwards as in Fig. I (2).

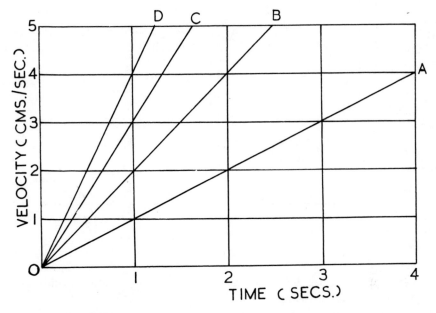

FIG. I (1).

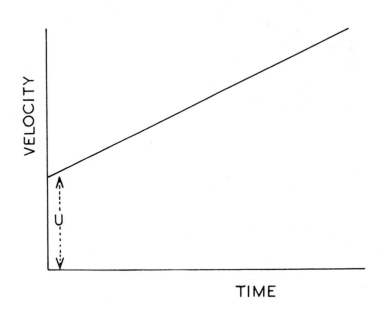

FIG. I (2).

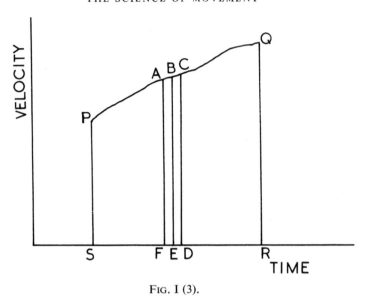

Fig. I (3).

Let us now consider the case of the motion of a body in which the acceleration need not be constant. Suppose that the curve *PABCQ* of Fig. I (3)
represents the velocity which the body possesses at a given time. At a certain
instant represented by the point *F*, its velocity will be represented by the line
AF. An instant later, at *E*, the velocity will be represented by *BE*. By taking
the instants *F* and *E* to be very close together, the difference between *AF* and
BE may be made very small. The distance traversed in the small interval *FE*
will be given by the product of the velocity and the time. This will be approximately equal to $AF \times FE$, or $BE \times FE$, since *AF* and *BE* will be approximately
equal when the interval between them is made very small. That is to say, the
distance traversed in the interval *FE* will be equal to the area of what is
approximately the rectangle *ABEF*. Similarly the distance traversed in the next
small interval of time, *ED*, will be given by the area of the rectangle *BCDE*,
and so on. Thus by adding up all these elementary rectangles it can be seen
that the distance traversed by the body in the finite interval *SR* will be
represented by the area *PQRS*, between the curve, the time axis, and the two
terminating ordinates, *PS* and *QR*. This is a very useful result of general
application.

Applying this result to the case of a body starting from rest and moving
with a constant acceleration, *a*, the velocity-time curve for which we have
already seen to be a straight line, we obtain the distance travelled as the area
of the triangle *OAB* (Fig. I (4)). This is equal to $\frac{1}{2}AB \times t$—that is, one-half
the final velocity multiplied by the time of motion. But the final velocity will
be equal to the acceleration, *a*, multiplied by the time for which it has been
operating—that is to say to $a.t$. The distance travelled will, therefore, be

$$\frac{1}{2}a.t^2.$$

This is the result which Galileo obtained for the motion of a ball rolling down an incline, and the above method is essentially the same as that which he employed after he had corrected his initial mistake arising from the failure to recognise the true nature of acceleration. Though this calculation may seem of extraordinary simplicity to us, equipped as we are with 'hindsight' and a much wider range of experience, it must not be thought remarkable that the result was not arrived at earlier than it was. Before the time of Galileo the difference between a velocity which increased uniformly with the distance and one which increased uniformly with the time was not appreciated, as we have already seen. It was Galileo who first recognised the essential role of time in this matter, as opposed to distance.

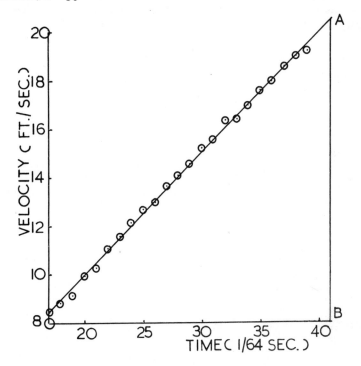

Fig. I (4). *The velocity of a billiard ball falling freely under gravity.*

We can obtain Galileo's results for a body falling freely under gravity, without having to dilute it by using an inclined plane to slow the movement down, by making measurements on the positions of the ball in Plate I (i). By measuring the successive positions of the ball, the distance it moves in a short interval of time may be determined. The points in the graph of Fig. I (4) were obtained by measuring the distances traversed in four frames of the ciné film, the measurements being made with a travelling microscope. An alternative method which gives results equally accurate is to project the film, frame by frame, in a projector and measure the distances moved by the ball by means of a metre rule. The graph shows how the velocity varies with the time of fall. Clearly it increases uniformly with time. In other words, a heavy body falling under gravity possesses a constant acceleration. The line on the graph is drawn to correspond with an acceleration of 32·2 feet per second per second, and the points representing the observed velocities of the ball are seen to lie very close to it. The results of these preliminary experiments, therefore, indicate that heavy bodies falling freely under gravity all fall with an acceleration of this magnitude, namely 32·2 feet per second per second, so long as they are not moving sufficiently rapidly for the resistance of the air to become appreciable.

Although not much use will be made of them in this book, the three simple kinematical equations connecting s, the distance travelled, and v, the final velocity attained, with u, the initial velocity, a, the acceleration, and t, the time, are given below for purposes of reference. They are:

$$v=u+at$$

$$s=ut+\tfrac{1}{2}at^2$$

$$v^2=u^2+2as.$$

CHAPTER II

The Role of Friction in Movement

WE are apt to look upon friction as being only a nuisance, as an impediment to motion, and, of course, it often is exactly that. Much of the advance of modern technology particularly in the case of transport, was made possible by reducing friction. Bearings of metal instead of wood, ball-bearings in place of plain ones, lubrication, all played their part. The railways succeeded because they were able to reduce friction by the use of steel wheels running on steel rails, a possibility that had been employed even before the advent of steam. The exhilaration of skating arises from the ease of movement which is possible when there is very little friction. Here friction is reduced by the lubricating action of a film of water. This film is produced by the melting of the ice, caused by the enormous pressure arising from the concentration of the weight of the skater on to the very small area of the base of the skates. As we have seen, it was friction that led to the development of Aristotle's mechanics in the way in which it took place. In his time it was difficult to imagine motion occurring in the absence of friction. All movement was impeded by resistances and it was on the steady state reached when the force applied became balanced by the frictional resistances, that attention was concentrated. This steady state was reached so quickly in all the most readily available examples that the important period prior to this condition of equilibrium was overlooked. Since, as soon as the force was removed, rest was again attained very rapidly, the idea that impetus and momentum could remain in the body after the force had ceased to act—a precursor of modern mechanics—was very long in being developed.

Friction, however, plays a more important role in movement than in just obscuring the basic principles and making them less easy to understand. Without friction the world would be a most difficult place in which to live. Starting and stopping would present very considerable difficulties and even holding things in our fingers would be next to impossible. The railways, where the steel wheels and the rails have reduced friction to so great an extent, often provide an illustration of this. When a steam locomotive starts to move a heavy train the driving wheels often slip on the track. There is insufficient friction to provide a grip, the engine races, and its pull is reduced. It has then to be turned off and a fresh start made, increasing the pull exerted less rapidly so that it does not reach the point where the wheels are caused to slip.

Some simple experiments with a long light trolley will illustrate the points involved. A trolley which moves with very little friction is desirable and one mounted on miniature bicycle wheels and ball-bearings works very well. The tyres should be blown up hard and a good, smooth, level floor is desirable on which they can run. It is an advantage if the trolley itself can be 'underslung' so as to give only just sufficient clearance over the floor to enable it to move

13

(A)

(B)

(C)

PLATE II (i). *An attempt to walk off a long light trolley. The result is that the trolley is propelled backwards while the walker makes very little progress in the forward direction.*

freely when fully loaded. Photographs of a trolley designed in this way are shown in Plate II (i).

If one stands on such a trolley the friction between one's feet and the floor is reduced very much indeed, and when first trying the experiments some little difficulty can even be experienced in maintaining one's balance and in not falling over. These difficulties, however, can soon be surmounted, so that it is possible to stand on the trolley and to attempt to walk off it in the forward direction. If this is done vigorously, and some little practice is usually neces- sary before sufficient confidence to do this vigorously enough is attained, it will be found that instead of walking forwards, as we have tried to do, the only effect of our efforts is that the trolley is propelled backwards from under- neath us. Three snapshots of this experiment showing the movement of the trolley backwards and the small movement forwards of the experimenter are reproduced in Plate II (i) (A), (B), and (C). The success of the experiment depends upon the trolley being made much lighter than the person performing the experiment, but there is not much difficulty in making even quite a large trolley weigh less than a sixth or a seventh of the weight of the experimenter, who, if necessary, can carry extra weight. When we start to walk forward the force which drives us in the direction in which we want to go is derived from the friction between our shoes and the floor. Interposing the trolley between our shoes and the floor reduces this friction with the result that we ourselves move forward very little. The fact that the trolley moves backwards shows that it must be acted on by a force in the opposite direction to that in which a force acts upon us. This we shall see is characteristic of all forces. They always occur in pairs acting in opposite directions. When one body exerts a force upon another it experiences a force itself in the opposite direction.

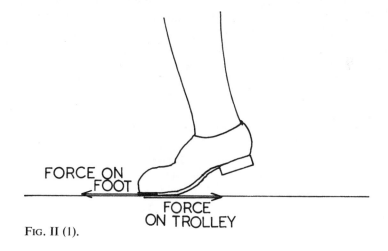

FORCE ON FOOT

FORCE ON TROLLEY

Fig. II (1).

If we make the trolley heavier, by placing weights upon it, we find that the task of walking off it becomes easier. We are able to get further forward before reaching the end of the trolley, and the trolley itself moves backwards more slowly. The heavier the trolley, the further forward are we able to get on it. When we start walking ordinarily with our feet in contact with the ground, two forces are still involved. Through the agency of friction we exert a backwards force on the earth, and the earth, also by means of friction, exerts a forward force on us. Although it is our own muscles that are responsible for the movement, they can only make us start to move forward by pushing backwards on the earth. It is the force that the earth then exerts upon us in the opposite direction that sets us going. The force which our muscles exert on the earth moves the earth backwards, although the earth, being so massive compared with ourselves, is moved quite undetectably.

We need a force to start us moving and then when we desire to stop we require another force to enable us to do so. As a rule this force is also provided by friction. A second simple experiment with the trolley will illustrate the truth of this statement. The trolley is placed in the middle of the room and we walk briskly on to it and stop in the middle—at least, this is what we try to do. This experiment also requires a little practice to perform safely and convincingly, because although we stop on the trolley, the trolley itself is carried forward with us on it. The action required is rather like that adopted when sliding on ice. Because the friction between our shoes and the floor has been reduced by the interposition of the trolley, there is little force available to stop our forward motion. By stopping on the trolley we carry the trolley forward with us but relative to the ground our movement continues. It is the force between our shoes and the floor on which we rely for stopping, and this it is which the trolley has reduced.

In the case of a motor-car these starting and stopping forces are exerted by means of the friction between the tyres and the ground. It is essential for both the processes of starting and stopping that the tyres should exert a good grip on the ground. This means that the frictional forces, which tend to prevent slipping between the wheel and the surface of the road on which it rests, must be as large as possible. Tyres are thus designed to achieve the maximum frictional force in this way. When the roads are wet or greasy the surface between the tyres and the ground is separated by a film of moisture or other liquid, the effect of which is to lubricate the interface and so reduce friction. To obtain a good grip on the road the tyre has to penetrate this lubricating film and come into contact with the road itself. This is helped by roughness in the road, which not only serves to drain away any liquid which may be present but also enables the weight of the vehicle to squeeze the liquid away from the points of contact of the tyre and the tops of the irregularities in the ground, on which the weight rests. The tyre itself is designed with a similar end in view. The crevices in the tread provide spaces into which the moisture can be squeezed so that the tyre itself can make contact with the road on the raised parts of indiarubber.

In ordinary movements the tyre does not slip over the ground, so that the roughening of the road and of the surface of the tyre does not add greatly to the resistance experienced by the car to its forward movement. However, in fact, it does cause a little additional resistance and there are some special cases where this has to be avoided. For purposes of advertisement, economy runs are sometimes staged for a particular make of car, in which a phenomenal

(A)

(B)

(C)

PLATE II (ii). *A small trolley is mounted on the larger one. When the lower trolley is towed to the right, the smaller one remains in the same position. The larger trolley is simply pulled from underneath it.*

(*A*)

(*B*)

(*C*)

PLATE II (iii). *A chock has been placed behind the wheels of the small trolley, and when the larger one is pushed forwards the smaller moves with it. However, when the larger one stops the smaller continues on its way.*

number of miles are travelled for each gallon of fuel consumed. In such tests special tyres may be employed in which the tread is very much diminished and perhaps even reduced to a narrow rim round the middle of the tyre. The tyre, itself, is also pumped up very hard to reduce flexion of the tyre walls, which is another source of resistance. Such conditions would not, of course, be tolerated in the course of ordinary motoring. A more legitimate use of similar principles is to be found in the case of the tyres fitted to aeroplanes. The modern high-speed aeroplane has to attain a very high velocity along the ground before it can take off. This velocity has to be achieved within the length of the normal runway. To reduce the drag of the wheels on the ground the tyres which are fitted, instead of being provided with 'tread' markings, are quite smooth. A tread could serve no purpose in the case of an aeroplane, since no part of the drive is transmitted to the wheels nor is there any problem of sideways skidding to be overcome. The only function which the wheel has to perform is to roll round and reduce friction with the ground, while supporting the weight of the aeroplane.

An amusing experiment, which illustrates the principles which we have just been discussing, is photographed in Plate II (ii). Here a smaller trolley has been mounted on the larger one, to which a pole has been attached so that it can be pulled along the floor. When this is done the small trolley is not carried forward by the larger one, but remains stationary in space. The large trolley is simply pulled away from underneath it. There is little friction between the two trolleys on account of the wheels on which the smaller one is mounted, and so little force is available to set it moving forward. The passenger is left ignominiously behind! If now a chock is placed behind the wheels of the small trolley to prevent it being left behind, the two trolleys move forward together when the bottom one is towed along. However, when the bottom trolley is stopped the small trolley continues on its way, again because of there being only small frictional forces available, this time to stop the motion. It is necessary to put chocks both in front of, and behind, the small trolley if it is to behave as though it were attached to the larger one.

Today few people indeed can go in ignorance of these forces which are necessary for starting and stopping motion, once their attention has been called to them. Standing in an omnibus we tend to remain stationary when the bus starts, so that we gravitate to the rear end of the vehicle. We provide ourselves with the necessary force to start us moving, so that we can keep pace with and remain inside the bus, by holding on to straps or standing with our feet wide apart. Similarly, when the vehicle stops we ourselves continue to travel forward inside. If we are not holding on to anything we may be shot to the front if the stopping is at all violent. If we are holding on to a strap or a seat, it becomes very obvious that a considerable force has to be exerted upon us to slow us down to a stop.

Still another amusing method of demonstrating these simple phenomena is to clear the breakfast table by first removing the tablecloth, leaving the crockery in position. This is not as difficult as it may sound, though it is as well to practise it first before trying it out with the best china! The experiment depends upon the fact that there is a limit to the magnitude which the force

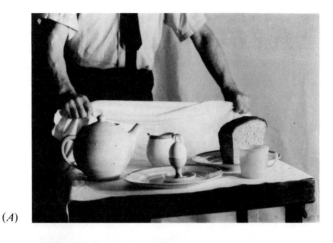

(A)

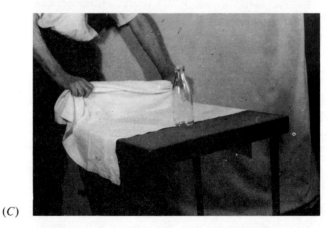

(B)

(C)

PLATE II (iv). *Removing the tablecloth from under the crockery. The photograph in Plate (C) shows how to practise this performance. Use an object of little value such as a milk bottle and begin by placing it only half over the edge of the cloth. Work up gradually from this position until it is well on the cloth.*

of friction can attain, so that if the cloth is removed very rapidly there may not be sufficient time for it to move the articles of crockery appreciably. They, therefore, remain in position. To try the experiment use a card table, the baize top of which will exert considerable friction on the pieces of crockery as soon as they come into contact with it and bring them to rest. They will acquire only a very small velocity as the cloth is removed from underneath them, and if the experiment is performed successfully no movement at all will be visible.

To practise this trick try it first with something of small value such as a milk bottle. For a first try lay the tablecloth only half-way across the table and place the bottle half on and half over the edge of the cloth. It will then be found very easy to snatch the cloth away without disturbing the bottle. From this beginning work gradually forwards with the cloth, so that the bottle is further and further on it. The limit to which it is advisable to go will soon become apparent. It helps very much to avoid jerking the crockery upwards and thus upsetting it, if the cloth is pulled downwards over the edge of the table, and it is sometimes advantageous, if using light plastic 'crockery', to weight it to increase its inertia. The cloth should be smooth and not too large. Sufficient should hang over the edge on one side to provide a good grip for the experimenter, but it should not hang down very far on the other side.

Brakes on vehicles are, of course, simply devices for providing frictional forces to stop movement. In a motor-car they may consist of shoes which, when the brake pedal is depressed, can be pressed against a drum which rotates with the wheels, or they may be pads which can be pressed against a disc similarly attached to the wheels. From our experience of the benefit obtained by having a tread on a tyre to provide a good grip on the road, one might, perhaps, expect to find a tread imprinted on the brake linings. A tread, however, is not provided on the brakes. The purpose of the tread on a tyre is to provide spaces into which liquid, lying on the road surface, can be squeezed to bring the rubber of the tyre into contact with the solid road. A similar problem should not occur with the brakes. To obtain the maximum retarding force which they are designed to give, it is essential that they should be operated dry and thus the problem of providing a grip on a wet slippery surface does not, or at least should not, arise. Spaces in the brake lining would only reduce the surface in contact with the drum and thus the maximum frictional force which could be obtained from the brake, before the surfaces are destroyed.

The force of friction can prevent motion taking place between two surfaces, but it never starts such motion. It is, in fact, a self-adjusting force which just balances any force which may be applied and so prevents sliding taking place. For example, it is possible to pull on a heavy packing case resting on the floor without moving it. The frictional force is just sufficient to neutralise the force we apply to the case. However, if the force which we apply is gradually increased there comes a point when the frictional force reaches a limit and movement occurs. Once sliding has started, the force of friction becomes somewhat less than the maximum value it attained just before motion commenced. This is an important fact which has a number of interesting consequences. Upon it, for example, depends the possibility of a violin bow maintaining the string of the instrument in vibration and thus producing a musical note. As the bow is drawn across the string the latter is pulled to one side by the friction. When the frictional force reaches its limit the string slips beneath the bow, the force of friction becomes less than it was, and thus the string returns towards its position of equilibrium. As soon as the string completes its oscillation and starts to return, slipping ceases and the frictional force can again attain its maximum value. The string is once again pulled to the side until slipping occurs once more. The cycle is repeated indefinitely and the string is maintained in oscillation.

This difference in the force of friction is said to be the difference between static and dynamic friction, the former applying to cases where slipping does not occur and the latter to cases where it does. The difference between static and dynamic friction has important consequences for the driving of motor-cars when the condition of the road is slippery. If slipping is allowed to occur between the tyres and the road, frictional forces, on which control of the vehicle depends, become less and the possibility of maintaining control is diminished. Once a skid starts it tends to go on, unless corrected. Brakes should, therefore, not be applied sufficiently vigorously to lock the wheels under the prevailing road conditions. When there is ice on the road this may mean that the power which can be obtained from the brakes is considerably reduced. Distances allowed for stopping have then to be enormously increased. Violent acceleration and deceleration, and violent cornering, which all give rise to slipping between the tyres and the road, must be avoided.

The experiment with the model motor-cars illustrated in the photographs in Plate II (v) is interesting in this connection. The results are rather surprising. The front wheels of the light-coloured motor-car, and the back ones of the dark car, have been locked by inserting a piece of paper between the wheels and the car. The cars are then slid down a slippery slope in the form of a smooth board. Most people, if asked beforehand to predict what will happen, would forecast that the dark car, with its back wheels locked, will slide down frontwards, the friction arising from the braking of the back wheels keeping it straight, while the light-coloured car with its front wheels locked will be stopped in front and will swing round so as to descend the slope backwards. Precisely the opposite occurs! The dark car with its back wheels locked swings round and goes down backwards while the light-coloured car descends the slope normally, front first. The reason, of course, is that by locking the back wheels of the dark car they are forced to slip. The friction between them and the 'road' is thereby reduced so that it is less than that at the front wheels. The back of the car, therefore, swings round and the slope is descended backwards. It is the car the *back* wheels of which have been locked which does this and goes down the slope out of control. In adjusting the brakes of a car, therefore, it is desirable that the back wheels should not be made to lock before the front. When the road has patches of ice on it, of course, slipping may occur with either front or back wheels unexpectedly and skids may be experienced.

There is another little trick which depends upon the difference between static and dynamic friction. A tumbler is raised up slightly from the table by

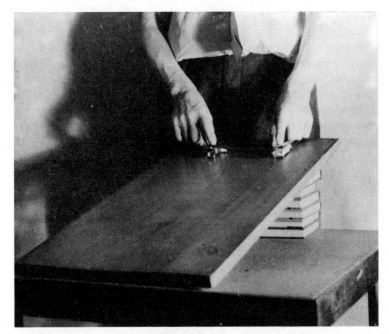

(A)

(B)

PLATE II (v). *The front wheels of the white car and the back wheels of the black car have been locked with a piece of paper inserted between them and the bodies of the cars. When released on a smooth slope, the car with its front wheels locked descends forwards, whereas the car with its back wheels locked skids round and descends backwards.*

placing its edge upon two forks or similar objects. A coin is placed under the glass where it cannot be touched without removing the glass. The problem is to obtain the coin without interfering with the glass. This can be done by scratching the tablecloth near the glass. The coin is thereby made to approach and can finally be brought outside the tumbler. When the cloth is scratched it is brought forward under the fingernail by the force of friction. As the finger continues its movement, slipping occurs, and the cloth slips back rapidly—just as the violin string did underneath the bow. At the coin similar happenings occur. When the cloth travels forwards under the finger, the coin is carried with it, but when the cloth slips back again the motion is very rapid, so that slipping between the coin and the cloth occurs. The coin can thus be brought gradually from underneath the glass.

PLATE II (vi). *Puzzle: How to get the sixpence without removing the glass.*

All that we have been discussing in this chapter, concerning the forces which are necessary to start a body moving, would have found a ready explanation on Aristotle's doctrine that nothing moves unless there is a mover. On the other hand, the fact that a force was necessary to bring the body to rest again would have perplexed him. He encountered a similar difficulty in the case of the arrow after it had left the string, but his method of escape from it by postulating that it was the air that caused the motion to continue would not have proved very convincing in some of the cases which we have been considering. Inside an omnibus one would expect to be able to feel the eddy in the air which he supposed occurred. The later medieval theory of a gradually diminishing impetus possessed by the moving body itself would have proved more successful. With the help of our trolleys we must now pass to consider a case which leads directly to the conclusions about motion in a straight line which were reached by Galileo and Newton.

Galileo rolled a ball down an inclined plane and arranged another inclined plane at the end of the first so that the ball had then to run up the second, as in Fig. II (2). He found that the ball mounted the second plane to a height which was approximately the same as that from which it had started on the first. He then decreased the slope of the second plane and found that his result was still approximately true. The ball had then, of course, to run further along the plane with the smaller slope to attain the same height as that from which it started. He then asked himself the question what would happen if the slope of the second plane was so diminished as to become nothing; surely the ball would go on rolling for ever, were it not for friction. He thus arrived at the conception of uniform motion in a straight line as being a 'natural' state of affairs requiring no further explanation. It was no longer necessary to invent forces to account for uniform motion.

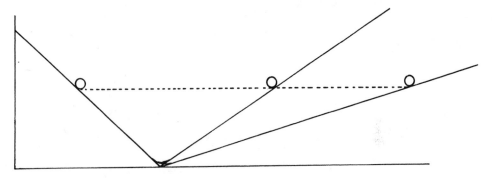

FIG. II (2).

We can illustrate this principle by means of our trolleys. When we push on the trolley in the forwards or backwards direction it starts to move. We can, therefore, employ it as an indicator of a force being applied to it. When we stood on it and attempted to walk off it in the forward direction, the trolley was propelled backwards. It indicated the force which we normally exert upon the earth when we start walking. Similarly, when we walked on to it and attempted to stop, the trolley moved forwards with us on it, indicating the force in the opposite direction to that in the first case, which we apply when stopping ourselves. Let us now walk steadily over the trolley and observe what happens. The result surprises many people when they see it for the first time. If the speed of walking has been maintained constant while passing over the trolley, the trolley is hardly disturbed at all. Photographs illustrating the effect are reproduced in Plate II (vii). We require very little force indeed to keep us moving so long as we maintain our speed constant. This is quite the opposite to what Aristotle, together with most other people right down to the time of Galileo, imagined. If we vary our speed while passing over it, the trolley will move. If we slow down, the trolley is carried forward, and if we speed ourselves up, the trolley is propelled backwards. Forces are required to vary our speed, not to keep it constant.

A word may, perhaps, be necessary to consider a possible objection. It might be pointed out that when we ride a bicycle on level ground, for example, a certain force is necessary to maintain a steady speed. This is certainly true, though the smallness of the force required when the speed is not too great

(A)

(B)

(C)

PLATE II (vii). *Walking over the long trolley. If the speed of walking is maintained constant the trolley is hardly disturbed. No force is required to maintain a steady pace.*

may well be surprising. It can easily be measured by means of a spring-balance employed to tow the bicycle, together with its rider, at a constant velocity. It is a matter of a few ounces only. However, as the speed is increased a greater and greater force is found to be necessary to keep the speed constant. Anyone who has ridden a bicycle, however, will not be long perplexed to find an answer to this apparent contradiction. Movement through the air occasions a resistance. We can feel it acting on our bodies when we face a strong wind. We find it necessary to brace ourselves to meet it. Also, even with the best of bicycles, friction has not been completely eliminated, though it is very small. We can then appreciate that such resistances lead to the introduction of forces which, though small compared with those exerted to start the movement, have still an appreciable effect. As the speed increases, so does the importance of all these resistances. They are, however, forces just like those we feel ourselves exerting whenever we push or pull on an object and set it in motion.

It was the realisation of the importance of uniform motion—that is, movement with a constant velocity—that was one of the most important factors contributing to the development of modern dynamics. The function of forces impressed upon a body was to alter the movement of the body, not simply to maintain it steady. Forces, in other words, produced accelerations. We shall return to this point, and to our trolleys, when we take up the question of the measurement of force. In the meantime we will leave the question of uniform motion as it was summarised by Newton in his first law of motion. 'Every body continues in a state of rest or of uniform motion in a straight line, unless it is acted upon by an impressed force.'

It was the presence of friction that prevented this simple truth from being recognised earlier than it was. Friction is of the greatest importance and is virtually ubiquitous. Without it life as we know it would be impossible. The existence of resistance to movement was certainly realised by Aristotle. What he failed to imagine was what motion could be like if it was absent. All motion, in his experience, was subject to resistance, and he made this fact the central point in his theory. Nevertheless, failure to recognise friction for what it is, namely a force like any other, which may or may not be present, impeded the progress of science for 2,000 years. Though we usually devote our attention to diminishing resistance to movement, there are many occasions on which we find it essential to increase it.

CHAPTER III

Simple Problems of Balance in Physics

WE shall consider in this chapter some problems of balance in physics, the explanation of which requires nothing more than the simple considerations of the previous two chapters. With some of these problems Aristotle himself would have felt quite happy, since they depend upon a body remaining at rest or upon its assuming a position so that its mass is, as a whole, as low as possible in the earth's gravitational field.

Let us examine the equilibrium of a simple object, such as the cylinder shown resting on a table capable of being tilted, in Plate III (i). The cylinder has a height approximately twice the diameter of its base. The photograph shows the table tilted at an angle of nearly 25°. The cylinder is then on the point of toppling and a slight increase in the angle of tilt is sufficient to cause it to fall over. What conditions determine the tilt to which the cylinder can be subjected before it reaches the point of toppling over?

PLATE III (i). *A cylinder whose height is twice the diameter of its base can be tilted through an angle of about 25° before it topples.*

It is easier to examine this question by a direct experimental method if a body possessing a more skeleton-like structure is employed, so that we may be able to get more nearly inside it on its axis. Such a structure is formed by the two discs, as nearly as possible equal to each other, which have been bolted to a piece of brass rod, as shown in Plate III (ii). In the photograph in Plate III (ii) (A) it is shown suspended by means of a piece of string. The

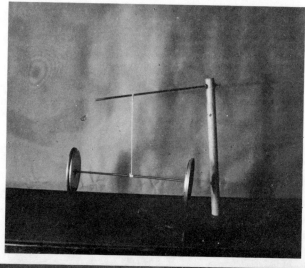

(A)

(B)

PLATE III (ii). *Two equal discs have been bolted to a brass rod. The point of balance is at the mid-point of the rod, as shown in the upper photograph. When the structure is on the point of toppling, as shown in the lower photograph, a plumb-line suspended from the point of balance points to the edge of the base.*

point of balance is, as we would expect of such a symmetrical object, at the mid-point of the rod, and it has been marked by a spot of white paint. In Plate III (ii) (B) the body has been stood upon the tilting table, the inclination of which has been increased until the structure is on the point of toppling over. A plumb-line has been suspended from the brass rod at the point of balance. When the structure is on the point of toppling, the plumb-line just points to the edge of the base which rests on the inclined table. The object evidently topples when the vertical line through the point of balance, or centre of gravity, just passes outside the base on which the object rests. In Plate III (iii) the original cylinder has been suspended by means of a piece of string from a point in the edge of its upper end. The centre of gravity of the cylinder will then clearly lie vertically underneath the point to which the string is attached, which, in turn, will lie vertically over the edge of the base. When it is suspended in this position the cylinder is seen to lie roughly at the same angle as it did when it was on the point of toppling over on the tilting table.

PLATE III (iii). *Here the cylinder has been suspended by a piece of string from a point on its upper edge. In this position its centre of gravity lies vertically under the point of support and over the lower edge. The cylinder is seen to be tilted at about the same angle as it was on the tilting table when it was at the point of toppling.*

Now let us make the cylinder heavier at one end than it is at the other. This we can do by fixing a heavy, tightly fitting lid, which has been weighted with lead, to the upper end. The cylinder will thus be very top-heavy. When it is placed on the tilting table with the heavy end uppermost, it can now be tilted through only about 11° before toppling occurs. It therefore topples at a much smaller angle of inclination than it did before. The photograph in Plate III (iv) (A) shows the cylinder on the tilting table in this position just before toppling occurs. However, if the weighted end is placed at the bottom it becomes possible to tilt the cylinder through an amazingly large angle before it starts to topple over. This is shown in Plate III (iv) (B). The surface of the table has been covered with coarse sandpaper, but even when made very rough in this way it is insufficiently rough to prevent slipping occurring before toppling. To obtain the photograph a small pin has been inserted in the table to prevent the cylinder sliding. The pin, in effect, simply increases the roughness of the surface.

(A)

(B)

PLATE III (iv). *The black-painted end of the cylinder has been weighted with lead. With the heavy end uppermost it is possible to tilt it through an angle of only about 11° before toppling occurs. With the heavy end at the bottom it can be tilted through an angle of over 60°.*

The case of the weighted cylinder can be investigated in a similar manner to that employed before if we use a skeletal object in which the centre of gravity is not at the mid-point. In Plate III (v) (A) two discs of very unequal weight have been connected together by means of the brass rod. For the composite object to balance when it is suspended by means of a piece of string as before, the string must be attached much nearer the heavier end.

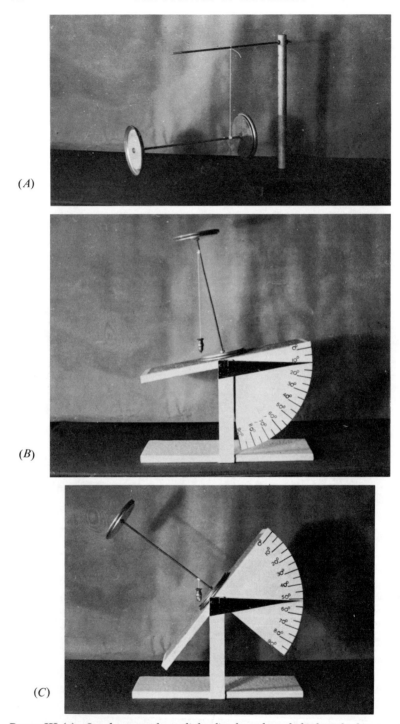

(A)

(B)

(C)

PLATE III (v). *One heavy and one light disc have been bolted to the brass rod. The point of balance is near the heavy end. When the structure is on the point of toppling, a plumb-line attached to the point of balance points to the edge of the base as before.*

The point of balance, or centre of gravity, has again been marked by a spot of white paint. In Plate III (v) (B) the structure has been placed upon the tilting table with the heavier end uppermost and the tilt increased until toppling is about to occur. We can see from the photograph that, as before, when toppling is about to take place the plumb-line attached to the point of balance points to the edge of the base. Thus toppling occurs when the centre of gravity just falls vertically outside the base. The photograph in Plate III (v) (C) shows the same thing but with the heavy end of the structure in contact with the table. The plumb-line has, of course, had to be shortened in this case to enable it to hang freely, but, once again, when the object is on the point of toppling, the plumb-line points to the edge of the base, as it did in the previous examples.

Similar conditions apply to the equilibrium of the human body. When standing still, the centre of gravity of the body must lie vertically over a point which is within the base formed by the feet. If we place ourselves in a position in which our centre of gravity cannot be placed vertically over the base formed by the feet, it will be impossible to stand without holding on to something. For example, if we try to stand with both feet along the edge of the floor next to a wall, we must inevitably fall outwards since we cannot get our centre of gravity sufficiently close to the wall to enable it to come over our feet.

It is possible, of course, for the centre of gravity of a body which is in stable equilibrium to be below the point of support. This is the case with all bodies which hang down, supported by a string or hook, like the cylinder in Plate III (iii). It is possible for a body to have its centre of gravity below its point of support and yet to have much of its volume above this point. Some of the well-known balancing toys depend upon this principle. Their secret lies in the fact that they have been weighted with a piece of lead, while the rest is kept very light. The centre of gravity is thus near the piece of lead and it can lie vertically underneath the point of support while most of the remainder of the toy can be above it. The centre of gravity of a body can easily lie outside the body. This is of common occurrence. The centre of gravity of a circular hoop, for example, is at the centre of the circle, although no part of the hoop is at this point. The centre of gravity of the human body can also be made to lie at a point outside if the body is curled round. This point is of some importance and will be one of the principal factors when we come to consider the technique of the high jump.

The centre of gravity of vehicles is made as low as possible so as to increase their stability. The body of a racing car is clearly slung as low as it can be, but even a fully loaded double-decker omnibus can be tilted through a remarkably large angle. This is because so much of the weight of the vehicle is in the engine, transmission, and chassis, all of which are low down, and this enables the load of passengers to be carried at quite a high level without raising the height of the centre of gravity unduly.

If a cylinder is loaded with a piece of lead near the curved side it can rest with this side on an inclined plane without running down. Bodies which are free to move do so in such a manner that their centre of gravity is lowered.

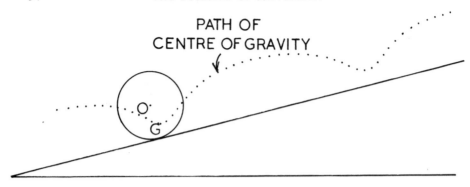

PATH OF
CENTRE OF GRAVITY

Fig. III (1).

With a uniform cylinder its centre of gravity would be lowered if it ran down the inclined plane in the usual manner. In the case of the weighted cylinder, however, the lead weight might be raised if the cylinder ran down the inclined plane, through the turning of the cylinder. If the lead weight is much heavier than the remainder of the cylinder, the centre of gravity of the whole would lie at some distance from the centre so that it can easily occur that the centre of gravity will be raised if the cylinder ran downhill, in spite of the fact that the general direction is downwards. The cylinder takes up a position in which its centre of gravity is as low as possible and it will not tend to roll down the plane if this entails raising its centre of gravity. There is a certain position in which its centre of gravity is in its lowest position, so that it would be raised whether the cylinder rolled up or down (Fig. III (1)). This is the position in which the cylinder will come to rest and it is here in stable equilibrium. If it is rolled down the plane by the finger, as in Plate III (vi), it will return to this position when it is released even though this entails its rolling up the inclined plane to do so, and it will oscillate about this position if displaced.

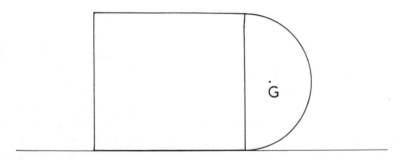

Fig. III (2).

The centre of gravity of a solid hemisphere lies at some point inside it, so that if such a body is held with its plane face vertical and then released, it will fall over on to its curved surface. If now a light cylinder is fitted to the plane

PLATE III (vi). *This cylinder does not roll down the slope.*

If it is pulled down with the finger and then released . . .

it will roll uphill again.

face of the hemisphere, it will be impossible for this plane face to be tilted past the vertical position when the whole object rests upon a horizontal surface (Fig. III (2)). If the light cylinder is sufficiently light, so that the position of the centre of gravity of the hemisphere is not altered appreciably when the cylinder is attached, the body will continue always to turn over on to the curved surface of the hemisphere when it is displaced from this position and left to itself. On this principle depends the performance of the weighted dolls which cannot be made to lie down, the salt-cellars which cannot be permanently tipped over, or the ashtrays which right themselves when upset. By using a large and heavy hemispherical base it is possible to mount such ashtrays on quite tall supports.

Some objects have to be supported on very small bases. For example, some wireless masts are supported on large ball-bearings and they have to be prevented from falling over by means of a series of guy-ropes. A very tall, slender structure is bound to give a good deal in the wind—even a rigid skyscraper gives quite appreciably—and to make it sufficiently strong for it not to buckle, if not supported, is not easy or cheap. Though tall, rigid towers are used, as for example at the Eiffel Tower or the new broadcasting tower at Charwelton, the cheapest construction remains the steel framework supported by guy-ropes.

Questions of stability require consideration, very often, in the design of domestic utensils. A tumbler, for example, may be given extra stability by lowering its centre of gravity by providing it with a thick base of glass; the stability of a wine-glass will depend upon the ratio of the height to the diameter of its base and upon how much liquid is in it. Tea-cups, tea-pots, and cream-jugs with unduly narrow bases will be easily upset.

The tendency for the centre of gravity of a body to take up the lowest position of which it is capable can be seen by immersing a very light body, like a hollow celluloid doll or a table-tennis ball, in dry sand in a box. When the box is shaken up or vibrated vigorously, the sand tends to go to the bottom and the light object to the top. By this process the centre of gravity of the whole system takes up a lower position. The doll or the ball will float on the top of the sand. Exactly the same thing happens when light objects rise to the surface and float on water. If the object weighs less than an equal volume of water, the centre of gravity of the whole will be lowered when the body rises to the surface so that the heavier water occupies the lower spaces and the lighter body the upper. If the object weighs more than an equal volume of water the centre of gravity of the whole system will be lowered when the body sinks. Such bodies, therefore, do not float but sink to the bottom. If the body weighs the same as does an equal volume of water, there will be no tendency for it either to rise or sink. The water will just support the body in any position. It must, therefore, exert upon such a body an upward force equal to the weight of the body. The pressures which the water exerts upon a body will not depend upon the nature of the interior of the body which is immersed in it, and consequently any body immersed in water will experience a force of buoyancy equal to the weight of the water which occupies the same volume as the body. This, of course, is the well-known Principle of Archimedes.

PLATE III (vii). *A table-tennis ball is placed at the bottom of a box of dried peas. After a few seconds' vigorous shaking from side to side, the ball pops out on top. It is advisable to place a hollow lid over the box during the shaking to prevent spilling the peas.*

When a heterogeneous collection of objects of various sizes is shaken up, the small ones tend to congregate at the bottom and the larger ones at the top. There are spaces between the larger objects which, if occupied by the smaller ones, enable the centre of gravity of the whole system to be lowered. When the mixture is shaken up the small objects can slip between the larger ones, whereas the latter cannot penetrate into the spaces between the smaller pieces. The larger objects, therefore, tend to rise to the top. If a tray of strawberries, for example, is shaken up gently, as may occur when a shopkeeper demonstrates the contents to a customer, the larger berries tend to come out on top and the smaller ones go to the bottom, which is a convenient fact for the seller but less advantageous to the purchaser! Macadam, the road-maker, discovered this fact and found that large stones in a road tend to work loose and so start the formation of potholes. To make his roads he used carefully graded materials so that the stones in any given place were all of the same size. It is because of the same reason that gravel paths should be raked over occasionally when dry. This enables the fine particles, which form mud when wet, to go to the lower levels and the larger stones to come to the surface to provide a dry path on which to walk.

All these cases are examples of equilibrium drawn from statics. The bodies are in a position of static equilibrium and do not require continual adjustment to maintain them in position. These are the cases which might well have been called examples of Aristotelian equilibrium, since Aristotle's mechanics would be quite adequate to explain them. We must now, how-ever, consider some of the simpler cases of dynamic balance for which the limited principles of Aristotle no longer suffice. On the whole they present considerations of much greater interest than do the cases of purely static balance, although we shall have to postpone to a later stage those cases of dynamic balance which depend upon the principles of rotational motion.

As an example of intermediate nature let us glance at the case of the equili-brium of ships. Just as in the cases of the equilibrium of solids which we have considered already, the stability of a ship floating in water is determined by the height of the centre of gravity. If the ship has its centre of gravity too high, it will be top-heavy and will turn turtle. The position of the centre of gravity of a ship will depend partly on the design of the vessel and partly on the cargo carried and upon how it is stowed. The total load which a ship can carry safely is determined by the level to which she sinks in the water, the limits to which are usually indicated by the marks on the vessel's sides, known as the Plimsoll lines. The position of the centre of gravity, however, also depends upon how the cargo is stowed as well as on its total weight. In the loading of a ship the heaviest articles should be placed low down and the lighter articles on top, any deck cargo which may be necessary consisting of the lightest articles only. The aim in arranging things in this way is to keep the centre of gravity as low as possible. However, it is not always practicable to do this to the maximum extent that is possible having regard to the articles themselves alone, since the order in which they will be required at the various ports of call along the route has also to be borne in mind. How high the centre of gravity may be placed before the vessel will capsize is rather more difficult to determine than is the point at which a solid, such as those which we have so far considered, will topple when tilted. The base which supports a ship is not so easy to define and the ship may well be liable to capsize even though its centre of gravity lies well over the area defined by the water-line. One has only to think of the equilibrium of a cylinder floating in water to realise this. If a weight is attached to its surface it will rotate until the weight is at the lowest point of the cylinder, if the latter floats with its axis parallel to the surface like a log of wood. Yet at no time need the centre of gravity of the body fall outside the water-line while this is happening. Also, as the vessel heels over, the water-line usually changes, but clearly the condition determining whether or not the ship will capsize has nothing to do with the centre of gravity at any time falling outside a base defined by the water-line.

The effect of raising the centre of gravity on the stability of a vessel can be studied in a simple manner by means of a model 'ship' made from a watertight box floated in a bath of water. A suitable box for elementary investigations is one made of transparent material and sold for holding sandwiches. One about 2 inches deep by 3 inches by 5 is a convenient size. A photograph of such a model 'ship' is shown in Plate III (viii) (A). It has been fitted with a thin wooden deck which partially covers the open top of the box, and to this is attached a mast from which hangs a very light plumb-line. The one in the illustration is made by a piece of thread to which is attached a blob of sealing-wax. A glass bead would serve equally well. A heavy plumb-line would, of course, by itself alter the equilibrium of so frail a vessel. A light scale graduated in degrees serves to indicate the angle of tilt. The model can be floated in a tank consisting of another sandwich box of larger size. A transverse beam is attached to the model from which a small weight can be hung to heel the ship over. A half-ounce weight forms the cargo.

The ship is floated in the water and the first thing that has to be done is to adjust the position of the cargo until it floats upright. This will be shown by the plumb-line indicating zero on the scale. We then hang the deflecting weight on the transverse beam at a specified mark, and note the tilt of the vessel as indicated by the reading of the plumb-line on the scale. Next we transfer the cargo to the deck from the bottom of the vessel and adjust it once again until the ship floats upright as before. We then hang the deflecting weight on the beam at the same mark as before and again note the deflection of the ship. It is easy to see from Plates III (viii) (B) and III (viii) (C) that the same turning force produces a very much greater angle of tilt when the cargo is carried high than when it is on the bottom of the vessel. The importance of keeping the centre of gravity of a ship and its cargo as low as possible becomes obvious. In the case of the box used in these experiments, a weight of 1 ounce placed upon the deck will cause the ship to turn turtle.

The stability of a ship is affected markedly by its beam. A vessel which is broad in the beam is more stable than one which is narrow, other things being equal. This can be shown with the same box used in the above experiments by simply turning it round. The beam is thereby increased from 3 inches to 5 inches. The photograph in Plate III (viii) (D) shows the effect of the same deflecting force as was used before. The tilt obtained is quite small, even though the cargo is carried on the deck in this case.

A tilt which a given turning force will produce when applied to a vessel will depend, of course, upon the shape of the hull and particularly on how the water-line changes as the ship is tilted over. On the one hand we have already seen how a flat-bottomed boat reacts as its cargo is shifted in position. On the other we have the case of the completely cylindrical vessel which will turn turtle as soon as the smallest weight is attached to the upper surface.

The forces which the water exerts upon a floating body balance the weight of the body. The body's weight is, of course, a downwards force and conse-quently the resultant of the forces which the water exerts must be an upwards

PLATE III (viii). *The stability of a ship may be investigated by means of a simple model made from a small plastic sandwich box. A 'deck', a mast, and a transverse beam to which deflecting weights can be attached have been added. A plumb-line, reading against a scale graduated in degrees, shows the angle of tilt. (The plumb-line has been thickened to render its position visible in the photograph.)*

The model has been floated in a larger sandwich box filled with water. It carries as cargo a half-ounce weight which has been placed on the bottom of the boat. The position of the weight has been adjusted until the boat floats in a vertical position.

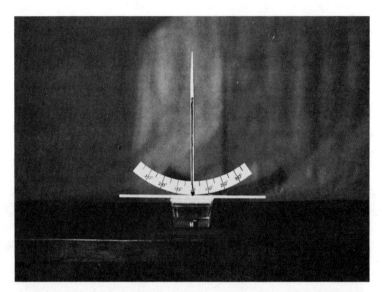

(A)

(B)

In the photograph of Plate (B) a deflecting weight has been hung on the beam and a tilt of about 8° has been produced.

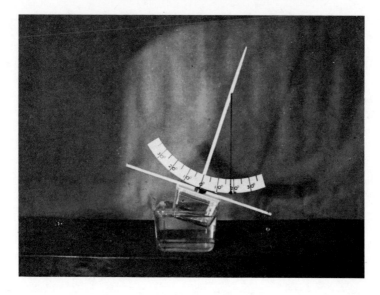

(C) The cargo has been transferred to the deck. The same deflecting force as before now produces a much greater angle of tilt.

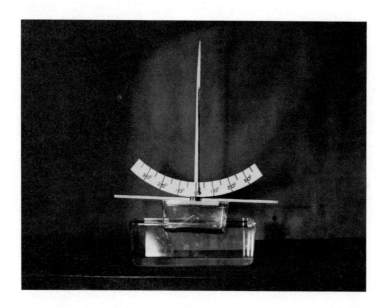

(D) By turning the beam round so that we use the length of the box we effectively increase the width of the boat. The same deflecting force now produces a very small tilt even though the cargo is still carried on the deck.

force acting at some point of the body. When the ship floats statically in stable equilibrium this vertical force must pass through the centre of gravity of the body in order that it may counteract the weight. Suppose now that the vessel is made to heel over at a small angle. The vertical force exerted by the water on it will pass through some point on the originally vertical axis of the ship. The point is known as the meta-centre. If the centre of gravity of the vessel is situated below the meta-centre she will clearly return to the vertical position when displaced from it and her equilibrium will be stable. If, however, the centre of gravity is above the meta-centre, any displacement will tend to get bigger and bigger, since the two forces acting on the vessel, namely her weight acting downwards and the reaction of the water acting upwards, will tend to turn her further from the vertical. (See diagram Fig. III (3).)

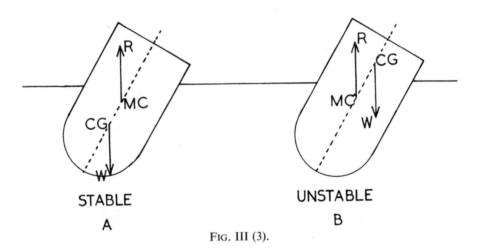

STABLE

A

UNSTABLE

B

Fig. III (3).

The height of the meta-centre above the centre of gravity is known as the metacentric height of the vessel. For a vessel of given weight it determines the magnitude of the turning force tending to right the vessel when she heels over.

The oscillation of a ship about an axis which runs fore and aft, such as these experiments have been concerned with, is known as rolling. If there is danger of the ship capsizing, it will be about such an axis that the vessel will turn over. In a sea-way a ship will possess other motions as well. She will also oscillate about an axis which runs athwart-ships which will alternately raise first her stern and then her bows. This movement is known as pitching. There may also be smaller oscillations about a vertical axis which is known as 'yawing'. This causes the direction in which the ship is pointing to oscillate first to port and then to starboard. The vessel may also be lifted bodily by the waves, a movement which is known as 'heave'. As well as this up-and-down movement there may also be displacements fore and aft and at right angles in the sideways direction, of similar magnitude though, as a rule, less noticeable.

The equilibrium of bodies which contain a fluid presents similar problems to those encountered in the equilibrium of ships. As the body is tilted the liquid alters its position and shape. The stability of many common vessels containing a liquid can be tested on the tilting table already used for solids. For example, the wine-glass shown on the table in Plate III (ix) can be tilted through only a small angle before toppling. When filled to the point in the photograph, it toppled at an angle of only 15°. If one of the tall glasses commonly used for Rhine wines had been tested instead of the Burgundy glass shown in the picture, it would have been even less stable. An ordinary tumbler full of liquid can usually be tilted through an angle of about 25° before it topples.

PLATE III (ix). *When a vessel contains liquid the shape of the system alters as it is tilted. The liquid shifts its position and this reduces the stability. The wine-glass with its small base can be tilted through only a small angle before it topples.*

The problem of the position of the centre of gravity is of even greater importance in the case of aircraft. Small variations in its position, such as are occasioned by limited movement of passengers, can be corrected by the controls. Special trimming controls are fitted to correct for loading on each flight and thus obviate the necessity for continual manual pressure. There are, however, strict limits to which the amount of more or less tail heaviness can be tolerated if the safety of the craft is not to be jeopardised. Fuel represents a considerable fraction of the load of an aircraft, and the consumption of it during flight could alter the position of the centre of gravity. The tanks are so positioned as to minimise this and the way in which the fuel is drawn upon is carefully regulated.

When a solid possesses a very small base it may, nevertheless, given patience, be possible to stand it up on its end. It will, however, be in constant danger of toppling over. Stray puffs of air or chance vibrations are sufficient to upset its equilibrium. Thus a long wooden rod may be stood on its end, but it is not very likely to stay in that position for very long. A pencil may be

PLATE III (x) (A). *Bodies with low centres of gravity are more stable than those with high. A stub of a pencil can be stood on its end very easily. A long pencil is less easy to stand on its end and a long stick is very difficult. It will only stay up for very short periods.*

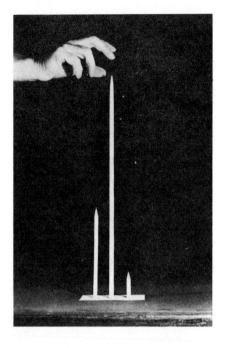

(B) *The stick can nevertheless be balanced on the tip of the finger. Paradoxically the stick with its high centre of gravity is easier to balance than the pencil. The pencil stub is very difficult to balance at all.*

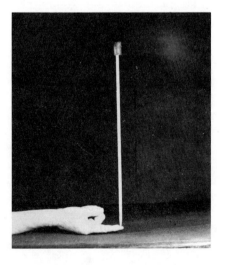

(C) *If the top of the stick is weighted with lead the task becomes easier still. Within limits the higher the centre of gravity of an object, the easier it is to balance.*

stood on its end without great difficulty and a stub of a pencil fairly easily. The stub is likely to remain longer in position than is the pencil, and the pencil, in turn, is more stably placed than is the long rod. In fact, the lower the centre of gravity of the object being stood on end, the more stable it is.

On the other hand, the long wooden rod can be stood on end on its point on the finger almost indefinitely if the finger is kept moving so as always to bring the point of support beneath the centre of gravity. This illustrates another possible method of balance, by means of a process of perpetual adjustment, of which considerable use is made in practice.

Not many of us find it necessary to balance a pole on the nose or to walk on stilts, but balance is maintained in both these cases by means of this process. The base is continually moved so as to keep it underneath the centre of gravity. Paradoxically enough, within limits, the higher the centre of gravity is placed in cases of dynamic balance, such as these, the easier is the feat to perform. The stick of Plate III (x) (B) is very easy to balance and can be maintained balanced on its point as long as may be desired. A full-length pencil can be balanced on its point on the finger, but the task is much more difficult, and a stub of a pencil is practically impossible to balance at all. The situation corresponds to that of an inverted pendulum. When a pendulum is short it oscillates to and fro very quickly, but when it is long its movement is slow. When a pole being balanced possesses a high centre of gravity it departs much more slowly from its position of equilibrium than it does when the centre of gravity is low. The movement is thus easier to recognise before it has gone too far and it is then more easily corrected. If the top of the stick in Plate III (x) (B) is weighted with a piece of lead, as in Plate III (x) (C), it is easier to balance than is the stick alone. Thus, what to the uninitiated may appear to be the more difficult feat may, in reality, be the easier.

In ordinary walking and running the same method of maintaining balance by the continual adjustment of the base is also employed. The feat having been learnt in infancy, the act is now performed as a reflex action without thinking. The staggering walk of the young child learning the art emphasises the fact that the technique does, in fact, have to be learnt. If the centre of gravity of our body moves more rapidly than we can move our feet to keep them underneath it, we will fall on our face. This may, indeed, happen if we make an attempt to alight from a rapidly moving vehicle. The body is moving forward with the speed of the vehicle when contact is first made with the ground, and it will continue to move forward at this speed since there are negligible forces available to stop it, apart from those which can be exerted by the feet. If this initial speed is greater than the maximum speed at which the person concerned can run, his centre of gravity will overtake his feet and he will fall forwards.

Similar principles to those involved in balancing a pole on the nose are also employed in maintaining balance while riding a bicycle. In this case it is only balance sideways which introduces any difficulty, the presence of the two wheels taking care of balance in the fore and aft direction. Balance is maintained by continually steering the machine so that the line joining the points of contact of the tyres with the ground remains beneath the centre of gravity.

The process amounts to a continual checking of incipient falling and, like walking and running, becomes entirely automatic after a little practice.

In connection with the balancing of a bicycle there is one further point which requires some discussion. It is possible to keep a hoop bowling along the ground, and it will not fall over so long as its speed is sufficient. Rotating objects possess peculiar properties, some of which will be investigated later on in this book. Hoops can run without falling over and tops can balance on their points without support. The wheels of a bicycle are also rotating like the hoop, and perhaps they contribute significantly to the balance of the rider. That they do, indeed, make some contribution may be seen from the fact that a bicycle possessing a light frame can be bowled along like a hoop, if it is set going fast enough, though the action is not simple and much depends upon the effect of tilt upon the steering. However, it is also clear that the rotation of the wheels cannot provide the entire explanation of how balance is maintained. Even if the wheels are heavily loaded, the author found it to be impossible to sit indefinitely on a machine mounted on a support which allowed freedom to rotate about a longitudinal axis, although the wheels were spun at a very rapid rate.

(A)   (B)

PLATE III (xi)

(A) Walking on stilts. Balance is maintained by moving the feet so that the points of contact of the stilts with the ground are underneath the centre of gravity of the body. (B) Riding a bicycle fitted with wheels side by side instead of fore and aft as is usual. In this case balance depends upon keeping the machine going at such a speed that the line joining the points of contact of the wheels with the ground is always underneath the centre of gravity of the rider.

It is interesting to set oneself the task of learning an entirely new technique from time to time. A bicycle can be constructed which sets new problems of balance if the wheels are set side by side, in place of the usual tandem arrangement. With a bicycle with the wheels set side by side, sideways balance presents no difficulties, just as longitudinal balance was taken care of auto-matically in the case of the ordinary bicycle. Fore and aft balance, however, has now to be maintained by a process of continual adjustment. In this case it is the speed which has to be adjusted so that the point of support formed by the points of contact of the tyres with the ground remains always under the centre of gravity. When one feels oneself falling forwards the speed has to be increased to bring the points of support forward more rapidly, and conversely, if there is a tendency to fall backwards the speed has to be reduced. Although the reactions required for these adjustments are perfectly natural ones—when the tendency is to fall forwards extra pressure is naturally applied to the forward pedal and this has the effect of increasing the speed, which is what is required, and conversely when the tendency is to fall back-wards—the machine requires a period of apprenticeship about as long as is required to learn to ride an ordinary bicycle, before it can be mastered. Unfor-tunately the accomplishment is of little practical value. The machine with the wheels side by side is ideal for the slow bicycle race since it is as easy to travel backwards as forwards, and one can remain stationary on it indefinitely, but it cannot be steered and it cannot be fitted with brakes!

The circus performer who rides a cycle with only one wheel has to face the problems of maintaining both his longitudinal and his lateral balance simul-taneously. This, therefore, combines both the problems of the side-by-side bicycle with those of the ordinary machine. It also raises some new ones as well. For example, he has to maintain his transverse balance as with an ordinary bicycle by steering it so as to keep the point of support always underneath him. But how can he manage to steer a machine which possesses only one wheel? He has no front wheel with which to steer and, furthermore, he can obtain no purchase on anything by which he can turn his single wheel round in the direction in which he wants it to go. The solution to this problem, together with that of how a cat is able to turn itself round in the air, to which it is related, must be left until later—until we have equipped ourselves with the necessary basis for their discussion. The monocycle rider has to employ methods of balance which the rider of the bicycle has no need to use. What these are will be appreciated when we come to study the problems of rotational motion.

CHAPTER IV

Biological Aspects of Balance: Straight Line Motion

WE have seen that on land a stationary object is in a stable position when its centre of gravity is directly above any point inside a line drawn round its supports. If its centre of gravity is outside this, the object falls, and when it stops falling the centre of gravity must be above part of the base area again.

Some animals are built with widespread legs and a relatively low body. In front view, tortoises, lizards, frogs, and toads are vertebrate animals in this category, while many insects, such as beetles and cockroaches, are invertebrate representatives along with spiders, crabs, and starfish. The approximate position of their centres of gravity can be imagined, and it can be seen that these examples must be tipped through a wide angle before they overbalance. A less stable category is represented by such as the hippopotamus, rhinoceros, bull, bulldog, and mouse, whose base widths are smaller in proportion to their heights. Following these might come a somewhat arbitrary series like elephant, sheep, cow, horse, lion, leopard, buck, man, giraffe, and a resting flamingo. The further along the series, the more unstable is the animal, and the finer must its adjustments be to avoid letting the centre of gravity cross an extremity of the base. The flamingo end of the series is approaching the case of the pencil standing on its end.

PLATE IV (i) (A). *Some wooden models and a terrapin and tree frog illustrating a stability series. The tree frog, on extreme right, is able to adhere to its substratum. The models are placed on the slope in positions where they are on the point of toppling. The terrapin and tree frog are living.*

PLATE IV (i) (B). *The underside of the foot of a gecko seen through the vertical glass to which it was clinging. Note the large area involved. No visible footmarks were left behind.*

From the biological success of the examples just mentioned, it seems there can be no great disadvantage in being unstable. Maybe if there were, it would be outweighed by the advantage of a longer leg, which helps faster economical movement, as discussed in Chapter IX, or in wading in deeper water as with the flamingo and heron. Further, there may be an analogy between an unstable animal and a fighter aircraft. The latter are often intentionally built to be unstable so that they can be flipped easily into manœuvres, whereas airliners and other aircraft are stable, and need their pilots only to keep them on the right course. An animal which is unstable will easily fall into a position suitable for swerving and thus be able to avoid its enemies easily. The condition that the centre of gravity should be inside the bounds of the base is only essential when the animal is stationary or moving with a constant velocity. This is no longer true during acceleration. Then reaction from the ground is not vertical but inclined, so that there is a component force to give the horizontal thrust. It is the direction of the resultant thrust which must now connect the centre of gravity to some point within the base. Of course, a running animal may have only one foot on the ground at a certain part of its pace, and it does not have to adjust its feet to be on this line. In this case an animal is in a state of falling between steps, maybe in addition to possessing an acceleration along its path, until another leg falls on the other side of the thrust line to restore the position. Averaged over a few paces, the thrust line does pass from the centre of gravity through the base.

Stable shapes, such as those of the cockroach and beetle, can, of course, swerve too, but in their case the legs are already in a good position to give a diagonal thrust.

Similar arguments on the direction of the line of thrust can be developed from the lateral view. With four-footed animals, the fore and hind legs are usually far enough apart to keep the centre of gravity well inside the base. During acceleration the thrust line becomes angled so that it passes closer to the hind feet. The hind legs must therefore be taking most of the strain, and the largest muscles for running are found in this region. If the thrust line should pass behind the rear feet, then the animal will rear up off its front feet. Such a state is seen occasionally with horses, as, for example, at the start of a race, and cannot last more than a moment if due entirely to acceleration. Animals such as horses, with heavy heads on long necks, have a centre of gravity nearer the shoulder than the hip. This helps to keep them from rearing during acceleration. Man, at the start of a race, adopts a slanting position (Plate IV (ii)) and similar forces are acting. Once he has attained full speed, however, his stance is bound to become more nearly upright, and he must put his feet down in front of his centre of gravity if he is not to fall over (Plate IV (iii)). In the 'on your marks' and 'get set' positions the centre of gravity must not move in front of the fingers, or toppling and a false start will ensue.

PLATE IV (ii). *The slanting attitude of the body during a sprint start.*

PLATE IV (iii). *After the start, and when velocity is steady, the body assumes a more upright position, so that the footfall is made in advance of a vertical line from the centre of gravity. This example is also during a sprint.*

Running is most comfortable when the surface is at right angles to the resultant force. When proceeding straight and steadily this is usually the case on running tracks. During starting, the angle of the starting blocks is about at right angles to the thrust, and when turning a corner, it is most comfortable if the track is banked so that it is at right angles to the slant of the athletes. Thus the best bank of the track in Plate IV (iv) (overleaf) can be estimated. As it is, there is a tendency to slip.

The slope on which an animal can stand, and also the acceleration it can achieve, are limited by the friction between the feet and the ground. If there is little, the body will slide before it overturns on a slope, as in the case of a tobogganing penguin, or, as with a physical object, in the case of the launching of a ship. The condition for slipping before overturning is that as the thrust line through the centre of gravity swings from the vertical, grip is lost before the line passes the extreme point of support. Most animals do not slip easily, for they are specially adapted to increase their grip. Some of those in our stability series use claws, and cats and leopards can, of course, obtain enough friction to climb vertical surfaces such as tree bark. Although they are

PLATE IV (iv). *Sprinters cornering on a cinder track. To avoid outwards forces, the track would have to be banked at the angle indicated.*

expert at going up, some cats seem to find difficulty in coming down, being averse to coming down backwards. If they turn round to descend forwards, then the backward pointing claws can no longer grip. No doubt with cats, muscular effort is expended in keeping the claws engaged, yet those of the squirrel are so curved that they must often be able to act as passive hooks.

The horse's hoof is another development of the fingernail, as is the cloven hoof of cattle, deer, goats, and their relatives. The cloven hoof is especially well formed to resist sideslip. Man changes his friction devices with the circumstances. Skates and skis give very little forward resistance, but much more lateral resistance; snowshoes spread the body weight and function like the pads of a camel; running spikes, crampons, football boots, and a great many other forms give resistance in various directions on their own special surfaces.

Several of the smaller animals employ adhesion or vacuum techniques. According to one hypothesis, the force obtained is proportional to the linear dimensions, while others imagine that it is an area effect, and hence goes up as the square of the length. The force the animal requires in order to remain secure goes up with the weight of the animal, which is proportional to the volume and hence the cube of the length, which makes these devices favourable to the smaller animals. There seems to be no reason why larger animals should not evolve extraordinarily large adhesive areas, but such are rare. The octopus is probably one of the extreme cases. The gecko, a small lizard, can walk on overhanging and inverted surfaces. Its foot pads are very finely divided like the foreshortened pages of a book (Plate IV (i) (B)). The housefly has adhesive pads as well as claws, and leaves behind marks of a fluid when it walks on a smooth surface. There has been controversy as to how the mechanism works, some suggesting that it is a sucker, the fluid acting as a seal. Others suggest surface tension, and others that the two surfaces seize together, thus using interatomic forces.[1] Adhesive methods such as these should enable an animal to hang without expending effort, yet some energy must be used during walking to undo the adhesion. An undoing action analogous to a zip would minimise such loss.

Most animals are unable to adhere to surfaces and they are concerned to determine, albeit unconsciously, the resultant thrust on their centres of gravity in order to take the appropriate balancing action. A variety of sense organs is concerned with receiving the information required from both outside and inside the animal. Sense organs activate nerves which communicate with the brain and spinal cord. Here, analysis of the data is made and the appropriate response composed. This is then passed down the correct nerves to the appropriate muscles and glands.

The basic animal units are cells, and these vary from each other according to the task they have to perform. Muscle cells are highly specialised in contracting; liver cells in the body chemistry; nerve cells with conducting electric pulses, and sense organs with translating their own specialised stimulus to the language of the nerves. Sense cells themselves present a wide variety of

[1] V. B. Wigglesworth, *Principles of Insect Physiology*, Methuen, 5th Edition, 1953, for a short Review.

appearances. Some, especially sensitive to light, are made up with a pile of microscopic plates which probably act as absorbers. Those sensitive to vibration often bear a minute hair-like process, and others are sensitive to such things as stretch, temperature, pain, and chemicals (Fig. IV (1)). As already

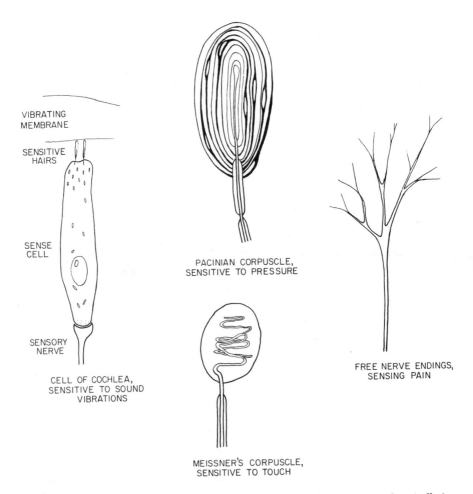

FIG. IV (1). *Some sense cells responding to mechanical stimuli. The muscle spindle is shown in the lower inset in Fig. IV (5).*

suggested, these qualities never pass down the nerves to the brain, for nerves are not empty tubes. The messages transmitted down all nerves are of the same nature—an electric pulse whose size is constant, but whose frequency can be altered. The only way the brain can distinguish between the senses is to be aware of *which* nerve fibre or fibres are active. The strength of the stimulus affecting the sense organ is indicated by the *frequency* of the pulses.

In the sense cell, the stimulus activates a chemical change, and the resultant chemical which appears between the sense cell and its nerve fibre causes the latter to become active in its turn. A nerve fibre starts activity only when its stimulus has reached a certain level called the threshold. As the stimulus increases in intensity the sense cell increases its output, and the frequency of pulses in the sensory nerve fibre increases. This continues until a level called saturation is reached, when a further increase in stimulus gives no further increase in response. A wider range of variability is a possibility if there is a group of sense cells with different thresholds. The response which would be picked up in the whole nerve running from a group of sense cells is shown in Fig. IV (2) and represents the summation of the activity of the individual fibres. Single sense cells in the skin are scattered among many other kinds of cell, but the response suggests that neighbouring ones have such a range of thresholds.

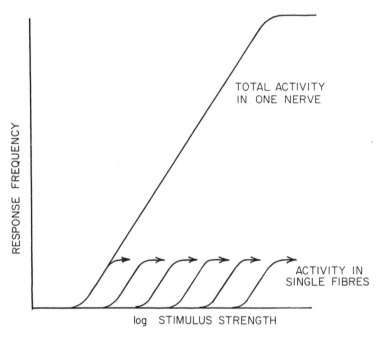

FIG. IV (2). *Diagram to illustrate the activity in a whole nerve as the sum of that in single fibres connected to sense cells of different thresholds.*

The eye is a more advanced apparatus in that the sensitive layer, the retina, is a sheet of densely packed cells, while other non-sensitive structures are present to channel the stimulus, in this case light. Spatial discrimination of two objects a long distance from the animal can be achieved if two separate sense cells are involved. In man, it can be about one-hundredth of a degree of arc, which is approximately 1 inch seen at a distance of 175 yards. Similarly, the large number of sense cells in the cochlea of the ear enable the fine discrimination of the pitch of a note, and in the quality of the sound, of which the ear is capable. As with the eye, non-sensitive accompaniments channel the stimulus. Here they are arranged so that the high notes peter out, or attenuate, before proceeding far down the cochlea (Fig. IV (3)), while the low notes penetrate further. Thus again two different stimuli, here a higher and a lower note, are translated into the activity of two different sets of sense cells, and their accompanying nerve fibres.

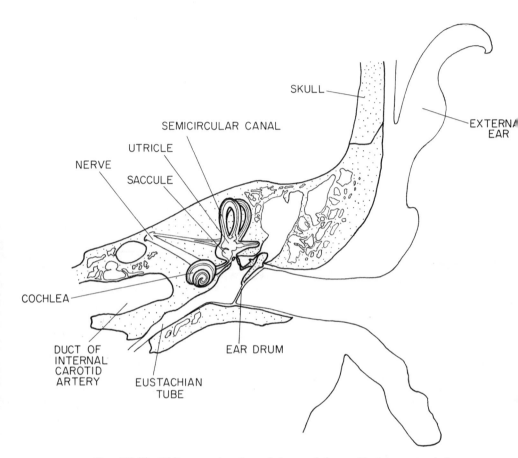

SKULL

SEMICIRCULAR CANAL

UTRICLE

NERVE

SACCULE

EXTERNAL EAR

COCHLEA

DUCT OF INTERNAL CAROTID ARTERY

EUSTACHIAN TUBE

EAR DRUM

FIG. IV (3). *Oblique section through human left ear, 1½ times natural size.*

Here we are concerned with balance and the co-ordination of posture. For simplicity, let us restrict ourselves to the organs found in vertebrate animals. No one sense organ is solely responsible for this facet of sensitivity, and the co-ordination of the relevant messages must rank among the more complex activities of the brain. One of the most important organs is the ear, which is more than a hearing organ. The inner ear is composed of a number of tubes, the intricacies of which have earned them the name of the labyrinth. The tubes, tunnels in the bone of the base of the skull, contain a fluid called perilymph. Inside these canals is a small replica of the system in the form of a thin membrane, itself filled with a similar fluid called endolymph. In certain parts of the membrane are sense cells, such as in the cochlea already mentioned. In two other chambers, the sacculus and utriculus, are found small patches of sense cells called maculae, which respond to sustained directional forces, such as those of gravity and acceleration, as opposed to the rapid multidirectional ones of vibration. In bony fishes these maculae are capped with large calcareous growths known as otoliths or earstones (Fig. IV (4)).

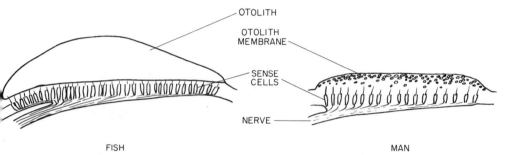

FISH   MAN

FIG. IV (4). *Diagrammatic sections through otolith organs of fish and man.*

Being denser than the endolymph in which they lie, they will exert a force on the sense cells of the macula. Different macula sense cells respond in different ways, some giving a steadily maintained response for any direction of the force, whilst others only act during a change of direction. Between them they signal the direction of the resultant force. A model of this mechanism is photographed in Plate IV (v), but only two sustained response cells are modelled. The utricular macula seems to be more important than the saccular one in this sense perception. Man has no earstones like the bony fish, but a layer of increased density is present over the macula sense cells in the form of small calcareous particles embedded in a gelatinous substance (Fig. IV (4)).

By itself, this sense organ is not sensitive enough to give the brain a clear story in all circumstances. Confusions do not normally occur, but they can be induced in experiments as well as in some more natural circumstances. If a blindfolded person be put on a freely running trolley and given a very gradual acceleration, he may not be aware that he is moving. Conversely, he may be unaware of having stopped if very gradually decelerated from a steady velocity. In less artificial conditions, the same result is often experienced when seated in a railway carriage which is standing next to another train. If the other train fills the field of view and starts moving, it is common to interpret this as the movement of one's own carriage. When the other train has drawn away a feeling of surprise and mild frustration results from finding the track and background quite stationary. The effect depends partly on the lack of vibration and sound clues in a normal slow-moving train and partly on the transmission of any vibration present from the moving to the stationary train. Similar illusions may be experienced in a train at night, or in a tunnel such as the 'underground', if there is a deceleration. This the observer is often inclined to interpret as the stopping of the train, whether it has actually done so or not. If it has not, a similar sensation of surprise may be felt on seeing a track-side light glide past.

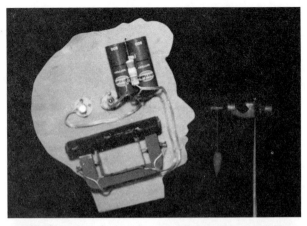

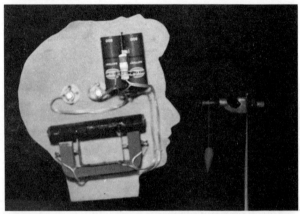

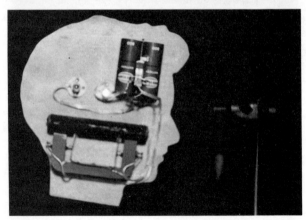

PLATE IV (v). *A model to show the action of the otolith organ of the ear.*
The dark cyclindrical weight (otolith membrane) rests on thin brass strips (sense cells)
connected to wires and lamps (nerve cells). Contact is made at the rear support when
the resultant force has a backward component; the opposite holds for the front support,
while in an intermediate position both contacts are made. The very much larger number
of sense cells in the real animal, combined with the variable message each is capable of
generating, gives the variability needed for the finely graded responses animals make.

In a vertical plane illusions are encountered in lifts, especially if they are totally enclosed and move with a relatively high velocity. The initial acceleration presents no problem in perception, but the final deceleration usually seems to last too long. Either one has failed to evaluate the initial acceleration correctly or has forgotten how great it was and for how long it lasted, since there was a lack of visual confirmation.

It is important to realise that sense organs relying on forces for their stimulation are incapable of recording velocity. The only sense organ which does record velocity is the eye, through the rate of movement of the image on the retina. When the eye is not available, the brain is inclined to interpret the messages from the force-sensitive organs rather coarsely in terms of velocity. The importance of several sources of sensory information in order to be really certain of what is happening is brought out by these illusions, and those sense organs which supplement the ear and eye must now be considered. One of the most important is found in the skeletal muscles, and is called the muscle spindle. It is an elongated capsule lying parallel to the muscle fibres, and itself containing some contractile material. To it are attached nerve fibres, some of which are sensory and transmit messages to the central nervous system, and others of which stimulate the spindle's own contractile fibrils. In any fixed position muscle spindles cause their sensory nerves to discharge steadily, and when the central part of the spindle is stretched, the pulse rate is increased. The sensory nerves run to the spinal cord where they activate other nerves through junctions called synapses. In the simplest cases the next nerve fibre runs back to the muscle directly, where it innervates a number of muscle fibres. Thus there is a simple circuit, or reflex arc, causing contraction. The shortening of the general muscle fibres will then relieve the tension on the muscle spindle, which then reduces its rate of pulse transmission, and the reflex arc settles down to a new rate of discharge. It acts as a feed-back mechanism, and the muscle can keep at the appropriate tension without any attention from the brain.

This mechanism is clearly demonstrated in the knee-jerk reflex (Fig. IV (5)). Here, the tap given just below the knee-cap causes a slight pull on the tendon connecting the tibia or shin-bone with the quadriceps femoris muscles through the knee-cap. The muscle spindles in the quadriceps femoris are thus slightly stretched, and they initiate the reflex arc just described. When the impulses demanding more tension arrive back at the muscle fibres, the contraction extends the knee-joint. It appears a useless movement since it happens after the stimulus has ceased, but normally when the quadriceps femoris is stretched an extra load has been added tending to flex the knee, and the reflex arc serves to resist it. Without such reflexes we would either have to give the brain a great deal more to do or allow ourselves to collapse at the slightest provocation.

When a voluntary movement is to be made the reflex must somehow become unlocked. A message from the brain goes to the contractile material of the muscle spindles. The sensory part of them is again stimulated, this time from a pull internal to the spindle, and the reflex arc again increases its activity, resulting in increased tension in the muscle. Thus the brain does not command the contraction as directly as might be expected; the arrangement is a natural servo mechanism.

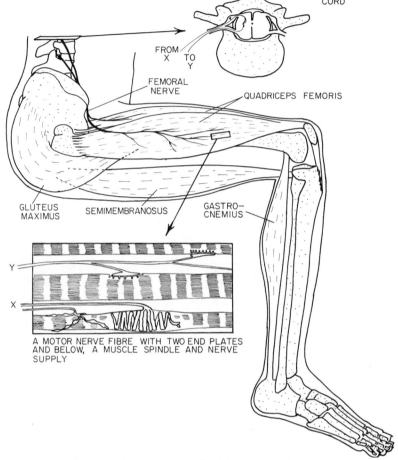

FIG. IV (5). *Simplified diagram of the right leg, showing the main extensor muscles and also the semi-membranosus, antagonistic to the quadriceps femoris. Nerve tissues associated with one simple reflex arc are shown.*

Other stretch receptors are found in tendons, joints, and in the skin. These supplement the information given by the muscle spindles. From a functional point of view they fall into two groups. One is concerned with recording a steady state, and the other with changes from one position to another. The steady-state recorders, such as the finely divided nerve twigs found in the joints, and the muscle spindles themselves, keep up a steady discharge whose pulse rate depends on the degree of stretch. Those concerned with transient movements, such as the *Pacinian* corpuscles of connective tissue and the structures in the joints which resemble them, give a burst of impulses during movement, followed by a decay in the rate to zero. This decay is known as adaptation, and is illustrated in Plate IV (vi).

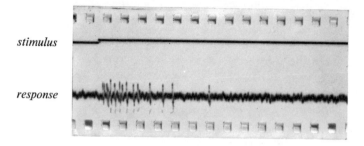

PLATE IV (vi). *Adaptation shown in the sensory nerve leading from a hair sensitive to touch, in the cockroach. A steady pressure was applied at the instant shown on the stimulus line. The whole trace represents nearly 0·3 of a second.*

This is a much simplified picture of the sense organs concerned with balance, but an example will give some idea of the number of messages with which the nervous system must deal. Let us take an athlete at the start of a race. About one hundred and fifty million sense cells in the retina of each eye are being stimulated to encode a picture of the track, and since the picture is not changing the brain is aware that the speed is zero. The image of the ground indicates the angle between the ground and the axis of the eye, but for the purpose of keeping appropriate posture it must be combined with messages from the stretch receptors in the structures connecting the eye with the rest of the head. Similarly, stretch receptors in the neck will relate the attitude of the trunk to the head. Each muscle is automatically maintained at the appropriate tension by its own reflexes from its muscle spindles, and the joint receptors will be giving information on the angles of the limb bones and other parts of the body. The utricular macula of the ear will be indicating the direction of gravity, and this will be combined with knowledge of the attitude of the head as with the eyes. Pressure from the ground and starting blocks on the ball of the foot and toes, and on one knee and parts of the fingers, if the athlete is 'on his mark', will supplement what the ear indicates about the vertical. The semicircular canals of the ear, which will be dealt with later, are indicating that there is no angular rotation. A casual glance down to check that the feet have been correctly positioned will cause nearly all these sense organs to alter their messages; the image of the ground moves rapidly across the retina but the stretch receptors in the neck and near the eye, coupled with the relative change in the vertical indicated by the maculae, show that the body is not falling; all the adapting sense organs affected by this movement will be brought into action, and their responses will then decay away; the movement of the head will alter the centre of gravity of the body slightly, and hence cause reflex alteration of the tension in each of the limb muscles; the feedback reflexes in each muscle will compensate automatically. The return of the head to look down the track will involve a similar number of events. When the starter says 'Get set', some of the limb muscles are voluntarily contracted, the tensions required in each muscle being dictated quite unconsciously from the brain, via the spinal cord and servo mechanisms involving muscle spindles.

At the same time, other muscles which oppose those whose tension has increased are inhibited from contracting. The adapting sense organs are again stimulated. As the starter's gun fires and the act of running begins, the central nervous system has the same kind of problem to solve. During the initial acceleration, it will be recalled, the thrust line from the centre of gravity will be slanting backwards and the utricular macula will record this. The stress in each muscle will be controlled to keep the footfall in the appropriate relation to the thrust line. As velocity increases and acceleration ends, the body must assume a nearly erect posture and each foot must fall in front of the centre of gravity in order to maintain balance (Plates IV (ii) and IV (iii)).

We must now look briefly at nerve conduction, for it is so fundamental to body co-ordination, and up to this stage has been taken for granted. The

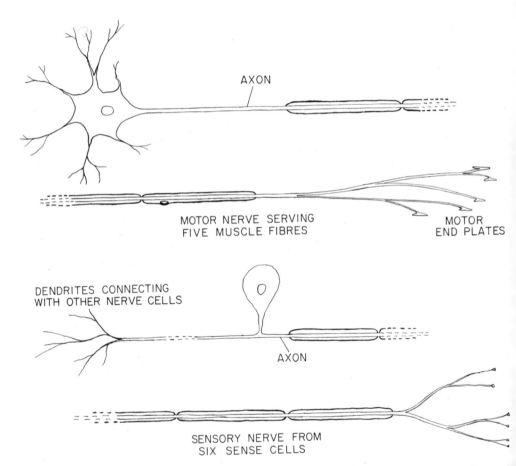

FIG. IV (6). *Diagram of two nerve cells, showing the extreme ends of each only. Note the sheathing cells, which stain with fat stains and are good insulators.*

visible nerves are bundles of a large number of fibres tied together with sheathing material. Each fibre represents a long process or axon of the more compact cell body. The cell body contains the nucleus as with most cells, and also other structures important in metabolism or the living chemistry of the cell. The nervous system may be divided into the central nervous system, which includes the brain and spinal cord, and the peripheral one, which embraces all the nerves running from the central one. The nerve fibres of the peripheral nervous system are divided into the sensory fibres and the motor ones. The former have their cell bodies near the spinal cord in swellings, called ganglia, while their axons run from the sense cells, and, in the other direction, into the spinal cord. The motor nerve cells conduct impulses from the spinal cord, where their cell bodies are to be found, to the muscles and glands. In the spinal cord are found the 'internuncial' neurones, which form the interconnections. Many neurones are in communication with a very large number of others (Plate IV (vii)). Some are of great length—for example, those in the leg of a giraffe.

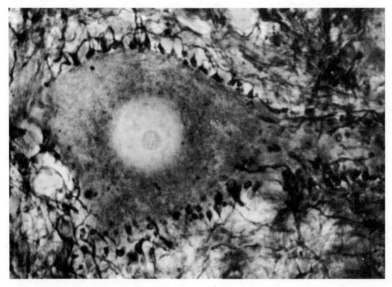

PLATE IV (vii). *A large number of dendrites from other nerve cells shown in contact with the cell body of a neurone (Mag.: × 775). Reproduced by kind permission of J. Armstrong, University College, London.*

The functioning of the nerves has been elucidated over the last twenty years by research techniques, such as the insertion of micro-electrodes into single nerve fibres, and the analysis of the movement of chemical substances across their boundaries. Names associated with these researches are A. L. Hodgkin, A. F. Huxley, B. Katz, and R. D. Keynes.

Nerve cells have been found to have the power of pumping ions, or charged particles, across their boundary membranes. Sodium ions are pumped outwards, and potassium ions concentrate inside the fibres. Since more sodium ions move outwards than equally charged potassium ions move inwards, the result is that the outside becomes positively charged with respect to the inside, to the value of between 0·06 and 0·09 volt, i.e. between about a tenth and a twentieth of a volt. This is called the resting potential. If the resting potential is reduced the threshold level is reached where the resistance of the fibre membrane to sodium breaks down. Sodium then rapidly diffuses inwards, and so much does so that the charge on the membrane actually reverses. This sudden change is called the action potential. Potassium ions then flow outwards and restore the resting potential; the pumping action then more slowly restores the initial concentrations.

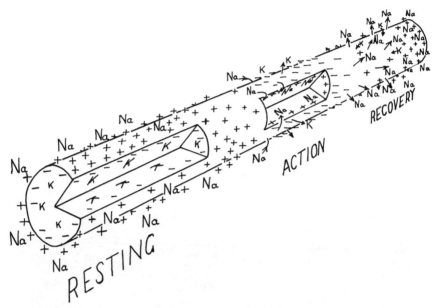

FIG. IV (7). *Diagram representing a small section of nerve axon to show surface charge and excess sodium* (Na) *and potassium* (K) *ions.*

The action potential lasts about one-thousandth of a second. Once an action potential has started it always rises to the full value, and this phenomenon is called the 'all or none' law. A small stimulus to a sense organ will give the same action potential as a larger one, provided it has crossed the threshold. This gives the need for the code already mentioned, where the magnitude of a stimulus is coded as the number of these action potentials, or pulses, per second. Values of several hundred per second may be reached, but a value of 100 per second is probably high for a motor nerve in man. It is limited by a period of insensitivity after the action potential has passed, called the refractory period.

So far the flow of ions described has been across the nerve membrane, but for a nerve to be of any use it must conduct at right angles to this, down its length. Imagine some stimulus to alter the resting potential at a certain point on a nerve. Shapes like nerves act as core conductors, which have the property that potential falls off with distance from any local disturbance as shown in Fig. IV (8) (a). When the threshold is reached an action potential fires off, and there will be a similar decay in potential as in Fig. IV (8) (b). All points between *A* and *B* will now, therefore, move across the threshold, and will generate their own action potentials. In this way the 'spike' spreads out in both directions from the initial stimulation. Normally conduction is in one direction only, for in the body the impulse starts from a sense organ at one end of a sensory axon or from the cell body in a motor nerve. The speed of conduction varies with the diameter of the fibre, and also according to whether it is electrically insulated or not. Non-insulated fibres of about a hundredth of a millimetre (10μ) in diameter conduct at under 5 metres per second (10 m.p.h.). The giant fibres of the squid, on which much of the research has been done, have a diameter of 700μ (0·7 millimetre) and conduct at over 20 metres per second. If they are specially insulated, however, rates of the order 100 metres per second (200 m.p.h.) are achieved in quite narrow fibres. With insulated fibres there is a linear relation between diameter and speed of conduction between the range of size known, from 1 to 20μ.[1] The insulation has been shown by the electron microscope to be a tightly wound spiral formed by special sheathing cells. The insulating material is fat. Each insulating cell covers about 1 millimetre of cell axon, and between this and the next is a gap called the node of Ranvier. The sheaths seem to have the effect of spreading out the core conduction decay curve, thus generating action potentials further away in a given time.

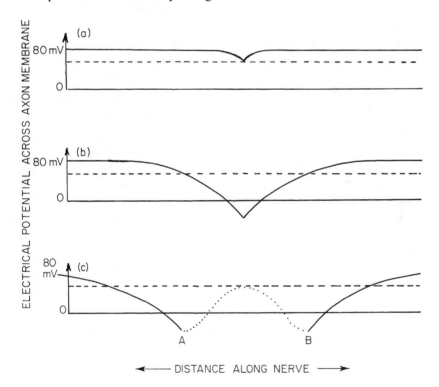

FIG. IV (8). *Generation and spread of an action potential.*

When the impulse reaches a synapse, it finds no direct connection with the next nerve cell. There is a minute gap which the impulse cannot bridge (Plate IV (viii)). Instead, a chemical is given off into this gap, and this has the

[1] Data from Ruch & Fulton, *Medical Physiology and Biophysics*, Saunders 1960.

effect of lowering the resting potential of the next nerve. The first pulse to arrive may not liberate enough chemical to reach the threshold of the next nerve, and in the time which follows the chemical is digested away by an enzyme. However, if another pulse arrives before it has all gone, the effect is cumulative so that the threshold of the next cell may be reached. Alternatively, the kind of chemical liberated may be one which increases the resting potential away from the threshold. Accumulation of this will tend to inhibit

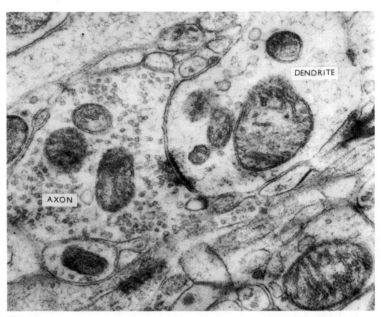

PLATE IV (viii). *A single synapse photographed by electron microscope. Note that a distinct membrane separates axon from dendrite. The axon is loaded with droplets which may be the transmitter chemical. Reproduced by kind permission of Dr. E. G. Gray.*

the activity of the next nerve cell. A cell, such as that shown in Plate IV (vii), in the central nervous system may possess a very large number of connections, and whether a pulse is started or not depends on a process like the counting of votes in Parliament. It is for this reason, and also because of the sheer complexity of the network, that the old analogy of the telephone exchange becomes a gross over-simplification of the nervous system.

The brain of man has been calculated to contain over 10,000,000,000 nerve cells. That is, three cells could be given to everyone in the world from the brain of one person, or to put it in a way which will not date with the current population expansion, put one to an inch, the nerve cells from one brain would encircle the earth six times. The problems of mapping nerve paths in this mass are very formidable, but short cuts have been taken by observing the effects of brain surgery. Another line of attack is to stimulate the brain with electrodes and observe the resulting movement, or ask the patient for the sensations he feels. Conversely, electrical activity can be picked up in certain parts of the brain following stimulation of a sense organ. A simplified version of the results is given in Fig. IV (9).

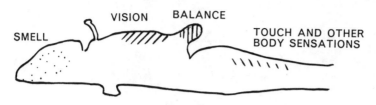

The brain of a primitive vertebrate animal,
giving key used below.

RITA
FROM FAST FLOWING WATER:
WELL DEVELOPED BALANCE

BIRD
WELL DEVELOPED VISUAL AND
BALANCING CENTRES

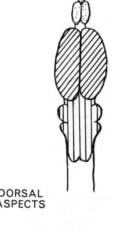

DORSAL
ASPECTS

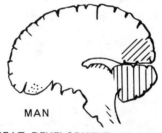

MAN

GREAT DEVELOPMENT OF CEREBRAL
HEMISPHERES NOT FOUND IN LOWER
VERTEBRATES

GURNARD

BOTTOM LIVING:
WELL DEVELOPED
TACTILE CENTRES

PIKE

HUNTER:
WELL DEVELOPED
VISUAL AND
COORDINATION
CENTRES

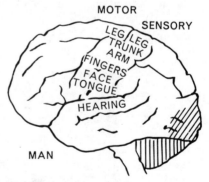

MOTOR

SENSORY

LEG/LEG
TRUNK
ARM
FINGERS
FACE
TONGUE
HEARING

MAN

SURFACE SENSORY AND MOTOR AREAS
OF THE BRAIN

FIG. IV (9). *Some vertebrate brains showing areas concerned with smell, sight,
balance, and other body sensations.*
Based on Part I zoology course, Cambridge (1957).

CHAPTER V

The Action of Muscle

MOVEMENTS on land, in the air, and in water pose very different external problems. Inside the animal, however, the problem is, in every case, that of moving some part of the body. A variety of solutions are found in the animal kingdom, the commonest of which is the use of actively contracting muscle, the same substance as lean meat. Alternatively small whip-like threads, called cilia and flagella, are used by many microscopic animals and even plants, and these must also contain contractile material. A third method is used by the famous Amoeba where pressure may be responsible for a bulge wherever the outer layer softens or liquefies. The protoplasm then flows slowly into the new bulge, expanding it in the process. The most important method from the present point of view is muscular propulsion.

Seen under the microscope, muscle is divisible into two main categories, striated and unstriated. A third and more specialised type is cardiac muscle, found in vertebrate hearts, which is immune from fatigue. Unstriated muscle, otherwise known as smooth muscle, is composed of discrete cells, each of which contains a nucleus in the normal manner. Smooth muscle is relatively slow to act and is found in the gut and bladder of vertebrates. In the gut it normally has an innate rhythm whose rate overall, rather than each individual contraction, is controlled by the nervous system. Such a rhythm is shown in Plate V (i) which was drawn on a revolving drum by a lever attached to an isolated piece of the gut of a worm. This preparation had no nervous input. Smooth muscle can exert a very large force for long periods in the closure of some mollusc shells, like the mussel. It seems that these muscles must be able to lock themselves in the contracted state, for they require little more energy then than when they are resting.

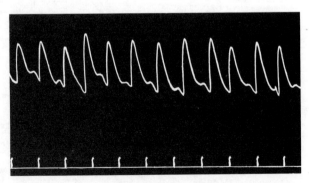

PLATE V (i). *Trace drawn on sooted paper on a revolving drum by a lever attached to an isolated piece of the gut of an earthworm. The lower trace is marked in half-minute intervals.*

68

Other muscle fibres are striated to various degrees, and these are normally associated with rapid movement. Insects, which probably use only this type, have representatives whose wings beat one thousand times per second. In vertebrate animals, striations are normally associated with muscles under the control of the will. A single unit, called the fibre (Fig. V (1) (A) and (B) and Plate V (ii) (A)), is between 10 and 100μ in diameter (1/100 to 1/10 of a millimetre) and varies greatly in length. In vertebrates they seldom extend the full length of the muscle, although some fibres a foot in length have been described. Each fibre contains a large number of fibrils or contractile elements which bear the striations and also many nuclei, unseparated from each other by cell walls. The striations seen under the light microscope were discovered by Leeuwenhoek and also about the same time by Baglivi—around the year 1700.

FIG. V (1). *The structure of striated muscles.*

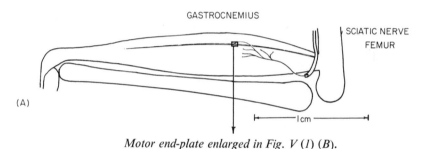

Motor end-plate enlarged in Fig. V (1) (B).

(A) *Calf muscle or gastrocnemius of frog, as used to obtain the traces in Plate V (iii). Only one muscle fibre is shown.*

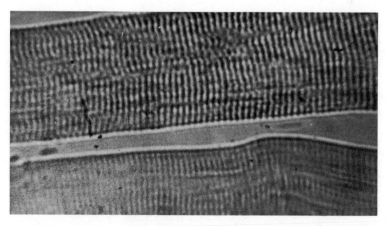

PLATE V (ii) (A). *Longitudinal section of part of two striated muscle fibres. Magnification is slightly greater than that of Fig. V (1) (B) but the resolution is slightly less. Reproduced by kind permission of Dr D. Harrison.*

FIG. V (1) (B). *Enlargement of part of the single fibre showing the motor end-plate.*

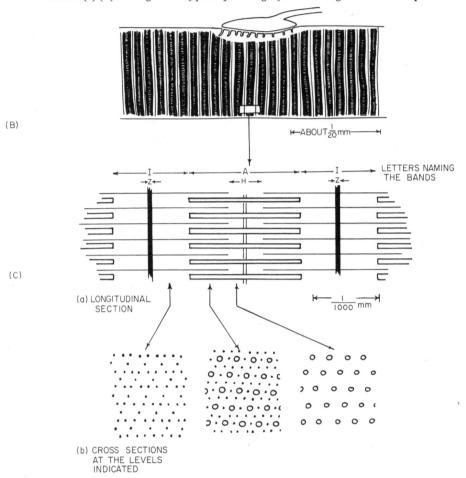

(B)

←—ABOUT $\frac{1}{20}$ mm—→

←—— I ——→ ←— A —→ ←—— I ——→   LETTERS NAMING
→Z←   →Z←   THE BANDS
←H→

(C)

(a) LONGITUDINAL
    SECTION

←— $\frac{1}{1000}$ mm —→

(b) CROSS SECTIONS
    AT THE LEVELS
    INDICATED

FIG. V (1) (C). *Interpretation of electron microscope photograph.*

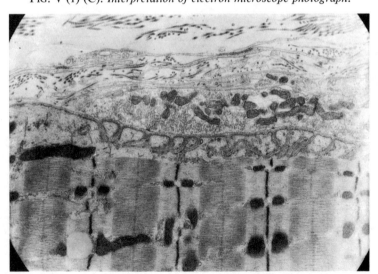

PLATE V (ii) (B). *Electron microscope photograph of longitudinal section of a motor end-plate. Intermediate in magnification between Fig. V (1) (B) and Fig. V (1) (C). Reproduced by kind permission of Professor Miledi.*

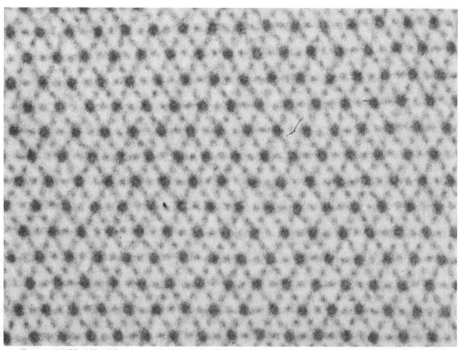

PLATE V (ii) (C). *Electron microscope photograph of cross-section in the* A *band at the level indicated by Fig.* V *(1)* (C) *(b)* (ii). *Reproduced by kind permission of Professor D. S. Smith. First published* Revue canadienne de Biologie 21, *1962.*

PLATE V (ii) (D). *Electron microscope photograph of longitudinal section of striated muscle showing a very small part of the width and length of one fibre. Reproduced by kind permission of H. E. Huxley, F.R.S.*

Various subdivisions of the striations have since been identified, of which the *A*, *Z*, *I*, and *H* are the most important (Fig. V (1) (c)). In 1954, A. F. Huxley was able to show by stimulation with micro-electrodes that the *A* bands move together on contraction of the muscle, reducing the width of the *I* band. The advent of the electron microscope allowed greater powers of resolution, and further striking patterns were observed. The cross-section is a regular pattern of dots which the longitudinal section shows to be bundles of rods. The rods are of two types which have been identified with the two types of protein, actin and myosin, found in muscles. The *A* band was found to be made of myosin, while the actin was present in all but the *H* band. The sliding of one set of rods into the other accounts for both the contraction of muscle and the light microscope observations on the striations. Some biologists were reluctant to accept this explanation, for no such mechanism had been encountered before in connection with living mechanisms. Many observers would have preferred some coiling arrangement. However, the sliding theory resulting from the elegant work of A. F. Huxley, R. Niedegerke, H. E. Huxley, and J. Hanson provides a very economical explanation of the observations. It makes no pretence at describing how the contraction is made forceful, i.e. how the energy-rich chemicals convert their energy into a physical pull, but the ideas of some easily reversible bonding between actin and myosin may prove to be the answer. Such bridges are, in fact, seen under the electron microscope. More detailed reviews are given by H. E. Huxley, *Sci. Am.*, December 1965, and D. S. Smith, *Sci. Am.*, June 1965.

The metabolism, or chemical processes of cells, depends for its energy on the process of respiration. This is normally a breakdown of carbohydrates and their subsequent oxidation to carbon dioxide and water. In animals, the reserve carbohydrate is glycogen, which is stored in muscle and also in the liver. Glycogen can be broken down into units of glucose which is normally taken to be the starting-point of respiration. The glucose molecules are split into two pieces, and if there is oxygen available, these smaller units join a cycle of reactions, called either the citric acid cycle or sometimes the Krebs cycle. As this goes round, the half glucose units which were put in are split up and eventually form carbon dioxide and water. The energy released in this process is stored in a complex chemical called adenosine triphosphate, or A.T.P., which comes from the lower energy form adenosine diphosphate, A.D.P., plus a phosphate group. This reaction is easily reversible, so that

A.T.P.$\rightarrow$A.D.P. + energy in a form which muscles can employ.

When 1 gramme of glucose is completely converted into carbon dioxide and water in this way, about 3,800 calories of energy are liberated. This quantity, if converted into physical work without loss, would lift a ton weight through 5 feet. Unfortunately the body is by no means 100 per cent efficient, and very much less than this is available for working on external objects.

If there is a lack or insufficiency of oxygen, as when strenuous exercise has used up the oxygen reserves in the muscles, and they could use more oxygen than the blood is currently supplying, the output of energy is not yet curtailed. Instead of producing carbon dioxide and water as end-products, respiration

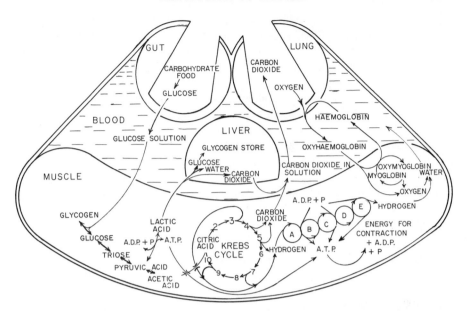

FIG. V (2). *Summary of the main processes of respiration in the body of a vertebrate animal. The numbers 2 to 10 in the Krebs cycle each refer to a different compound. The compounds referred to as (A) to (E) form an 'oxido-reduction chain' passing hydrogen from the Krebs cycle to join with oxygen.*
A.D.P. is Adenosine diphosphate.
P. is a phosphate radicle.
A.T.P. is Adenosine triphosphate.

reactions shunt off down a line ending in lactic acid, before reaching the citric acid cycle. This course needs no oxygen, but unfortunately only yields about one-twentieth of the energy liberated the other way. Lactic acid is poisonous, so only a limited quantity can be held by the body. It produces a feeling of tiredness—a useful safeguard against poisoning oneself! When exercise slackens, and more oxygen becomes available, the lactic acid is operated upon in the liver. Some is broken down completely via the citric acid cycle to carbon dioxide and water, liberating energy which is used to build the rest back into glucose and eventually, maybe, glycogen. The panting which results from hard exercise lasts while this excess of lactic acid is being converted, and whenever there is an accumulation of it in the body, the latter is said, very appropriately, to be in an oxygen debt.

The chemistry of the process is very strictly related to the energy obtainable. Thus if a man uses a certain amount of oxygen, this can be related exactly to the amount of sugar he uses up, and hence to the energy he will make available. His efficiency, expressed by,

$$\frac{\text{work done in moving forces external to the body}}{\text{energy liberated from sugar in respiration}}$$

or more briefly by the ratio,

$$\frac{\text{work done}}{\text{energy used}}$$

is disappointingly low, varying from about 20 per cent to nothing, depending on the type of activity. No heat engine approaches 100 per cent efficiency, and about 25 per cent is a very good figure in ordinary engineering practice. The conversion of biological energy into work in athletic activities is discussed later.

The respiratory activity of cells occurs in small intricate bodies, called mitochondria. The equivalent of these in muscle fibres has been termed 'sarcosomes'. In one kind of muscle they are associated with deposits of myoglobin, a material related to haemoglobin, the red substance of blood. The myoglobin gives these muscles much of their red colour, and as with haemoglobin in the blood, holds oxygen in readiness for respiratory activity. This type of muscle is often found in the parts of vertebrates where there is much work to be done.

Smaller, more delicate movements are often controlled by 'white muscle'. There is no distinct division between the types, which thus represent the two ends of a range. White muscle may be more uneconomical in maintained action owing to its higher speed of contraction. This quicker action may be due to there being a higher proportion of contractile material, and less ground-substance in the fibres.

As we have seen, muscle fibres are stimulated to produce energy, and hence contract, by the arrival of nervous impulses. The wave of changing resistance giving rise to the action potential arrives at the nerve ending, which is enlarged into a pad called a motor end-plate. This area of juxtaposition between muscle and nerve is greatly increased by a folding of the muscle fibre membrane. As with nerve synapses, the nerve action potential does not jump the gap. Minute globules have been observed in electron microscope preparations of end-plates which may be stores of the transmitter chemical (Plate V (ii) (B)).

Muscle fibre membranes have resting potentials across their boundaries, just as nerves do, and action potentials can be made to run down them once threshold values have been reached. The speeds of propagation in vertebrate striated muscle are similar to those of the slower nerves, varying between about 1 and 6 metres per second, being nearer the upper limit in mammals.

A single nerve impulse is usually sufficient to produce an action potential, and hence a contraction in vertebrate striated muscle. The result has the nature of a twitch, which does not reach the force which is the maximum the fibre is capable of exerting. A. V. Hill, in 1951, described a system in which there is an elastic element in series with the contractile one, and for the muscle to exert full force the elastic portion must be fully stretched, the achievement of which takes more than the duration of the single twitch. The closer the twitches, the more do they add up (Plate V (iii)) until there is no relaxation between them, when the state is called a tetanus. Red muscle needs about ten a second for a tetanus and white muscle about thirty. Thus individual muscle fibres can make a graded response instead of the all or none pull they would be reduced to giving if there were no elastic element. The whole muscle has another way of grading its response, for there is no need for all its fibres to be active at once. It will be remembered that a single motor nerve fibre divides and innervates a group of muscle fibres. The group is called a motor unit.

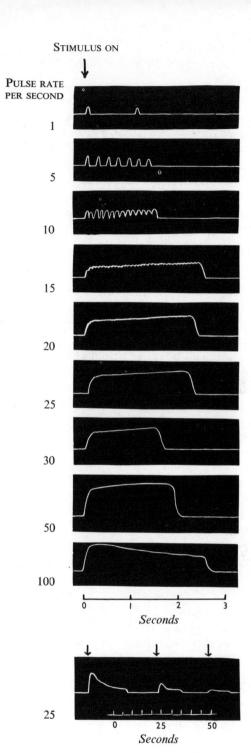

PLATE V (iii). *Records of the contraction of the gastrocnemius muscle of the frog. The muscle is dissected out with the sciatic nerve, which is given electric shocks at variable frequency. One end of the muscle is pinned down, while the other is attached to a lever which acts against a spring when the muscle pulls. The end of the lever draws a trace in soot on a revolving drum. Time runs from left to right.*

The nine upper traces on the fast time-scale show the effect of increasing the stimulus frequency. The lowest trace shows three contractions on a slower time-scale at a stimulus of 25 impulses per second. Fatigue sets in rapidly, but there is partial recovery between periods of stimulus.

Thus when one motor nerve fibre transmits a pulse, all the muscle fibres of its motor unit are caused to twitch, but the rest of the muscle need not make any response. A graded response is therefore possible, ranging between contraction due to the activity of one motor unit to the stage when all the units in the muscle are active. The fairly steady pull which muscles give is the result of summation of the contributions from different motor units.

The number of fibres in a motor unit depends on the job the muscle has to perform. When very accurate control is needed, such as in the eye muscles, it may be as low as two.[1] In postural muscles control can be coarser, and values of 750 in the gluteus maximus, and from 1,000 to 2,000 in the biceps, are quoted.[2]

One of the fundamental properties of muscle is that it can only contract actively. For the return to the original length to be accomplished a second muscle, acting in opposition or 'antagonism', must be used. In vertebrates the skeleton is jointed and internal, so antagonistic pairs of muscles are usually found acting on either side of a joint. Tendons, made of tough white fibrous tissue, form cords allowing large numbers of fibres to act on a small region of bone, and ligaments often loop round tendons, allowing them to act round the concave side of flexed joints, as in the fingers, toes, and wrist. An exception to the situation of antagonistic muscles on either side of a bone is found in the main flight muscles of a bird. Here, they lie beside each other, and while one pulls directly on the humerus or upper arm-bone, the other acts through a long tendon which runs over the shoulder bones to insert on the opposite side of the humerus (see Fig. XII (1)).

Arthropods, a group including crabs, lobsters, insects, and centipedes, combine their skeleton with the outer protective layer. In this case antagonistic muscles lie inside the skeleton, but on opposite sides of a joint hinge. The arthropod equivalent to a tendon is an inpushing of the exoskeleton called an apodeme.

If an animal has no hard parts for muscles to act upon, antagonism is obtained across some fluid pressure system. The earthworm, for example, is soft-bodied, and made of a line of fluid-filled segments. The main muscle system consists of two sheets lying just under the skin. The outer contains fibres wrapped round the body, and the inner one is made of longitudinally running fibres. When the former contract, the segment becomes long and thin, while the longitudinal muscles cause the reverse action. Smaller muscles cause short spines to protrude and retract in the body wall to grip or release the ground in accord with the changing length of the segment. Insect caterpillar larvae depend on a similar system, although here the segments are not isolated by bulkhead-like septa. They have many small muscles whose sole function is to keep up the fluid pressure by pulling the body wall tight round the fluid.

Slugs and snails move on single large feet. Sections of these show muscle fibres running in all directions, not grouped into bundles as in vertebrates. Here a system somewhat similar to the worm's probably holds, in that the

[1] J. Z. Young, *The Life of Mammals*, p. 112.
[2] Starling and Lovatt Evans, *Principles of Human Physiology*, 13th Edition, 1962.

gelatinous foot tissues have a more or less constant volume, and distortions in one direction come at the expense of opposite movements at right angles.

The jellyfish makes use of its non-contractile elastic bell to antagonise the bell-pushing muscles. Thus when the bell pulsates, the muscles which are on the inner surface of the bell are working not only against the water, but also against the natural shape of the bell.

TABLE V (I)

The Approximate Mechanical Disadvantage of some Human Muscles

Muscle	Load, and action	Mechanical disadvantage
Triceps	Load on hand, elbow being extended	22
Quadriceps femoris	Load on foot as in kicking a football	17·5
Semimembranosus	Flexion of knee, load on bal' of foot	8·5
Gluteus maximus	Load on ball of foot, leg extended	8·2
Biceps	Weight in hand, palm upwards	7
Temporalis	Biting with incisor teeth	3·5
Gastrocnemius	Raising body on to ball of foot, leg vertical	2·3
Temporalis	Biting with back molar teeth	1·7

From Table V (I) it will be seen that man has muscles arranged under a mechanical disadvantage; that is, a lever system where they have to exert much greater forces than the loads to which they are applied, since their insertions move through smaller distances than the loads. Such gearing is found in the faster animals—the vertebrates and arthropods. The advantages of this are that limbs can be slim, since muscles can lie alongside bones to insert near joints, and secondly that since striated muscle can only contract through about 30 per cent of its length, the system can magnify the movement which is possible. It is sometimes said that the efficiency of a muscle is greater if it moves through only a short distance, since the loss against viscous forces in distorting itself is less. However, since a larger muscle would be needed to pull against the greater mechanical disadvantage, this would appear to cancel out the saving through having a small velocity of contraction—viscous forces being proportional to velocity.

The lifting strength of a muscle varies as the area of cross-section (see Appendix II). The graph of Fig. V (3) shows an approximate measure of this for a group of people. The area represented is a cross-section of the arm in the biceps region, which will also include a layer of skin, fat, and bone. If we can assume that the relative proportions are the same in arms of various sizes —an assumption which can obviously be only roughly true—this will not affect the shape of the curve, but only the absolute values. The load was always lifted with the arm in a standard position, the elbow flexed at right angles. The points are scattered not only for the reasons already mentioned but also because the mechanical disadvantages of different arms may vary, as well as the relative size of the brachialis muscle, whose widest part did not contribute to the cross-section actually measured. However, despite all these variables, a fair line is obtained. Isolated muscle, which can be connected to weights and measured directly, gives values of 4 to 5 kilograms per square centimetre of cross-section.

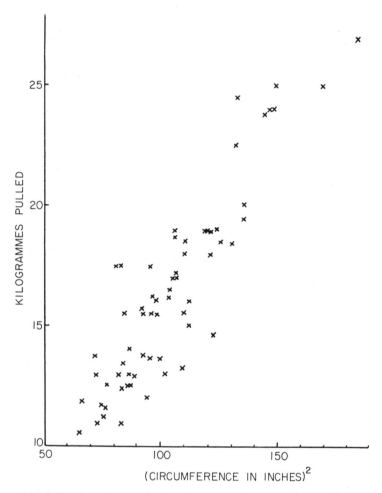

FIG. V (3). *A function of strength plotted against a function of area of cross-section of the forearm in the biceps region.*

It is interesting to compare this force with those required to break certain substances. The following figures are derived from those given by Koch,[1] and represent breaking tensions. Different values apply for compression and shearing forces:

Bone	1,260 kg. per sq. cm.	=	18,000 lb. per sq. in.
Tendon	700 kg. per sq. cm.	=	10,000 lb. per sq. in.
Muscle	5·6 kg. per sq. cm.	=	80 lb. per sq. in.
Hard steel	9,000 kg. per sq. cm.	=	130,000 lb. per sq. in.

[1] J. C. Koch, 'The Laws of Bone Architecture', *Amer. Journ. Anat.*, vol. xxi, p. 177, 1917.

Muscle is very much weaker than bone and tendon, which indicates that the intermolecular forces pulling it together must be very differently arranged from those in normal solids. The greater strength of tendons enables them to be much thinner than the muscles to which they are attached. The architecture of bone is more complicated, since it has to stand compression and shearing as well as tension. Bone substance appears to be laid down partly in response to the internal stresses and strains. Long bones are usually hollow, allowing for strength and economy of weight (Plate V (iv)). Bone compares favourably with steel when the densities are taken into account. Depending upon the variety of either, steel has from about 3·8 to 4·6 times the weight of an equal volume of bone. Thus for equal weights, steel has only just under twice the tensile strength of bone.

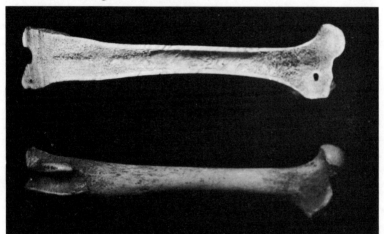

PLATE V (iv). *Internal and external aspects of a dog's femur sectioned longitudinally.*

Although muscle is so weak in the scale of tensile strengths, it makes a much better showing when the force which it can exert is compared with those of some man-made engines. Aircraft engines are suitable, since their weights are reduced as much as possible. Table V (II) shows the thrust to weight ratio for

TABLE V (II)

Table of thrust/weight ratios of five jet engines

Type	Year	Thrust (lb. wt.)	Weight (lb. wt.)	Thrust/ weight
Whittle, W.1	1941	850	560	1·5
Adder	1950	—	—	2·0
Ghost	1947	5,000	1,950	2·6
Derwent	1946	3,500	1,250	2·8
Conway	1960	13,000	3,473	3·75

a number of them built between 1941 and 1960. Care must be taken in choosing a comparable value for muscle. Some authorities quote lifting forces per gramme of muscle, but this means very little if the area of cross-section is not defined (see Appendix II). Taking a muscle the shape of a bicep's, with an area of cross-section of 8 square centimetres, the muscle weight would be about 100 grammes and as it would exert about 35 kilograms, the thrust to weight ratio is about 360—nearly 100 times better than the best engine listed.

We have seen that under a mechanical disadvantage, muscles exert greater forces than they would have to if applied directly to their loads. This does not imply that energy is wasted. Work and energy are defined as the product of the force and the distance it moves its point of application along its line of action. By the principle of levers, if the joints move freely, the muscles exert a large force but move through a small distance. The system only becomes inefficient if the joints do not move easily, but vertebrate joints, well oiled with synovial fluid, probably waste little energy.

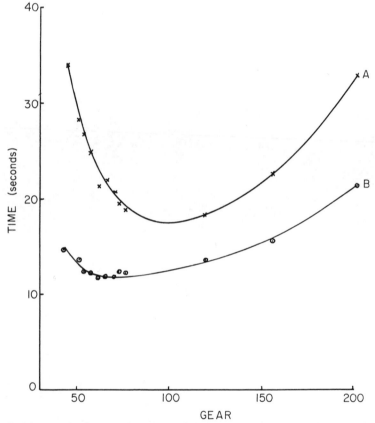

FIG. V (4). *Graph showing the effect of different gears on the velocity and power output of two cyclists.*

Each point indicates the time taken to cycle at maximum speed from a flying start up a slope 100 yards long. The vertical rise was 15 feet 6 inches. The units on the gear axis represent the number of feet travelled by one pedal with reference to the frame of the cycle. Curve (A) is for an eleven-year-old boy and Curve (B) is for a man. Since the course was the same for each record, and there was no acceleration, the time-scale is inversely proportional to the power output of the rider.

(The crank radius was 6·5 inches for the extreme left and four right-hand points in each curve, while for the others it was 6·75 inches. A cycle was specially modified for the three right-hand points which represent gears which would have no commercial value.)

Another simple deduction can be made about the work done by a muscle, and consequently about its power output, or rate of doing work. Vertebrate striated muscle, normally contracting through about 20 per cent, must move its point of insertion through a distance proportional to the length of the whole muscle, as measured parallel to the fibres. Now the force exerted will be proportional to the area of cross-section, so that the work done, which equals the force multiplied by distance, is proportional to length multiplied by the area of cross-section, namely to the volume of the muscle. Assuming a constant speed of contraction, the power or rate of working will thus be proportional to the volume of the muscle also. This assumes that it is being supplied with an adequate quantity of fuel in the form of carbohydrate and oxygen, and having its waste products cleared away.

If it is required to get the maximum work out of a muscle in a given time, there is an optimum gearing to be set. Imagine that a load is applied to the muscle which it cannot shift; then no matter how long our time limit, no work will be done on it. If the gearing is altered to the other extreme, so that the muscle must contract through a great total distance because the force needed is negligible, again hardly any work is done on the load. In this case it is all wasted against the internal viscosity of the muscle itself. Somewhere between these two limits there is an optimum arrangement which allows the muscle to do more work in the set time than any other. This sort of consideration applies to the cyclist. Fig. V (4) shows the performances of a boy and a man riding up a constant slope, using in turn each of the thirteen gears with which their machine was specially fitted. The lowest points on the curves represent the highest outputs of power. An oarsman should have the leverage of his oar and sliding seat adjusted to the similar optimum for the muscles he uses.

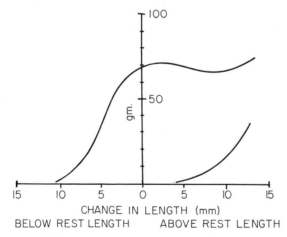

FIG. V (5). *Force pulled by a muscle at various degrees of stretch. The lower right-hand curve represents the static tension during rest. By permission of D. R. Wilkie. First published* Brit. Med. Bull. 12, *pp. 177–182, 1956.*

In the case of both the cyclist and the oarsman, the machinery should be adjusted so that the man is neither too cramped nor stretched out when he is working with his biggest force. Fig. V (5) plots the force exerted by a muscle

CHAPTER VI

The Conservation of Momentum

WE are aware of forces which act upon ourselves and of the fact that they accelerate us. We would also be prepared to say, no doubt, that the bigger the force which we feel—that is the more acutely that we experience the pressures exerted upon our bodies—the greater is the acceleration which we are given. Though we might conceivably draw up a rough scale for forces, like the Beaufort Scale for winds, based upon these general impressions, it would not be possible to obtain a scale capable of being applied quantitatively and accurately in this way. Almost all accurate measurement in physics depends upon the sense of sight, in being able to note the position of bodies at certain times—in the more sophisticated parts of the subject particularly, the position of pointers relative to a scale. In a final analysis it is necessary to base the measurement of force upon something which can be seen. The basic fact of the science of dynamics which is capable of visual demonstration concerns the conservation of momentum, and it is upon this that the system of measurement has been based. Since all other branches of physics assume the validity of mechanics and all other sciences the validity of physics, the conservation of momentum is one of the most fundamental propositions in the whole of science. It is worth spending some time discussing it.

We shall have first to clarify what we mean by the term momentum and some preliminary experiments with our trolleys will help to point the way. The trolleys move with very little friction and so enable us to apply a single force to them and note the result. We will begin with the series of experiments illustrated in Plate VI (i). In this experiment the total weights of the two trolleys have been equalised by mounting the necessary additional load behind the boy on the small trolley. The boys then tow each other by means of the piece of rope. When they do this they approach each other at the same speed. That this is so can be shown by setting up two small pieces of wood in the paths of the trolleys so that they will be knocked down when the trolleys pass. If each piece is mounted the same distance in advance of its trolley, it will be found that they go down simultaneously. On a hard floor they fall with a single sound. The result, moreover, is the same whether the large boy pulls the small one, the small boy pulls the large one, or if they both pull together. The only condition for the success of this experiment is that the pulling should be sufficiently vigorous for the small amount of residual friction to be negligible in comparison with the tension in the rope. A good floor is therefore desirable so as to reduce the friction, and, of course, it must be level. It is better performed indoors than out.

We next examine the similar set of experiments illustrated in Plate VI (ii). Here the additional weight has been removed from the small trolley and other weights added to the large one so that the large trolley and its load weighs twice as much as the small one. Now when the boys tow each other the small trolley approaches with twice the speed of the large one. This can be shown by setting up the pieces of wood so that the small trolley has twice as far to go as the large one before knocking down its piece of wood. Again, it will be found that both pieces of wood fall down together and again, perhaps surprisingly at first sight, it makes no difference whether the boy on the light trolley pulls the boy on the heavy one or vice versa, or whether both pull together.

(A)

(B)

PLATE VI (i). *The interaction of equal trolleys. The total weight of each trolley has been made the same and the boys tow each other with the rope. To show that they approach each other with the same velocity two small pieces of wood have been stood up in the paths of the trolleys at the same distance from each. Both pieces are knocked down at the same instant. The result is the same whether the large boy pulls the small, the small boy pulls the large or both pull together.*

(A)

(B)

PLATE VI (ii). *In this experiment the weight of the large trolley has been made twice that of the small one by placing additional weights on the former. The pieces of wood are set up so that the small trolley has twice as far to go as the large one before knocking them down. In this experiment only the small boy is pulling, but as before it makes no difference whether one or both of them pull.*

In both these sets of experiments we see that if we multiply the total weight of each trolley by the velocity generated in it, the result is the same for both trolleys. When we double the weight of a trolley in comparison with the other, the velocity generated is halved. We might now be tempted to define the momentum of a body as the product of its velocity and its weight. In our trolley experiments momentum so defined would be conserved. The system of the two trolleys started with no momentum, both being stationary, and it ended with equal and opposite momenta in each trolley separately, so that the total would remain zero. However, to do so would make us very liable to circularity of argument when we came to use the quantity so defined in the measurement of force. The weight of a body is itself a force—the force with which the earth attracts the body—and so cannot be specified until we have decided upon a system for measuring forces. We have, therefore, to proceed somewhat differently. Instead of weight we must use mass.

The difficulty in using apparatus like the trolleys just described or the various devices using solid carbon dioxide to reduce friction is that they are not homogeneous. The only way of estimating the total amount of matter in them is by weighing them and this, as we have seen, is difficult to justify before we are equipped with the laws of dynamics which it is the purpose of the experiments to establish. The difficulty can be got over to some extent by including other experiments in the discussion depending upon the property which forces appear to possess of deforming bodies, and the behaviour of elastic bodies, but this is not necessary and is better avoided. If we experiment with homogeneous solids then the quantity of matter in them can be estimated simply from their volumes, so long as they are made of the same material. Suitable objects to use for the purpose are large spherical steel ball-bearings. They are homogeneous—if we wish this can be checked after the experiments by grinding them down and examining the various cross-sections exposed for cracks and cavities—and it is a reasonable assumption that those, at least from the same batch, are made of the same substance to a very high degree of accuracy. We can examine changes in their velocities as they collide and interact with each other. In doing this it is desirable not to roll them over a smooth table like billiard balls because, as we shall see later, rotation then plays an important part, and, as any billiard player knows, spin can markedly affect the behaviour of balls when they collide on a billiard-table. A billiard ball can be made to come back, go forward, or come off at an angle at will, after a head-on collision with another ball simply by imparting spin to it in different ways.

We have to arrange that the ball-bearings can move without appreciable friction and without rotating, and the simplest way of doing this is to suspend them by long threads and study their direct impacts. Such an arrangement is known as a ballistic balance. In the experiments now to be described the velocities were measured by taking photographs of the spheres silhouetted against a very bright background, in an 8-mm. ciné camera running at 64 frames per second. To make the movements sufficiently slow so that satisfactory definition can be obtained, the supporting strings were made long— 18 feet in the experiments recorded in the photographs which are reproduced here. A diagram of the apparatus is shown in Fig. VI (1).

Each ball was supported by two threads so that its motion was confined to one plane. One ball was initially stationary in the centre and the other released to collide with it by switching off a small electro-magnet which holds it to one side. If the incident ball travels in from a distance of about 3 feet 6 inches, its velocity over the central 6 inches or so will be found to be constant to within about 1 per cent. The film is developed as a negative on which the spheres are recorded as white patches on a black background, so that it can be projected and rephotographed on to another plate in a still camera and a number of frames superimposed. Except for Plate VI (iii), as reproduced here the spheres appear also as the negative on the ciné film. The process is very economical of film, each experiment requiring only about 18 inches of the 8-mm. film.

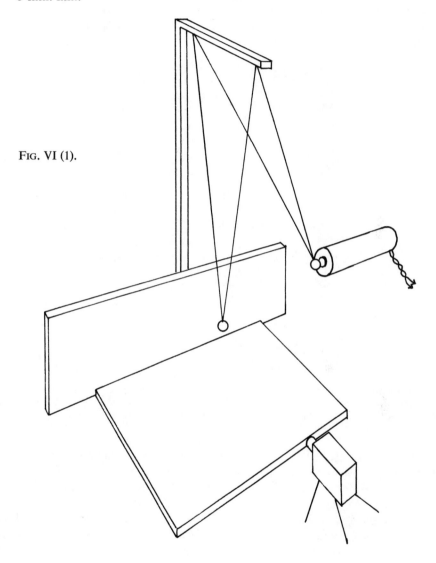

Fig. VI (1).

The first experiment illustrated in the photographs is a repetition of those already performed with the trolleys towing each other. A small spring made of steel piano wire and possessing a volume of about one-tenth that of the small sphere is attached to one of them, so that, when released, it pushes vigorously against the other sphere. Plate VI (iii) is a photograph of the spring and its release mechanism and Plate VI (iv) reproduces successive frames from the film. The two spheres had diameters of 1 inch and $\frac{3}{4}$ inch respectively, so that the volume of the large sphere was 2·37 times that of the small one. The photographs show that, as with the trolleys, the results are practically the same whether the spring is attached to the large or the small sphere. The spring itself, of course, takes up some of the momentum which has to be added to the balance-sheet. Since both the spring and the spheres are made of the same stuff, the volume of the spring has simply to be added to that of the sphere to which it is attached.

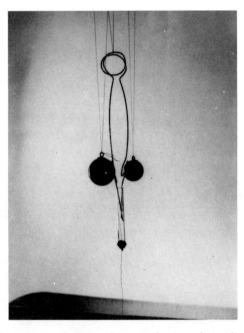

PLATE VI (iii). *The spring set between the two spheres and attached to the larger one. The glass tube at the bottom which holds the spring set is arranged so that it is on the point of falling off. The spring can be released by pulling on the thread at the bottom of the glass tube.*

The velocities of the spheres were determined by projecting the film on to a screen and measuring the successive positions of the spheres by means of a large scale. Taking the unit of mass to be that of the small sphere, so that the mass of the large sphere is then 2·37, the unit of distance to be 1 inch on the screen and the unit of time the interval between successive frames in the film, the momenta generated in the two spheres (the product of the masses and their respective velocities) in the two experiments were measured to be:

     (1) Spring attached to small sphere
        Momentum of small sphere and spring $= 55\cdot0$ units
        Momentum of large sphere $= 55\cdot1$ units
     (2) Spring attached to large sphere
        Momentum of small sphere $= 56\cdot6$ units
        Momentum of large sphere and spring $= 56\cdot6$ units

The momentum generated in the small sphere is equal to that generated in the large one. The agreement is better than one has a right to expect with the apparatus, but errors should not exceed more than a few per cent.

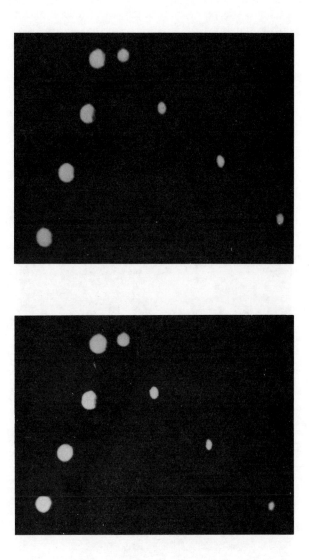

PLATE VI (iv). *Interaction of two spheres.*
Top: *A spring, which does not show in the photograph, has been attached to the large sphere on the left, and when released it pushes against the small sphere, on the right. The photograph shows 4 frames of a film of the subsequent movement of the spheres, when the spring is released. The large sphere moves slowly to the left and the small one rapidly to the right.*
Bottom: *A similar 4 frames from a film taken with the spring attached to the small sphere. The subsequent movement is the same as when the spring was attached to the large sphere.*

The results of a further series of experiments performed with the apparatus are recorded in Plates VI (v) to (viii). It will suffice if we discuss only the first of these in detail. Let us take the case of the inelastic impact of two equal spheres. Here the spheres adhere together, as the result of a small piece of Plasticine attached to the point of contact, and proceed as one body after impact. Measuring the film in the same way as before, we find for the momentum of the incident sphere before impact, 32·0 units and for the momentum of the two together after impact, 31·4 units. In other words, the two spheres together, possessing double the mass of the incident sphere, go away after the impact with approximately half the velocity with which the incident sphere approached before.

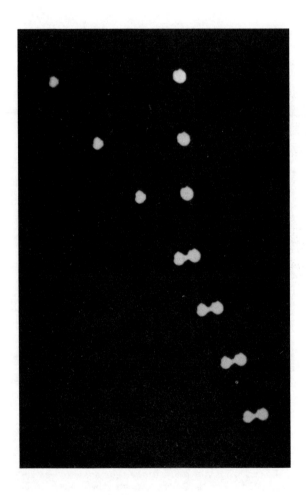

PLATE VI (v). *The inelastic impact of equal spheres. The moving sphere comes in from the left. After the impact, the two spheres adhere and move to the right with half the velocity possessed by the first sphere initially.*

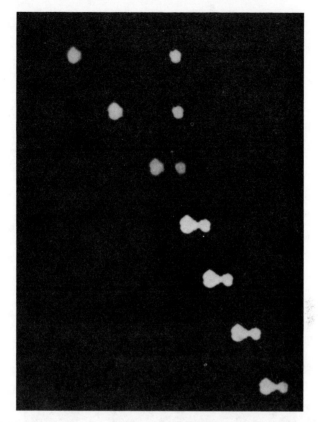

PLATE VI (vi). *Inelastic impact of a large sphere on a small. The large sphere comes in from the left-hand side. After impact the two spheres adhere and move towards the right with a velocity smaller than that possessed by the large sphere initially.*

Plate VI (vi) shows the impact of a large sphere on a small one, the two again adhering together after impact. Since the mass which is moving is only increased by a relatively small fraction when the small sphere adheres to the large one, the velocity of the two spheres combined after impact is only a little less than the velocity of approach of the large sphere. When, however, it is the small sphere which impinges on the large one, as in Plate VI (vii), the velocity of the pair after impact is much less than that of the small sphere before. Measurement of the films as before shows that the total momentum after impact is the same as that possessed by the moving sphere before, within the small experimental errors.

In Plates VI (viii), (ix), and (x) the collision is elastic. No adhesive has been added and the spheres proceed independently after impact.

Plate VI (viii) shows the impact of one sphere upon an equal one. In this case the incident sphere stops completely upon impact and the target sphere moves off with the same velocity as the incident sphere had initially. Measurement of the film as before showed that the incident sphere possessed 44·9 units of momentum before impact and the target sphere 43·6 units after. No movement could be detected in the incident sphere after impact.

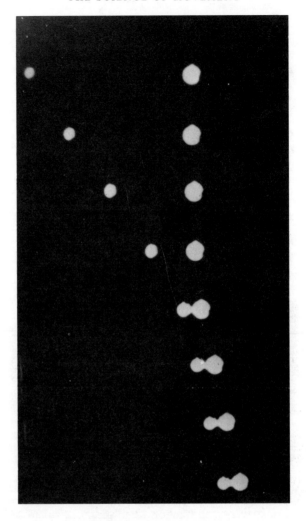

PLATE VI (vii). *Inelastic impact of a small sphere on a large. The small sphere enters from the left and after impact adheres to the large sphere. Both move towards the right after impact, but with diminished velocity.*

Plate VI (ix) shows the elastic impact of a small sphere on a large one. In this case the small incident sphere is reflected backwards after the impact. It is necessary to take into account the fact that its momentum is in the opposite direction in the balance-sheet which works out as follows:

> *Before impact*
> Momentum of small sphere   =   55·6 units
>
> *After impact*
> Momentum of large sphere   =   74·0 units
> Momentum of small sphere   = −19·8 units
> —————————————————————————————————
> Total momentum after impact =   54·2 units

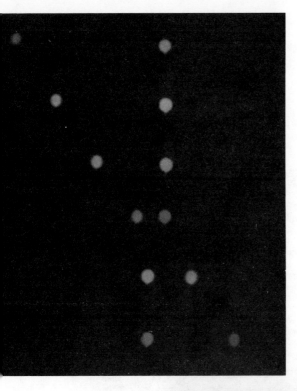

PLATE VI (viii). *The elastic impact of equal spheres. The moving sphere comes in from the left. After impact the moving sphere is brought to rest and the formerly stationary sphere moves away with apparently the same velocity as that with which the sphere initially moving approached.*

PLATE VI (ix). *Elastic impact. Frames from a film showing the impact of a small sphere upon a large one. Every fourth frame is printed.*

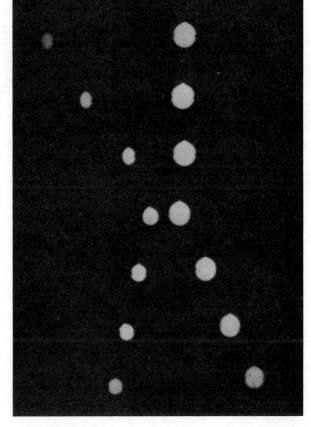

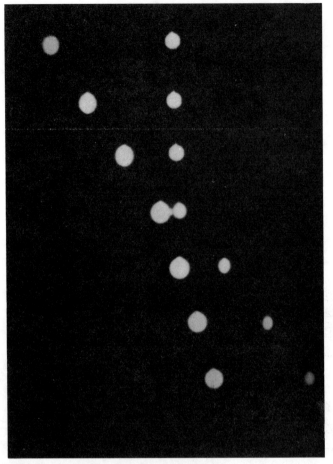

PLATE VI (x). *The elastic impact of a large sphere on a small. The large sphere moves in from the left. After impact both spheres continue to move to the right, the large sphere with a smaller velocity than that with which it started and the small sphere with a higher velocity.*

When, as in Plate VI (x), the large sphere collides with the small one, the large sphere continues on its way after impact but with reduced velocity. The small sphere is knocked on with a greater velocity. Measurement of the film gave the momentum before impact to be 114 units and the total momentum afterwards to be 113 units.

All these experiments confirm the law of the conservation of momentum to within a few per cent. No doubt more accurate measurements could be made given more elaborate apparatus but this is hardly essential. What we require are sufficiently accurate results from which we can derive the laws of motion to a first approximation. The real confirmation of the laws comes when they are applied in astronomy, a procedure which is much more accurate than anything we could do in an ordinary laboratory. By a simple generalisation, our experiments give us a first approximation to the law of the conservation of momentum in a form from which we can argue further. This law is that the total momentum of a system left to itself, measured by the sum of the velocities of the parts of the system multiplied by the quantity of matter in each part (i.e. by the mass of each part), remains constant throughout any interaction between the parts.

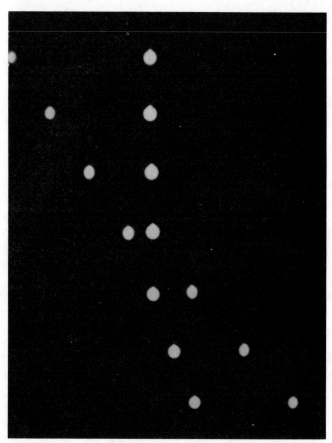

PLATE VI (xi). *Elastic impact of a steel sphere upon a glass one of about the same size. The steel sphere moves in from the left. After impact it continues to move forward with a smaller velocity. The glass sphere moves forward with a greater velocity.*

Plate VI (xi) is of some further interest. It is of the elastic impact of two spheres of equal volume, as before, but here the incident sphere goes on after impact instead of being brought to rest. The target sphere, moreover, goes on with a greater velocity after the impact than the incident sphere had before. The explanation is that the two spheres, although of the same volume, were not made of the same material. The target sphere was of glass, whereas the incident sphere was of steel as before. We can retain the law of the conservation of momentum in this case, however, if we assume that the masses of the two spheres were different in spite of their volumes being the same. Measurement of the film shows that, in round numbers, the incident sphere had a velocity of 9 units before impact and 5 units afterwards, while the target sphere was given a velocity of 12 units on impact. As before, let us call the mass of the incident steel sphere 1 unit and let the mass of the glass sphere be M of these units. Then, if the law of the conservation of momentum still held sway, we would have:

Before impact
Momentum of incident steel sphere $= 1 \times$ 9 units

After impact
Momentum of steel sphere $\quad = 1 \times$ 5 units
Momentum of glass sphere $\quad = M \times 12$ units

Hence, according to the law of the conservation of momentum,

$$9 = 5 + 12M.$$

Giving $$M = \frac{1}{3}.$$

In other words, the glass sphere had only one-third the mass of the steel one. The ballistic balance, therefore, gives us a method of comparing masses which is quite independent of gravity. It is from this fact that it derives its name. The method could be used in a spacecraft in a condition of weightlessness. In such a case, of course, there would be no necessity to support the masses by means of strings; they could be fired at each other directly by hand or by springs.

The conservation of momentum applies in any given direction. If a system possesses no momentum in a certain direction, whatever it may possess in others, it will continue to possess no momentum in that direction so long as there are no external forces acting upon it. Plate VI (xii) illustrates this point. Unlike the pictures of the ballistic balance, which were taken from the side, this photograph is taken from directly above. It is a composite picture obtained by superimposing 6 frames, 3 before impact and 3 after, by re-photographing them on to a plate in a still camera. The two equal steel spheres used were suspended by single threads, the same length as before, instead of double ones, so that they were free to move in two dimensions. They behave like balls on a billiard-table except that the incident ball possesses no spin as would the billiard ball rolling over the table. The incident ball comes in from the top of the picture and strikes the object ball a glancing blow. After the impact the two go off at different angles. The three positions of the object ball shown after the impact are, of course, on the same frames as the three positions of the incident ball after impact. Before the impact the incident ball possessed no momentum in a direction at right angles to that in which it was travelling. It follows from the conservation of momentum that the two spheres must have equal and opposite momenta in this direction, after impact. Since the two spheres were of the same size and material, this can easily be seen to be the case, since both balls travel to the left or the right the same distance in the same time. The two dotted lines from the target ball drawn at right angles to the original direction of motion are respectively equal to the two dotted lines drawn from the subsequent positions of the incident ball. In the longitudinal direction the incident ball travelled 24·5 units between

successive frames before impact. After the collision the incident ball travelled
16·5 and the object ball 8 units in the direction taken by the incident ball
initially, the sum of which is the distance travelled by the incident ball in the
same time before impact.

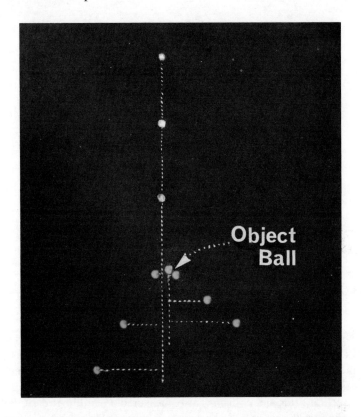

PLATE VI (xii). *Glancing impact of equal spheres. Six frames from a ciné film of the
impact of two equal spheres taken from above. The spheres were supported by means
of threads 18 feet long. The first 3 frames show the approach of the moving sphere
before impact with the 'object ball', as it comes in from the top of the photograph in
which the frames have been superimposed. The final 3 frames show the movement
of both balls after impact. The two balls then move at different angles to the original
line of approach, shown by the dotted line which has been added to the photograph, but
they both move through equal distances at right angles to this line, in equal times.*

It will be seen that after impact the paths of the two spheres are at right
angles to each other. This is not a chance occurrence but is true generally for
the collision of two equal, smooth, and perfectly elastic spheres, whatever the
nature of their impact. To see that this is so let us consider the momentum of
the system, measured along the line traversed by the object ball after impact,
CF (Fig. VI (2)). If *AB* is drawn to represent the velocity of approach of the
incident sphere, its velocity along the line *CF* will be represented by *CB* (see
Chapter VIII). Along *CF*, which is the line joining the centres of the spheres
at the moment of impact, the interchange of momentum will take place as in
the case of direct impact, which we have already studied. The velocity *CB* will

be transferred to the object ball, which will therefore travel along *EF*, while
the incident ball will lose all its velocity in this direction. The latter will,
therefore, travel in the direction *BD*, parallel to *AC*. Thus after impact the
two spheres will travel on paths at right angles to each other.

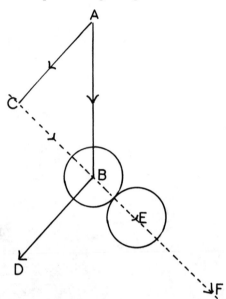

FIG. VI (2).

Measurements on the photograph of Plate VI (xii) confirm this theory.
Fig. VI (3) is a tracing from it. *AC*, which will be proportional to the velocity
of the incident sphere at right angles to the line of impact before the collision,
was measured to be 19 millimetres, *DE*, which will represent its velocity in the
same direction after the collision, also measured 19 millimetres. *CB*, representing the initial velocity of the incident sphere along the line of impact,
was 15 millimetres. *FG*, representing the velocity given the object ball after
the collision, was 13 millimetres.

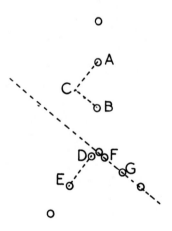

FIG. VI (3).

The theory applies strictly only to spheres which are perfectly elastic, to which spheres of steel are a good approximation. When the elasticity is not perfect we approach the case of inelastic impact, which we have also studied, in which the velocity of the incident sphere is not completely transferred to the object ball. Steel, though highly elastic, is not perfectly so, and the velocity of the object ball after impact is not quite equal to that of the incident ball before. As a result, the two paths, if measured accurately, are found to be only approximately at right angles, although they are very nearly so as can be seen from the photograph.

We are now equipped with as much information as we can readily obtain from elementary terrestrial sources for the basis of dynamics and the next step is to try to build upon this foundation. As has been pointed out before, we are, in fact, in command of more information of this nature than the originators of the science had at their disposal. In his process of 'deducing' the laws of motion from the phenomena, practically the only terrestrial experiments Newton had to go upon were those of Galileo. Newton was, of course, also guided by Kepler's laws of planetary motion. In this book we shall seek to base Newton's laws upon terrestrial experiments only, and leave their celestial applications to furnish their ultimate justification, to render them in Newton's own words, 'general by induction'.

CHAPTER VII

Force and Mass

NEWTON propounded three laws of motion and it is upon these that the whole science of mechanics is founded. It is convenient to consider the second of the laws first. This one deals with the measurement of force and mass. It defines the meaning to be attached to these terms and specifies how a scale of magnitudes is to be applied to them. A definition is a specification of the meaning an author intends to assign to the words he uses and, as such, cannot be said to be capable of being either right or wrong. However, in framing a definition, the author has to have an eye for the happenings in the world of nature. By choosing an appropriate definition, the quantity which is defined may be useful, whereas an inappropriate definition will furnish something which is of little value.

Our general experience of what we would ordinarily term force is that when it is applied to us and is not balanced by any other force of which we are aware, we experience an acceleration. Our experience would also suggest that a large force produces a large acceleration and a small force a small acceleration. An obvious first step to take in setting up a quantitative scale for the measurement of force would be to see what would be the consequences of saying that the magnitude of a force acting upon a body is *proportional* to the acceleration it produces in that body. We can easily measure an acceleration quantitatively by observing how the velocity of the body changes. On the other hand, there is no independent means of checking this concept of a force so that, apart from more or less vague general impressions, we cannot establish the validity of the relation in another way. To this extent the choice of the criterion of acceleration for the measurement of force is perfectly arbitrary. We could equally construct our scale on the basis that the force is proportional to the square—or any other function—of the acceleration. So long as we were careful always to stick to the particular specification we selected, it would make no difference. It is merely a matter of securing agreement upon what is to be meant.

In making our choice of the particular relation to use we would want to be sure that the quantity obtained as the measure of the force fitted in with our general experience in an easy manner. Making the proportionality between force and acceleration the basis of our measurement—by saying that when we observe that the acceleration of a body to have been doubled, the force acting on the body must also have been doubled and so on—implies that when the force is reduced to nothing the acceleration will also be reduced to nothing. In other words, when circumstances appear to make it reasonable to assume that no force is acting upon the body, then we ought to observe no acceleration of its movement. Any motion which the body possesses should then be uniform. The experiments in which we attempted to walk off the long trolley, and when we walked steadily over it without moving it, suggested that this is so. Galileo arrived at the same conclusion as a result of his experiments in rolling balls down inclined planes as the inclination was gradually reduced to nothing. But there is no guarantee that there is no force acting in these cases. When a trolley is set moving and left to itself it slows down gradually. We say that this is due to the force of friction, but friction is only a force which we invent to account for the fact that the movement of the trolley is not uniform.

Another fact which the definition we are considering would imply is that when the force is constant, so also is the acceleration of the body upon which it acts. How are we to recognise a constant force in practice, in a way which does not make use of the acceleration it produces, the appropriateness of which, as a measure of force, we are considering? Historically there was one case which seemed to fall into this category and this was the force of gravity. It appeared reasonable to assume that the force with which the earth attracted a body was constant at a given place on the earth's surface. In particular it seemed reasonable to assume that it would be the same whether the body was moving or not. There was, of course, no alternative method of ascertaining whether this was, in fact, the case or not, apart from measurements of the acceleration, and it remained an assumption, although a plausible one. If the force with which the earth attracted a body did remain constant in this way, however, then the definition of the magnitude of a force as proportional to the acceleration would imply that the acceleration of falling bodies should also be constant. It was this consequence which led to the importance of the experiments of rolling a ball down an inclined plane carried out by Galileo. There was a further assumption in these experiments, of course, but it seemed probable that if the force with which the earth attracted a body remained constant, so would the force which caused a ball to roll down an inclined plane. Timing the ball would, therefore, furnish a test of the constancy of the acceleration of a body when under the influence of a constant force. Our own experiments with the freely falling billiard ball also showed that when moving under the action of gravity alone, the ball acquires a constant acceleration. They, therefore, support the conclusion that the acceleration of a body is an appropriate direct measure of the force acting upon it.

Motion under gravity was practically all that Newton had to go upon in formulating his second law of motion. Using our trolleys we can carry out a simple experiment to demonstrate a similar fact in a different way. It has the advantage of being independent of gravity. A spring requires a certain force to extend it by a certain amount, and, as with the weight of a body, it is a reasonable assumption that when a spring is extended by a constant amount, the force which it exerts will also be constant, however the spring may be moving. On the basis of this assumption we can use a spring-balance to tow our trolley forward with a constant force. We can adjust the rate at which we pull so as to keep the reading of the balance constant. To determine the acceleration we could fit the trolley with a speedometer or, alternatively, we could photograph its movement in a ciné camera as with the experiments of Chapter VI. The graphs in Fig. VII (1) show the results of such an experiment, using a speedometer. The three lines show the results of these experiments, in each of which the trolley was towed with a constant force as indicated by the spring-balance. It is seen that when the trolley is acted upon by a force which the extension of the spring-balance would seem to indicate as being constant, as with motion under gravity, the acceleration is constant.

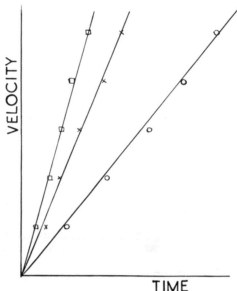

FIG. VII (1).

TIME

Other apparatus in which a presumably constant force is applied to a body by means of a spring stretched by a constant amount has been designed. They all show that under these conditions the body so acted upon acquires a constant acceleration, and the upshot of all of them is to indicate that a definition of the magnitude of a force as proportional to the acceleration it produces would be a reasonable one. Nevertheless, it is of importance to remember that the decision to adopt this method of measurement is arbitrary and that other definitions are possible.

Adopting this definition we would have, using F for the magnitude of the force and a for the acceleration it produces in a given body,

$$F = Ma$$

in which M is a constant. This relation merely says that if we notice that the acceleration of a body is doubled we agree to say that the force acting upon it is also doubled, and so on.

Common experience tells us that it is more difficult to accelerate a large body than a small one of the same kind, and that we would expect that the same force applied to the large body would produce a smaller acceleration than when it is applied to the small body. This is supported by observations in which the identity of the force applied in the two cases is made very plausible, for example by the constant extension of a spring-balance. The constant M will therefore depend upon the body upon which the force acts. When the body is large and the resulting acceleration is small, M must be large (M multiplied by the acceleration must remain the same when we use the same force). The constant M which is characteristic of the body being acted upon is called the body's mass. The mass of a body, therefore, measures the difficulty we experience in setting it in motion—in giving it, that is, an acceleration.

Newton's relation,

$$F = Ma,$$

provides us, therefore, with a means of measuring both force and mass. If we take a standard body and allow various forces to act upon it, the accelerations produced give a measure of the forces. For example, if our standard body is the pound, which is a piece of platinum kept in a certain standardising laboratory, then the unit of force would be that force which produces in it an acceleration of 1 foot per second per second. It is called the poundal. A force of 2 poundals would be that force which produces an acceleration of 2 feet per second per second in the standard pound.

If the standard pound were allowed to fall freely, the force with which the earth attracts it would produce in it an acceleration of about 32 feet per second per second. This force, which is called the weight of the pound (or 1 pound weight), will be about 32 poundals. Put round the other way, a poundal is about the weight of half an ounce.

If instead of the pound we use the standard kilogram, which is another lump of platinum kept in a different standardising laboratory, then the force which produces an acceleration in it of 1 metre per second per second is called the newton. Since gravity produces an acceleration of 9·81 metres per second per second, the weight of the kilogram is 9·81 newtons.

If we denote the acceleration produced by gravity by g then the weight of a body of mass M will be

$$W = Mg.$$

If M is in pounds and g is in feet per second per second, the weight will be expressed in poundals. If M is in kilograms and g is in metres per second per second, the weight will be in newtons.

By writing Newton's relation

$$M = \frac{F}{a}$$

we see that it provides us not only with a means of measuring force but also with a means of measuring mass. Suppose that by means of a spring-balance extended by a constant amount we apply the same force to a number of different bodies, then their masses will be inversely proportional to the accelerations produced. If the acceleration of one body is double that of another, then it follows that its mass must be half that of the second one. When we double the acceleration we halve the time taken to acquire a given velocity. Thus mass may be defined as the time taken by a standard force to generate unit velocity. This definition of mass is important. We shall need to return to it when we come to consider the analogous case of moment of inertia in the dynamics of rotation.

In particular, if as our standard force we take the poundal and as our unit of velocity 1 foot per second, then a body will have a mass of 1 pound if it takes the poundal 1 second to generate in it a velocity of 1 foot per second. It will have a mass of 2 pounds if it takes 2 seconds for the same force to generate the velocity of 1 foot per second in it, and so on. Similarly, any body will have a mass of 1 kilogram if it takes 1 second for a force of 1 newton to generate in it a velocity of 1 metre per second.

As we shall see later, in rotational mechanics we measure the inertia of bodies to rotation by applying rotational forces to them and noting the time taken to generate a given angular velocity. In practice, however, the mass of a body—that is its inertia towards linear motion—is not measured in this way. We do not measure masses by accelerating bodies with known forces, because there is another and much more convenient and accurate method of arriving at the same result. In practice the effect of gravity is employed for comparison.

Since all bodies acquire the same acceleration under the action of gravity it follows from the relation,

$$W = Mg,$$

g being constant, that the weight of a body is proportional to its mass, M. If, therefore, we compare the weights of two bodies we automatically compare their masses. Two bodies will only be counterpoised when placed in the pans of a balance if their masses are the same. The accelerational constant g varies slightly from place to place on the earth's surface, but since it will always be the same for both bodies in the balance at the same place, two bodies which counterpoise each other at one place will always counterpoise each other wherever the balance may be set up. So long as the same set of 'weights', or accurate copies of them, are employed, a balance will, therefore, always weigh out the same quantity wherever it may be. A spring-balance, on the other hand, does not compare the weights of two bodies but measures one at a time. Its readings give the value of $W = Mg$. They will thus vary as the value of g varies.

An ordinary balance compares the weights of two bodies at the same place, and since g will then be the same for both it also compares their masses. There is no call to be pedantic about it, however. If we are thinking about the forces exerted by gravity upon the pieces of brass inside the box which goes with our balance, there is no reason why we should not call it, if we wish, a box of weights. If we are thinking about the masses of the pieces of brass, we can call it a box of masses, but in either case it is about an attribute of the pieces of brass that we are thinking and neither the weights nor the masses are really inside the box. To be strictly accurate it is a box of standardised pieces of brass.

Newton expressed his second law, which we have been considering so far in this chapter, in the form that the rate of change of momentum of a body is proportional to the impressed force and takes place in the same direction. If the mass of a body is constant its rate of change of momentum is equal to its mass multiplied by the rate of change of its velocity, which is the form in which it has been given above. It is, as we have seen, of the nature of a convention defining how force should be measured.

It follows from the second law that if no force acts upon a body then its acceleration will be zero; that is to say, its velocity will be constant. This is Newton's first law of motion, which he expressed in the form that every body continues in a state of rest or of uniform motion in a straight line unless it is acted upon by an impressed force. Since it is a particular case of the second law, which is a convention, it follows that the first law is also a convention. We can easily see that this is so if we remember that we have no means of telling whether a body is acted upon by a force or not, other than by observing whether or not it possesses an acceleration. We agree to say that a body which is in uniform motion in a straight line is acted on by no resultant force. The experiments, such as those of Galileo and our own of walking over the trolley, show that this convention is a reasonable one and is in line with our qualitative experience.

It now remains to consider Newton's third law of motion. This is that when two bodies act upon each other with forces, the force which one exerts upon the other is equal and opposite to that which the second exerts upon the first. This law is a statement of fact and is not, therefore, a convention. We cannot decide upon the properties of matter by issuing a definition from the study. Given Newton's second law, however, it is a simple matter to deduce the third from the law of the conservation of momentum, which we have demonstrated experimentally to a first approximation, by the experiments described in the last chapter.

Suppose that we have two bodies which act upon each other and let F_1 be the force acting upon the first body and F_2 that on the second. Both forces will act for the same time, t. Let M_1 and a_1 be the mass and acceleration of the first body, and M_2 and a_2 those of the second. Then we shall have

$$F_1 = M_1 a_1$$
and
$$F_2 = M_2 a_2.$$

Multiplying by t we have,

$$F_1 t = M_1 a_1 t = M_1 v_1$$

where v_1 is the change in the velocity of the first body.

Similarly,

$$F_2 t = M_2 a_2 t = M_2 v_2$$

where v_2 is the change in the velocity of the second body. But from the law of the conservation of momentum we have,

$$M_1 v_1 = - M_2 v_2.$$

Therefore,

$$F_1 = -F_2.$$

That is to say, as Newton put it, action and reaction are equal and opposite.

On the basis of our qualitative experience and the experimental law of the conservation of momentum, we have arrived at Newton's laws of motion. Upon these three laws the whole of Newtonian mechanics was erected. It is true that we have only obtained the laws to a first approximation, of the order of a few per cent, but this will suffice for a discussion of most of the problems of movement which we meet in everyday life. The laws of motion, however, are thought to be accurate with very much greater precision than this. Confirmation of the laws of motion to a high degree of accuracy is a different matter and lies outside the scope of this book. Here it must suffice to say that the labours of mathematicians of the eighteenth century applied Newton's laws to the movement of the planets and other celestial bodies with almost complete success. The laws were confirmed to a very high degree of accuracy indeed. In fact, the laws remained entirely intact for over 200 years. The theory of relativity has now made some modifications in the results, but none which are of any effect in the consideration of the common problems to which we shall turn our attention in this book.

CHAPTER VIII

Weight and Weightlessness

WE have seen from the fact that all bodies fall with the same acceleration under gravity when released that the force of attraction exerted by the earth on a body is proportional to its mass. It follows from the third law of motion that the body will also exert an attractive force on the earth. When Newton saw the apple fall from the tree, the possibility struck him that it might be the same force which kept the moon in its orbit round the earth as made the apple fall. He was thus led to investigate the effects which would occur if every particle of matter in the universe attracted every other particle with a force which is proportional to the product of their masses. If Newton's force of universal gravitation was the agent which maintained the solar system in being, it is a comparatively simple matter to show that the force must also vary inversely as the square of the distance between the particles, but we shall omit the calculation in this book since it does not affect the terrestrial movements in which we are primarily interested. It was not until the closing years of the eighteenth century that gravitational attraction between bodies which could be handled in the laboratory was demonstrated by Henry Cavendish.

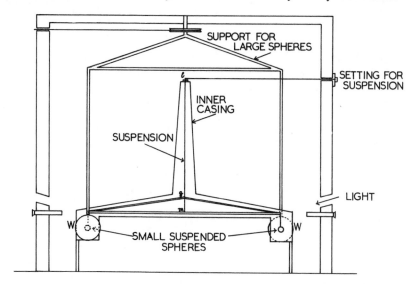

FIG. VIII (1). *Cavendish's apparatus for the measurement of the Constant of Gravitation.*

The original plan for such an experiment was conceived by the Rev. John Michell, who actually made the apparatus for the purpose but did not live to perform any measurements with it. After his death his apparatus passed to Professor Wollaston, who gave it to Cavendish. Cavendish, however, remade most of it and set it up in a special room to prevent draughts, which he constructed in an outhouse in his garden at Clapham Common. A diagram of his apparatus is reproduced in Fig. VIII (1). Two large spheres of lead, W, each 1 foot in diameter, were brought near the two small spheres, also of lead and of 2 inches diameter, which were suspended from an arm carried by a torsion wire lgm. The twist in the torsion wire as the large weights were changed from one side to the other of the small spheres was measured by means of a fixed ivory scale. The difference in the two positions was of the order of a third of an inch. Cavendish measured the force required to twist the torsion wire through this angle and thus obtained the force of attraction between the masses. If the force of attraction between two bodies whose masses are M_1 and M_2 kilograms is F, then

$$F = \frac{GM_1M_2}{r^2}$$

when they are r metres apart.

In Cavendish's experiment, F, M_1, M_2, and r are all measured and so the constant G can be calculated. It is known as the gravitational constant and must not be confused with the acceleration caused by gravity at the surface of the earth which is usually written g.

The value obtained by Cavendish was close to that obtained from modern experiments, which is $6 \cdot 670 \cdot 10^{-11}$ M.K.S. units. From it we can easily calculate the mass of the earth. Consider a kilogram at the earth's surface. It is acted upon, as we have seen, by a force of 9·81 newtons. The surface of the earth is 6,360,000 metres from the centre of gravity of the earth where its mass can be taken to be concentrated. Thus if M is the mass of the earth

$$9 \cdot 81 = 6 \cdot 670 \cdot 10^{-11} \frac{M}{6,360,000^2}$$

which gives $M = 5 \cdot 98 \cdot 10^{24}$ kilograms.

The mass of the moon is only $\frac{1}{81}$ of that of the earth and its radius is 1,770,000 metres, so that the force of attraction exerted by the moon on a kilogram on its surface is

$$6 \cdot 670 \cdot 10^{-11} \frac{5 \cdot 98 \cdot 10^{24}}{81 \cdot 1,770,000^2}$$

which is approximately 1·57 newtons. Weights on the moon are thus about one-sixth of what they are on the earth.

Before leaving this topic the methods whereby the size and mass of the moon were obtained should be explained. The size of the moon is obtained by straightforward trigonometrical survey. The points on the earth's surface which are as far apart as possible (e.g. Greenwich and the Cape of Good Hope where there are observatories) provide a sufficient base-line for the moon's distance to be determined. The angular diameter of the moon (about $\frac{1}{2}°$) is also easily measured and the two results combined furnish the moon's diameter. The mass of the moon is obtained from the fact that it is not the earth which traverses the elliptic orbit round the sun, but the centre of gravity of the earth : moon system. The earth and moon circle round their common centre of gravity once a month. The result is to introduce a monthly fluctuation in the position of the sun as seen from the earth, and the size of this fluctuation gives the position of the centre of gravity of the earth and moon. It is 81 times nearer the earth than the moon, so that the mass of the moon is only $\frac{1}{81}$ of that of the earth. One result of the moon's smaller mass is that it is not large enough to retain an atmosphere.

When we stand upon the surface of the earth all parts of our body are attracted downwards with the force of their weight. They are prevented from descending, however, by the reaction of the ground, which takes the form of an upwards force applied to the soles of our feet. All parts of the body have to be supported, however, and so they each press downwards on the body tissue which carries them. The supporting tissues, in turn, exert upward forces on the parts they support. The resulting thrusts and tensions experienced in the body give rise to the sensation of weight.

Suppose that we now stand on the floor of a lift which starts to descend with a certain acceleration, less than that of gravity. Some part of the weight of our body is then required to generate the same downward acceleration in us as the lift possesses. The force between the floor of the lift and our feet will be lessened. Only the difference between our full weight and that fraction of it which was required to produce our acceleration would have to be balanced by the upwards force exerted by the floor. Similar considerations would apply to each part of the body. A fraction of their weight would be used up in generating their downward acceleration and only the remainder would have to be carried by the supporting tissues. The sensation of the possession of weight would decrease.

If now the lift descended with the acceleration of gravity, all our weight would be required to generate our downwards acceleration so that we kept pace with the lift. We would simply fall downwards at the same speed as the lift, keeping station inside it wherever we might happen to be. We would be in a condition of free fall and the sensation of weight would have disappeared entirely. We would experience a state of weightlessness. Whenever we fall freely we experience the same thing. The experience is thus a common one, though normally it lasts for only a very short time. We have it whenever we jump off a height until we land on the ground. Apart from the parachutist, who experiences it for some time as he falls before his parachute opens, the longest common experience of it is provided by a high dive or a high jump on a trampolin. The parachutist continues to experience it until he falls fast enough for the resistance of the air to be sufficiently great to support his weight. As soon as he reaches his terminal velocity, the air resistance equals his weight and he falls at a steady speed. His downwards acceleration disappears and with it the experience of weightlessness.

Jules Verne, that pioneer of science fiction, wrote a book called *Journey to the Moon* in which he anticipated much of modern space travel, but he did not appreciate the phenomenon of weightlessness. His voyagers were shot to the moon in a large shell. According to the story, while they remained within the gravitational field of the earth they rested comfortably on the base of the shell, but as they entered the field of the moon their weight became less and was finally directed towards the nose. This is incorrect. During the whole flight they would be in a state of free fall and would experience weightlessness all the time.

If our lift descended with an acceleration greater than that of gravity, then the top of the lift would have to press downwards on us to accelerate us sufficiently to keep pace. Our weight would be insufficient of itself to do this. We would, in fact, be able to stand upside down on the ceiling. If the lift descended with twice the acceleration of gravity, we would press on the ceiling with a force equal to our weight. We would experience the sensation of weight just as when standing ordinarily on the ground, except that our weight would be directed upwards towards the ceiling apparently.

The sensation of weight can be increased, decreased, or removed altogether by the acquisition of an acceleration. The effects of weight are identical to those arising from the possession of an acceleration in the opposite direction. If we are accelerated upwards we feel as if we possessed an additional weight acting downwards. This equivalence of weight and acceleration was the basis of Einstein's theory of gravitation which is known as the General Theory of Relativity.

PLATE VIII (i). *One ball has been projected horizontally at the same time as a second has been allowed to fall vertically. Both balls cover the same distance vertically in the same time. The picture consists of successive frames from a ciné film superimposed. The ball which has been projected horizontally covers equal distances horizontally in equal intervals of time, at the same time as it falls vertically.*

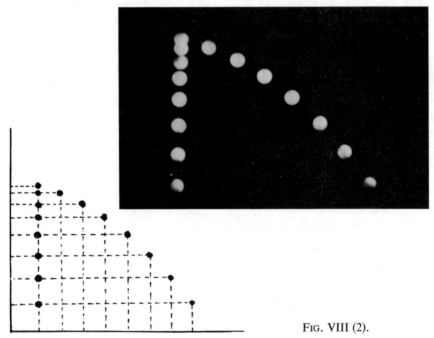

FIG. VIII (2).

The weight of a body is a vertical force and therefore alters the vertical momentum of the body only. It leaves unaltered any momentum the body may possess in a horizontal direction. Plate VIII (i) shows successive frames from a ciné film of a ball which is released and allowed to fall vertically at the same time as another is projected horizontally. Both fall through the same vertical distance in the same time. The ball which is projected horizontally travels uniformly in the horizontal direction, covering equal distances in equal times. Fig. VIII (2), which is a tracing from the photograph, illustrates these points. Plates VIII (ii) and VIII (iii) show a rather pretty variation on this. If

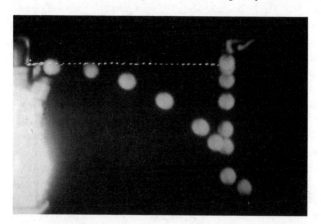

PLATE VIII (ii). *A ball projected horizontally and aimed directly at another which is dropped at the same instant, collides with it in mid-air.*

PLATE VIII (iii). *A ball which is aimed, at an angle to the horizontal, at another which is allowed to fall at the same instant that the first is projected will always collide with it in mid-air.*

the ball which is projected horizontally is aimed at the other ball from a point some distance away, then the two will collide in mid-air if both balls are released at the same time. The simultaneous release of the two balls is easily arranged if the one which is projected horizontally interrupts the current in a small electro-magnet which supports the other. An even more striking demonstration is to project one of the balls upwards at an angle to the horizontal. So long as the initial direction of projection passes through the position from which the other ball starts, the two will again collide in mid-air. This is shown in the photographs of Plate VIII (iii). The same point is sometimes illustrated by a simple story. A man shot at a monkey hanging from a branch of a distant tree. On seeing the flash of the gun the monkey dropped from the branch. However, the shot hit him just the same. The shot will have fallen the same distance below the point aimed at, as the monkey dropped in the same time. The story supposes that the gun used was not provided with sights adjusted to counteract the effect of distance but was simply pointed at the monkey direct, and the monkey reacted instantaneously.

Suppose that a ball is attached to the roof of a lift descending with the acceleration of gravity. Its position after successive intervals of time would correspond to those of the ball which descended vertically in Plate VIII (ii). If a man in the lift threw the second ball at the first, then its successive positions would be those of the left-hand ball in the same plate. The man in the lift, however, would accelerate downwards, so that he and the two balls would always be in the same straight line—all three being at equal distances below their initial positions. To the man, therefore, the ball he threw at the first would appear to travel in a straight line towards it and finally hit it. The man in the lift would be in a state of weightlessness and thus not only he himself but also all the objects which travelled with him would appear to him to be without weight.

With a lift accelerating upwards, on the other hand, the apparent weight of everything on board is increased. Extra forces, over and above their normal weights, have to be applied to objects to give them the upward acceleration. If the upward acceleration of the lift is a feet per second per second, the apparent weight of an object of mass M pounds becomes $M(g + a)$, instead of Mg poundals. With violent accelerations the effects of these increased forces can be very great. At two or three times the normal gravitational acceleration—at 2 or $3g$ as it is called—the increased weight of the blood causes it to drain into the lower parts of the body. If the body is vertical, blood leaves the head and causes a black-out. Above $9g$ the body no longer is strong enough to support its own weight. Astronauts, being rapidly accelerated to high speeds by means of rockets, lie flat on their backs in form-fitting rubber couches to enable them to withstand the effects of their increased 'weights'. Insects which collect on the windscreens of motor-cars travelling at moderately high speeds actually disintegrate in the air before striking the vehicle. They are displaced by the air currents to which the car gives rise, and they are not built sufficiently robustly to withstand the accelerations involved. A bird can similarly be killed by a vehicle travelling rapidly, although it does not come into direct contact with it. It can be thrown so vigorously over the top while flying that it suffers fatal internal injuries.

The fact that the vertical and horizontal velocities act independently of each other is a particular case of an important principle. If a body is given two displacements, s_1 and s_2 (Fig. VIII (3)), it will clearly be transferred to the end of the diagonal, R, of the parallelogram formed by the two displacements.

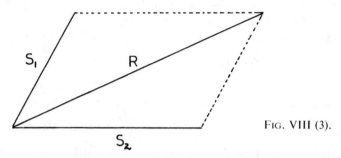

FIG. VIII (3).

Velocities, which are rates of change of displacements—that is to say, displacements divided by the times in which they occur—will similarly combine by the parallelogram rule. The same is true for accelerations which are rates of change of velocities. Since forces are proportional to accelerations, they too will combine according to the same law.

A velocity may be looked upon as being equivalent to a pair of velocities which have it for the diagonal of the parallelogram which they form. There are many such pairs as Fig. VIII (4) shows. A velocity v at an angle θ to the horizontal can be decomposed into a horizontal velocity $v \cos \theta$, together with a vertical velocity $v \sin \theta$. These are known as the horizontal and vertical components of the velocity.

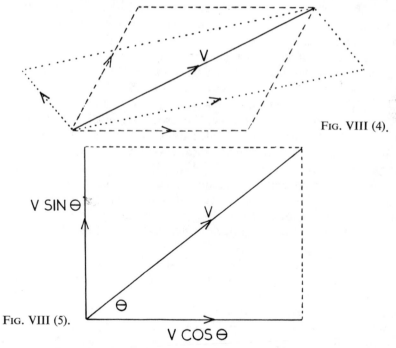

FIG. VIII (4).

FIG. VIII (5).

When a body is projected with velocity v at an angle θ to the horizontal, it travels upwards and then downwards in the vertical direction as though it had been thrown vertically upwards with the velocity $v \sin \theta$. In the horizontal direction it travels uniformly forward with the velocity $v \cos \theta$.

Its time of flight is determined entirely by the vertical component. In the vertical direction it has an acceleration of g feet per second per second, downwards. Its vertical velocity, $v \sin \theta$, will therefore be destroyed in $\dfrac{v \sin \theta}{g}$ seconds. The projectile is then at the top of its flight. It then descends and takes as long in coming down as it did in going up. The total time of flight is thus $\dfrac{2v \sin \theta}{g}$ seconds. During this time it travels forward with a velocity $v \cos \theta$, so that the distance it travels before it strikes the ground (its range) is

$$R = \frac{2v^2 \sin \theta \cos \theta}{g}.$$

When a ball is thrown into the air, it will stay up longest if thrown up vertically. It will then, however, possess no horizontal velocity, so that its range will be zero. If, on the other hand, it is projected nearly horizontally it will be given a large horizontal velocity, but, since it has only a small vertical velocity, its time of flight will be small. Again its range will be small. Somewhere between these two extremes will be an angle for which the range is greatest. Plate VIII (iv) shows the flight of a tennis ball projected at various angles by means of a simple catapult stretched by always the same amount. When the angle of projection is high, the range is short and it is also short when the angle of projection is low. Maximum range is obtained for an intermediate angle of projection.

Elementary textbooks often contain a discussion which purports to show that the maximum range is obtained when the angle of projection is 45°. The discussion assumes that the velocity of projection remains constant as the angle of projection is varied, but this is rarely the case. In spite of the apparent simplicity of the act of throwing, the process is highly complicated and difficult to deal with by a simple calculation. In many cases of interest to the sportsman the force exerted by the thrower on the object to be thrown is not many times greater than the weight of the object itself (for example the shot and the long jump), and this fact alone renders it impossible to project it at various angles with the same velocity. Those trajectories with a high angle of projection entail a lower velocity of projection than those with a low initial angle, and thus the lower trajectories are favoured and the angle of projection for maximum range is less than 45°. This is shown by the trajectories of the tennis ball shown in Plate VIII (iv). Maximum range was obtained in that case for an angle of projection of about 40°. The angle depends upon the ratio of the force applied to the weight of the ball. The smaller the force of projection the lower is the angle required to achieve maximum range.

When the object is thrown by hand a number of other variables enter into the question. The muscles moving the arm work more effectively in certain directions than in others. Thus the force applied to the projectile will also vary according to the angle of throw. While it can be seen in a general way

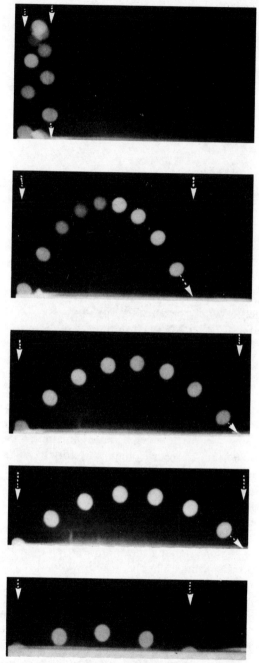

PLATE VIII (iv). *The trajectory of a tennis ball. Superimposed pictures of the flight of a tennis ball projected at various angles with the same force. The range on the horizontal plane is indicated by the dotted arrows. It is short for high angles of projection and also for low angles. The catapult used to project the ball exerted an average force on it of about four times the weight of the ball. Maximum range under these conditions would be expected to be obtained with an angle of projection of about 40°, corresponding roughly to the photograph of trajectory number 4.*

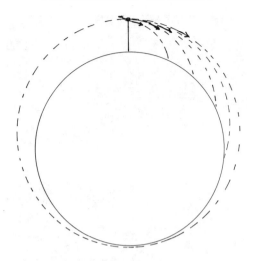

FIG. VIII (6).

that the effect of this is also likely to favour the lower angles of projection, it is a matter which can only be satisfactorily approached experimentally. As will be discussed in Chapter XX the transference of momentum from the arm to the object being thrown, through the whip-like action of the throwing arm, is another factor of which account must be taken. Abdominal muscles enter into this process and again the lower angles of projection are likely to be favoured.

Objects are rarely thrown by a person who remains completely stationary himself. A running throw introduces a number of further considerations. The velocity of running, on the one hand, adds horizontal momentum which makes it profitable to try to secure a high trajectory to make as much use of it as possible, while, on the other, it lengthens the distance over which the force can be applied, which favours a lower trajectory. The effect is different according to whether the run is limited by the top speed of the runner, or by a fixed distance for the run, and by whether or not he starts from rest.

To illustrate the effect of some of the factors which enter into the selection of the correct angle for attaining maximum range, a couple of calculations have been given in Appendix VI. The resulting curves may help towards an understanding of the processes, but since they cannot take account of all the factors involved they must not be taken as accurate indications of the angles to be employed, which can only be decided upon as a result of trial. The graphs, however, do emphasise the fact that, as a rule, lower trajectories are likely to be more advantageous than the higher ones. The fact that projection does not take place from ground-level also tends to favour the lower angles to some extent.

Probably, in practice, the example which comes nearest to the elementary estimate of 45° for the optimum angle of projection, occurs in the hitting of a cricket ball with a bat. The time the ball remains in contact with the bat is very short and the force applied to the ball is enormous compared with its weight. Wind resistance and the effect of spin are not predominant in this case, and if it is desired to slog a ball right out of the ground, 45° is probably not far from the best angle at which to aim it. The throwing of a cricket ball must also come fairly close to the simple calculation, though here run and the relative effectiveness of the muscles in different directions will also have an effect. The dominant factor in the flight of a golf ball is air resistance and the effect of spin, as will be discussed in Chapter X. This is also the case with a rifle bullet in which there is a high force to weight ratio. In shot putting the best angle of projection is a good deal less than 45°, and so it is in the case of the long jump. In general it is best to treat the elementary calculation with a good deal of reserve.

When a projectile possesses a range sufficiently great for the curvature of the earth to affect it, the distance it goes is greater than its range would be on a horizontal plane. To illustrate this point Newton constructed a diagram similar to that in Fig. VIII (6). He imagined a projectile being fired horizontally from the top of a mountain. With small velocities of projection it would land close to the foot of the mountain. As the speed of projection is increased, however, it would land further and further away, and as it did so the curvature of the earth would come into play. As soon as the velocity of projection is sufficient to take the projectile past the antipodes, however, it would continue on its way and would then be in orbit round the earth. Of course, the resistance of the air would vitiate Newton's argument if projection actually took place from the top of any mountain on the earth, but now that objects can be transported above the atmosphere, his picture comes into its own. In so far as its vertical motion is concerned, an object in orbit is continually falling towards the earth, but at the same time it possesses a horizontal motion which makes the radius of curvature of its path greater than that of the earth. An object in orbit is thus perpetually in a state of free fall and anything contained in an orbiting spacecraft will appear weightless even though the craft is well inside the gravitational field of the earth.

CHAPTER IX

Movement on Land

So far we have considered animals first as simple physical shapes, and then in terms of their internal mechanisms. The sense organs present coded information about the environment to the nervous system, which analyses it and commands the subsequent action from the muscles. The internal problems of movement are much the same in all vertebrate animals, and the same basic machinery is used to exert thrust on the outside, whether it be water, land, or air. It is now time to consider the special problems connected with each of these habitats, and a few of those connected with movement over the land, being the most familiar, will be taken first. The horse, relying in its natural state on speed in order, it is commonly supposed, to escape from predators is more specialised than many in the art of movement on land. This, together with its long-established connection with man, makes it an interesting example on which to base arguments, but other animals will follow many of the same rules, although only a few can be mentioned.

The two pairs of limbs of land vertebrates are anchored to bony girdles (Plate IX (i)). The anterior, or pectoral, girdle is slung to the rib cage and backbone by extensive muscles. In man, and many climbing animals, there is, in addition, a bony connection, the clavicle or collar-bone, joining the shoulder to the breast-bone, but it is absent in the horse and many other animals whose limbs normally receive little sideways stress. The hind limbs, joining the pelvic girdle, are more firmly supported since there is a fusion of the girdle with the sacrum, part of the back-bone.

The joints between girdle and limb are ball and socket ones in all tetrapods, the socket being in the girdle and the ball on the limb-bone. Fundamentally it is a universal joint, but the articulation is restricted to varying degrees in different animals, by tendons, muscles, ligaments, and other bones. The horse, for example, cannot readily swing its legs far to the side. Correspondingly, its muscles are grouped to give power longitudinally.

Distal (i.e. moving down the limb) to the shoulder and hip joints are the humerus and femur bones respectively, which at their distal ends bear simple hinge joints, allowing rotation about one axis only like the hinge of a door. These joints are again found in nearly all tetrapods, although the parallel between those of the horse and of man are not immediately evident. The knee and elbow of a horse are obscured somewhat by the surrounding muscles, and in a silhouette lie inside the outline of the main body. Distal to the elbow and knee, the basic vertebrate condition is, as in man, for there to be two bones side by side. The one simply makes the elbow and knee joint hinges already mentioned, but the other, rotating on its own axis, enables the wrist or foot to be twisted. In the horse, and indeed many other quadrupeds which use their limbs solely for running, these two elements are joined together and no twisting of the hand or foot is possible.

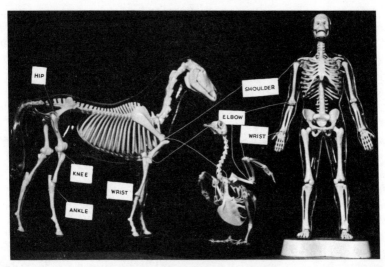

PLATE IX (i). *Model skeletons of man and horse, with original skeleton of a pigeon.*

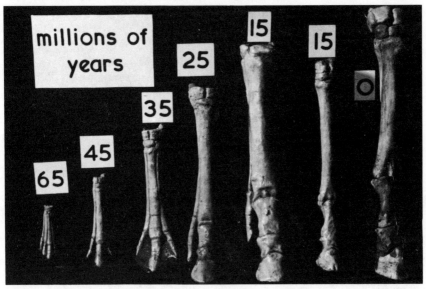

PLATE IX (ii). *Bones of the fore-foot of the modern horse* (right) *and casts of the fossil remains of the fore-feet of some of its ancestors.*

The greatest variety in tetrapod limbs is seen at their distal ends, and since these are concerned with contacting such a wide range of environments, this is to be expected. Taking just man and the horse, the only obvious homology is that the number of joints in series is the same in the feet and hands of both creatures, and that they bend in the same directions. The relative proportions of the bones, and the number of fingers, are very different. Nevertheless, we are very fortunate in being able to point to a common plan for both man and horse, from another line of evidence, the fossil record. The ancestors of the horse have left us with one of the best fossil series, and those shown in

Plate IX (ii) relate the unspecialised foot of Hyracotherium, sometimes known as Eohippus, to the foot of the modern horse, which is adapted for movement on hard level surfaces. One of the fingers in the hand, and one toe in the foot, developed to carry more and more of the body weight at the expense of those on either side. The result has been something resembling stilts, but even in the modern horse two splint bones, rudiments of the lost toes, are found along- side the first long bone in each foot, which is termed the cannon-bone by equestrians.

The study of horse teeth over the same period shows that the animals changed from a browsing to a grazing diet in the Miocene period, about ten million years ago. This supports the evidence from the feet to suggest a change from forest life to one on the kind of open grassy plains found in much of America and Asia. On surfaces such as these, and with a herbivorous diet, there is no need for the grasp given by a many-fingered and possibly clawed foot.

It is often tacitly assumed that a long leg gives greater speed with less effort, but the relation is not so favourable as a simple linear one and several factors must be taken into account when seeking an answer to the problem. First imagine the leg as a pendulum. If set swinging, it will oscillate at a natural frequency which depends on the length and how the mass is distri- buted. At its natural frequency the only energy needed to maintain it is that required to overcome air resistance and the friction of the supporting joint. These factors are relatively small. In the case of a real animal, muscles will, of course, have to work against their own internal resistances as well, for the swinging of the leg will alter their length. The remainder of the animal's strength can be used for acceleration or moving uphill. If faster progress is to be made, effort will be spent not only against the viscosity of the muscles and in doing external work, but also in forcing the limb to oscillate faster than it would of its own accord. The most economical leg, therefore, will be one whose tip traces out the greatest distance in a given time when oscillating like a pendulum. The longer a pendulum, the lower its frequency of swing, but nevertheless the tip of a long one does move faster than that of a shorter one swinging through the same angle. Pictorially this is seen in Plate IX (iii), where the tip of a pendulum 4 units long covers twice the distance in a given time that the tip of one only 1 unit long does. The same result can be deduced from the fact that the number of swings per minute, n, is propor- tional to $1/\sqrt{L}$, the length of the pendulum being L. (See Appendix IV.) In one minute the distance covered by the tip will be proportional to the product of the number of oscillations and the length, i.e. to $n.L$.

That is to say, the distance covered will be proportional to

$$\frac{1}{\sqrt{L}}.L=\sqrt{L}.$$

In other words, to cover twice the distance in a given time, the pendulum must be four times as long. Thus, although the increase in length is indeed helpful, it is not so favourable as direct proportion. The effect is qualitatively obvious if the speed of a gently trotting dog is compared with that of a gently trotting horse.

PLATE IX (iii). *Time exposure of the illuminated bobs of three pendula of lengths of 1, 2, and 4 units, all swinging through the same angle. During the exposure, the camera was tilted progressively upwards to avoid superposition of the traces from later oscillations. The common support of the pendula bore a fainter light whose trace is seen at the top of the picture. The pendulum 1 unit long performed 7 oscillations while the longest performed 3½. Since the angle of swing was the same for all, the shortest covered 1×7 units of distance, while the longest covered $4 \times 3 \cdot 5 = 14$ units. The length of the traces may be measured to confirm this even more directly, but the irregularities in the swinging of the shortest, resulting from axial swinging of the bob, somewhat obscure the issue.*

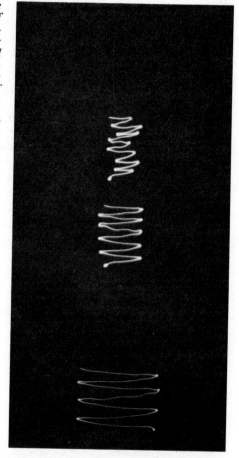

This advantage of extra height, however, diminishes and finally disappears, when the animal forces its rate of pacing above the natural gait determined by the period of swing of the leg under gravity. To show that this is so is not difficult (see Appendix III), but as it involves using the results of later chapters, the calculation has been deferred and placed in an appendix. There it is shown that for animals of similar build, taking into account the variation in the size of their muscles, the frequency of forced oscillation of a limb will vary inversely as its length and not, as in the case of a free oscillation under the influence of gravity only, as the square root of the length. Thus the distance covered in a given time being proportional to the product of the length and the frequency, we see that an animal's top speed should be independent of its size. Thus the tall man will walk faster than a short one when out for a leisurely stroll, but the short man can run as fast as the tall one when both put their maximum effort into a sprint.

To move the limbs at other than their natural frequency requires muscular effort and is tiring. This is so whether the limbs are being moved more slowly or more quickly than they would when swinging freely. That is why it is tiring to walk when circumstances demand a continual change of speed, as when out with children or in crowded streets. When walking freely with a shorter companion the speed can be adjusted by altering the length of the stride.

At first sight, the result that long-legged animals have no higher top speed may seem surprising, but in fact the *top* speeds of animals of similar shape are not widely different. The fox, the hound, and the horse all have legs of much the same shape and can maintain similar top speeds of the order 25 to 30 miles per hour.

As far as running goes, therefore, the advantage of being long-legged is that one can move faster without exertion, but it does not confer a significantly higher top speed. An important advantage is gained by running on four legs rather than on two. The principal running muscles of the horse and the dog are attached to the hind limbs. The fore limbs serve mainly as props to support the animal during strides, the hind limbs providing the forward bound when the animal is moving fast. Since the hind limbs land just in front of the fore limbs, the effect is to add one body's length to each stride. This effectively doubles the speed, and thus the top speed of a man running is about 15 to 20 miles per hour, and that of the horse 30 to 40.

We may carry out a similar order-of-magnitude calculation concerning the importance of size in jumping. We have seen that the force exerted by a muscle is proportional to its area of cross-section and will thus vary as the square of the linear dimensions of the animal. The work done by the muscle in contracting, being proportional to the product of the force and the distance moved, will vary as the cube of the linear dimensions, that is as the volume or mass of the animal. Equating this (constant times M) to the initial kinetic energy of the animal when jumping, which will be shown in a later chapter to be $\frac{1}{2}Mv^2$, we see that the velocity of projection, v, would be expected to be constant and independent of the size. In other words, all animals should be able to jump to the same height.

This seems, at first sight, at variance with experience. We have to remember, however, that the height of the jump which we have calculated is the height to which the centre of gravity is raised and not the height above ground-level which is cleared. For example, a horse jumping over a five-barred gate need raise its centre of gravity only a foot or so, while a man clearing 6 feet will raise his centre of gravity by about 3 feet. It would seem that 3 feet is a very good jump for any animal. Even the familiar flea is not so much below this figure in performance! In the case of a tiny animal, like the flea, air resistance is relatively very much greater than it is with larger creatures, and of course the flea is built on a completely different plan to the other animals we have been considering in this connection. However, the argument depends upon considerations of energy and it is not closely dependent upon similarity of shape. It does assume that the jumping muscles account for a constant fraction of the total mass of the animal, and it is further assumed that the jump takes place from rest. By running, the velocity of projection can be increased since the speed of running can nearly all be added to it. This is sufficient to account for such differences in jumping ability as strike the eye, but, of course, the argument must not be pressed too far. It is only an order-of-magnitude estimation.

To return to the running animal whose speed depends upon the product of the length of its leg and the frequency with which it can be swung, we have seen that to a certain extent any advantage gained by lengthening the leg is offset by a decrease in the period of swing. The frequency of a pendulum is increased by raising the bob, and in a similar manner the frequency of swing of a limb can be increased by concentrating as much of the weight as possible near the pivot. This can be done without shortening the limb itself and thus the speed of running can be increased. In running animals this is achieved by arranging the leg muscles as near to the top joint as possible. The legs of the horse demonstrate such a concentration of matter near the pivot, the muscles providing the main power being concentrated within the outline of the main body, the parts projecting below the level of the body being relatively slender (Plate IX (iv)). The principle of the homology of structures of all vertebrates extends beyond the bones to the muscles which are attached to them. Feet and hands contain very few muscles, the digits being operated like puppets on strings by very long tendons pulled by muscles lying just below the elbow and knee. Elongation of the foot and hand can be achieved without moving the heavy musculature away from the pivot.

The horse has further reduced the musculature needed away from hip and shoulder by the fusion of the radius with ulna, and tibia with fibula, so that muscles are no longer needed to keep these bones in the right positions relative to each other.

The most massive muscles, those in the shoulder and hip region, are attached to the girdles and spine at one end, and the humerus and femur at the other. It is interesting to note that these particular bones have remained relatively short in proportion to the size of the horse, and have not taken so much part in the lengthening of the limb as they have done in slower man. These muscles, working under a very great mechanical disadvantage, are very weighty and thus well fitted to do a large amount of work before tiring.

When running fast the limbs do not swing as a pendulum of constant length; the length varies during each pace. The flexing of the joints during recovery tucks the leg up beneath the body and shortens the length of the equivalent pendulum and hence increases the natural frequency of swing (Plate IV (iii)).

A horse in a hurry will, as we have seen, oscillate its limbs more rapidly than when it is trotting or walking comfortably, and energy will be wasted in forcing up the rate of swing. We can see how the frequency of pacing rises with increasing speed by watching the actual animal. As the speed rises, so does the rate of pacing, but as can be seen from Fig. IX (1), a doubling of the speed does not entail a doubling of the rate of pacing. The actual relation between these two factors depends on the gait being used. For the slower gaits, the walk and the trot, the line of the graph rises more steeply than it does when the horse is cantering or galloping. In the latter, the speed was more than doubled for an increase in the rate of pacing of only 20 to 30 per cent. The horse thus increases its speeds while economising on the energy-consuming process of raising the rate of oscillation of the limbs. It achieves this, of course, by increasing the amplitude of swing of the leg (Appendix IV).

(A)

(B)

PLATE IX (iv). *The four common gaits of the horse.*
(A) Walk. (B) Trot. (C) Canter. (D) Gallop.
Note that in the canter one of the fore-legs is in the same phase as the opposite hind leg,
while this is no longer so in the gallop. In the trot the other fore-leg is also in phase
with its opposite hind.

(C)

(D)

Another factor which is important in deciding the mass of a limb, and hence its swinging properties, is the weight of the animal supported. Also a taller animal must have more strength in its bones than a shorter one of the same weight. Where the proportions and shape are much the same, a large animal carries a great deal more weight than a small one. If one is double the other in length it will possess eight times the volume. Since animal matter is all roughly similar in density, this also implies an eightfold difference in weight. The larger animals, therefore, possess bones with a greater area of cross-section in proportion to their size. The natural period of swing of a limb is determined by the length, but the more massive structures will require greater forces to force them to swing at a higher rate.

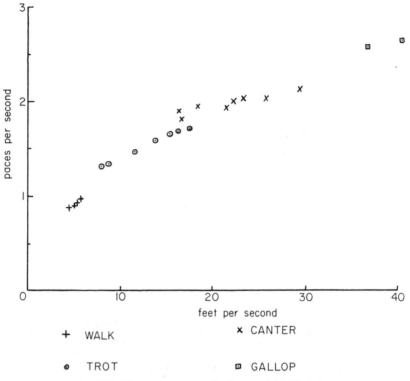

FIG. IX (1). *Performance of a horse of 14·3 hands.*

Despite man's long association with the horse, it is only since the development of the camera that he has been able to appreciate accurately how a horse co-ordinates its four limbs. The greatest difficulty occurred in perceiving what happens in the gallop, and since this is the horse's fastest gait, attempts to draw it had to be made in pictures suggesting movement at speed. Early representations, such as the white horses on the chalk hills and the pictures in the Bayeux Tapestry, lack anatomical detail besides depicting the gallop incorrectly. One of the turning-points came with the work of George Stubbs, who lived from 1724 to 1806. He was the first artist to use knowledge gained by actual dissection. Consequently, his paintings show much more insight into the skeleton, musculature, tendons, and blood system, which all play their part in moulding the outline of the skin. In 1766 he published his *Anatomy of the Horse* which has become a standard work of reference. Yet in spite of Stubbs's care, although he portrays the slower gaits accurately, he was unable to reproduce what photographs have since told us actually happens in the gallop. Subsequent paintings, such as those of Ben Marshall and Alken, show the influence of Stubbs.

In the 1880s Clarence Hailey first used the camera to freeze the motion of the horse. The most notable discovery from this was that the horse when off the ground during the gallop was seen to have its legs bunched under its body, and was never in the spread-eagle position as previously imagined. Further,

WALK TROT CANTER GALLOP

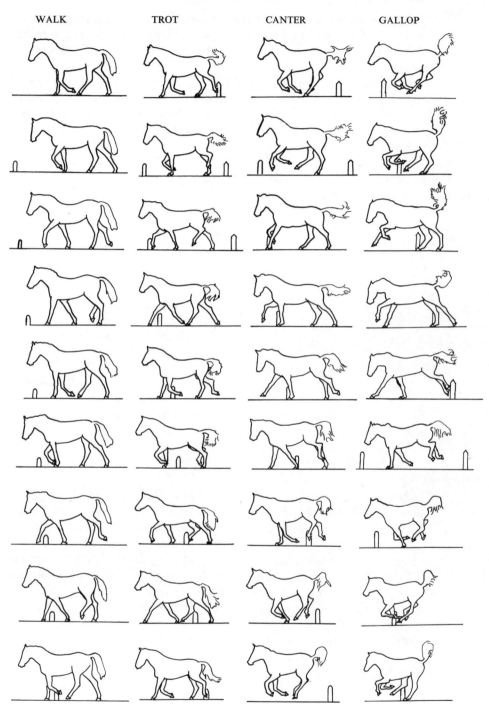

FIG. IX (2). *The four gaits of the horse, drawn from ciné film. The vertical columns represent film lasting for Walk—1 second; Trot—$\frac{2}{3}$ second; Canter—$\frac{1}{2}$ second; Gallop—$\frac{2}{5}$ second.*

when outstretched behind or in front, the hind legs were discovered never to be together, and the same applies to the fore-legs when stretched forwards. Subsequent paintings, such as those of Munnings, show Stubbs's influence and that of the camera.

Sequences of photographs taken during a few paces resulted from the work of Muybridge in 1878. He arranged a series of trip wires, each of which was attached to the shutter mechanism of a separate camera. The photographs were then processed and arranged in order. The movement could be recaptured by arranging them in a zoëtrope.

The series of drawings from modern ciné film (Fig. IX (2)) show the position of the legs for the four main gaits of the horse.

When walking the footfall is:

1. Left fore
2. Right hind
3. Right fore
4. Left hind

each foot falling separately. Thus the walk is a four-time pace. The number of hooves on the ground at any instant depends on the speed of walking. If grazing, all four may be, and they are lifted in turn as the centre of gravity moves forward. In the rapid walk there are always two hooves on the ground, and for parts of the cycle, three. This happens since the one rising leaves the ground just before another falls.

On moving faster, the amplitude increases, and so does the frequency of pacing (Fig. IX (1)) and eventually the animal breaks into a trot. This is a pace in two-time, diagonally opposite feet rising and falling together. Thus this pace can be written:

1. Left fore + right hind
2. Right fore + left hind

and can be seen to be derived from the walk by running the first two actions into one, and the other two into the other beat. Normally there is insufficient spring for all hooves to be clearly off the ground between footfalls, but halfway between there is very little pressure downwards, and the hind footprints are very close to those from the fore-feet. They may even fall on top of them.

When trotting, a horse may easily break into a canter. This does not necessarily mean an increase in speed, for fast trots can be quicker than slow canters for any one horse (Fig. IX (1)). The change is like a change of gear, for the canter does enable a much higher speed to be attained. The canter is a pace in three-time, in which a hind foot may be taken to fall first. If it is the left hind, the sequence is:

1. Left hind
2. Right hind + left fore
3. Right fore

When the right fore has swept through there follows a period of no contact with the ground, which lasts for about one-eighth of the time of the cycle.

Then, the hind legs are recovering in advance of the fore-legs, and hence all feet are bunched beneath the animal. The horse may lead with its right hind, and then the gait is the mirror image of the one described. An individual horse usually prefers to lead with the same foot, but when turning in a circle may change if its leading foot would not be on the outside of the circle. This gait is potentially faster than the trot because the leading hind foot can take off before the last hoof has landed, and thus increase the length of pace. The body axis thus rocks up and down, while in the trot it remains horizontal. Another reason for the increased potential speed is that while the animal is off the ground it is being carried forward in a leap, without the legs having to be moved as rapidly as would otherwise be necessary.

As speed increases and more effort is put into the movement, the canter develops into a gallop. Here, the second beat of the canter is split, creating another four-time pace. As with the canter, this can exist as the mirror image, giving:

1. Left hind	or	1. Right hind
2. Right hind		2. Left hind
3. Left fore		3. Right fore
4. Right fore		4. Left fore

In the gallop, the horse is off the ground for a greater proportion of the cycle, the actual fraction depending on the speed, but being of the order of $\frac{1}{5}$ to $\frac{1}{2}$.

An approximation to the old idea of the airborne horse with its legs extended is achieved by animals which bound, such as the cheetah (Fig. IX (3)). In a bounding gait the animal is completely off the ground twice during the cycle, once after the hind legs have swept through, when all the legs are extended, and once when the fore-legs have just left the ground, when the legs are bunched under the body, as in the horse's gallop. The bound involves a much more supple backbone than does a gallop. Although the hind legs or the fore-legs may appear to be parallel when in the extended position, they are, in fact, slightly out of phase, for they do not fall together. The double bound of the cheetah gives it a potential speed almost twice that of the horse.

The *Guinness Book of Records* mentions a test in London in 1939 when a cheetah covered a distance of 500 yards at an average speed of 44 m.p.h. A. V. Hill quotes 65–70 m.p.h. (*Science Progress* April 1950). The cheetah drawn in Fig. IX (3) was running beside a camera vehicle whose driver stated that at times he reached 50 m.p.h. At no time did the animal appear to be exerting itself, and it seems that speeds of 70 m.p.h. are not out of the question.

The *Guinness Book of Records* gives record speeds for the horse as 43·26 m.p.h. over $\frac{1}{4}$ mile, 38·63 m.p.h. for 1 mile, and 34·29 m.p.h. for 3 miles.

Another gait of the horse is to amble, not done by horses unless they are trained to do so, as in 'American Pacing'. Bears and camels often adopt this. In silhouette it looks like a trot, but in fact the legs in phase are both in the same side of the body. As with the trot it can be considered as a development of the walk, but this time by telescoping actions 2 and 3 of the walk into one and 1 and 4 into the other movement.

FIG. IX (3). *Bounding gait of the cheetah. Drawn from the film taken by Granada TV of Sir Frank Houston Bowden's specimen. Reproduction is by kind permission of the Kenion Press.*

CHAPTER X

Hydrodynamics

THE movement which we have considered so far has been of solids. But liquids and gases also move. Both possess mass and require forces to accelerate them just as solids do, and they are subject to the same laws of motion. Action and reaction are equal and opposite. However, they possess some features which are peculiar to themselves, which we shall consider in this chapter. The science of fluid motion is known as hydrodynamics. Newton himself made some initial moves towards its study, but it was Daniel Bernoulli (1700–82) who developed the mathematical theory of the subject.

The conservation of momentum, and its corollary in Newton's third law of motion, applied to fluid motion is the basis of many forms of propulsion. Action and reaction are equal and opposite, and forward propulsion is achieved by propelling fluid backwards. The fluid which is propelled backwards is usually that in which the vehicle is immersed. In the case of a ship it is the water in which it floats that is forced backwards; in the case of an aeroplane it is the air. With a rocket the fluid is contained within the vessel itself. It is, therefore, the only vehicle capable of propelling itself in a vacuum. Paddle wheels, screws, aeroplane propellers, and jets all act by propelling fluid backwards. In the case of the jet engine, what is thrown backwards is partly air taken in from the front and partly the products of the combustion of the fuel. It is thus intermediate between the rocket and the piston engine, although even in the latter the exhaust is thrown backwards and so makes a small contribution to the forwards force. Both jet and piston engines rely upon the oxygen of the atmosphere for the combustion of their fuel and neither will function in the absence of air. In the water wheel, the windmill, and the turbine the same phenomenon is seen in reverse. These take energy out of a stream of fluid and use it for the performance of work. In propelling a vehicle, on the other hand, work is performed in order to generate backwards momentum in a fluid and thus forward momentum in the vehicle at the same time.

Like solids, fluids can be accelerated only by forces, but they do not retain their shape and thus a force applied at one point of a fluid may not affect fluid some distance away. In the case of fluids it is necessary to study the action of pressures (the force per unit area) acting over finite areas. The forces to which a particle of fluid is subject usually vary from place to place, and it is thus necessary to consider the distribution of pressure. When the pressure is uniform there is no tendency to move any of the parts of the fluid. Any small part of it will experience the same force in all directions and so will remain in equilibrium. If, however, the pressure decreases in a certain direction, there will be a force urging the particles of the fluid in that direction. When the pressure decreases in this way there is said to be a pressure gradient in the

131

direction of the decrease. The term arises by analogy with a ball situated on a slope. It experiences a force which tends to make it move downhill. As the particles of fluid move down a pressure gradient they become speeded up just as does the ball rolling downhill. On the other hand, if, as a result of momentum they possess, fluid particles are able to move against a pressure gradient, they experience a force tending to slow them down, just as a ball rolled uphill is slowed down. In a fluid, therefore, we find the fluid moving fastest where the pressure is least and moving slowest where the pressure is greatest. Conversely, if we notice that certain parts of a fluid are moving faster than other parts we can infer that the pressure there is less, since the particles can only have acquired their greater velocity by moving down a pressure gradient. We are, of course, assuming in all this that the fluid is not acted upon by any other force in this process. If, in the course of its movement, the fluid travelled to a lower level in the earth's gravitational field, for example, its weight would speed it up. What we have said, therefore, applies to movement on the level.

Put in this way the conclusion that the pressure is least where the velocity of the fluid is greatest, seems obvious enough, but it leads to some results which are very surprising when met for the first time. For example, if we hold a visiting card flat against the end of a sewing cotton reel and blow down the hole, instead of the card being blown off, as would appear inevitable at first sight, it actually does the opposite and adheres to the end of the reel. The harder we blow, the more tightly does the card stick. In this experiment the place where the air is moving the fastest is in the narrow space between the card and the reel, and consequently here the pressure must be least. The decrease in pressure can easily be sufficient to support the weight of the card. The card tends to slide off the reel if not held exactly horizontally, but it can be prevented from doing so by inserting a drawing-pin through it, the point of which fits loosely into the hole in the reel.

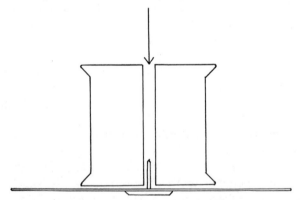

FIG. X (1). (*Reproduced from* Bores, Breakers, Waves, and Wakes *by R. A. R. Tricker.*)

Similarly, when a fluid flows along a tube in which there is a constriction, it moves fastest at the constriction and here the pressure is least. Before giving the matter much thought one might tend to imagine that the pressure would be highest at this point. A diagram of an arrangement to show this is given in

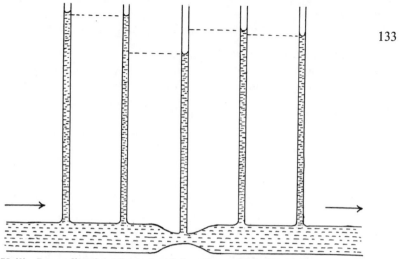

FIG. X (2). *Bernoulli tube.* (*Reproduced from* Bores, Breakers, Waves, and Wakes.)

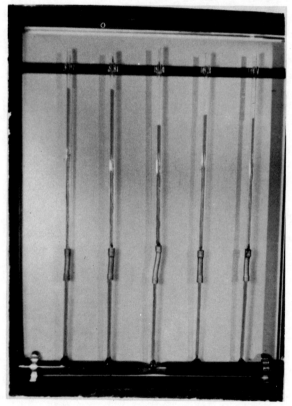

PLATE X (i). *Fall of pressure along a tube along which water flows. The side tubes indicate the pressure in the horizontal tube at the bottom. In the middle of the horizontal tube is a constriction and at this point the pressure is lowest.*

Fig. X (2) and a photograph of the apparatus showing the effect is reproduced in Plate X (i). Side tubes have been sealed to the horizontal tube along which the flow takes place, to indicate the pressure at various positions by the height to which the fluid will rise in them. There is, as one would expect, a pressure gradient along the tube as a whole. This gradient gives rise to the forces necessary to maintain the flow. However, there is a sudden fall of pressure at the constriction and a rise afterwards. In traversing this rise in pressure the fluid is like a ball which, having acquired a certain velocity, say by rolling down a slope, is then able to mount a small hill in its path.

If two table-tennis balls are suspended about an inch apart by threads a foot or two in length and one blows between them, it will be found that instead of being blown apart they are driven together. If two ships steaming in the same direction on nearly parallel courses gradually approach each other as if they were attempting to proceed side by side, a similar low-pressure region would develop in the water between them and they would be in danger of colliding.

This decrease in pressure as the velocity of a fluid increases is known as the Bernoulli effect. It explains a number of important occurrences in fluid flow. A direct consequence of it is the phenomenon sometimes known as the Magnus effect. If a current of air flows past a rotating cylinder the air, which clings to the cylinder to some extent, is speeded up on one side and slowed down on the other. A difference of pressure therefore develops between the two sides and the cylinder experiences a force directed from the side that is moving against the current of air towards that which is moving with it. It is, of course, immaterial whether air flows over the cylinder or whether the cylinder moves forward through the air in the opposite direction. The cylinder of Fig. X (3) would experience a force in the upwards direction.

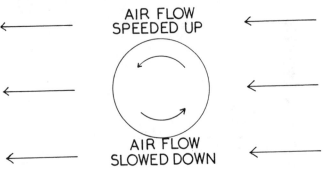

FIG. X (3). *Magnus effect.* (*Reproduced from* Bores, Breakers, Waves, and Wakes.)

Spinning balls which are projected through the air show the same effect. If a golf ball, for example, is driven with bottom spin, it experiences such an upwards force which tends to keep it in the air and thus extend its range. All good drives must be given such bottom spin in order to obtain maximum range. The markings on a golf ball are put on to give the ball a 'grip' on the air and facilitate the effect. In a good drive the ball will remain in the air until air resistance has all but exhausted its horizontal momentum. It then drops very nearly dead, the remaining bottom spin preventing any appreciable run. Much less useful is spin about a vertical axis! This occurs when a drive is pulled or sliced. If the spin is clockwise when viewed from above, as when the ball is sliced as it is driven, it will drift away to the right. On the other hand, when the drive is pulled the spin is counter-clockwise seen from the top and the ball drifts away to the left. As any golfer knows only too well, the extent of these drifts can be very considerable indeed. Had Newton played golf it is to be feared that he might have taken longer to be convinced about the validity of his first law of motion! When a drive is 'topped' and top spin imparted to the ball, it results in a very ignominious flight indeed. Low pressure develops underneath and high pressure above, which quickly bring the ball to earth. Because of its spin, however, the ball may run along the ground for considerable distances.

The spin is imparted to the golf ball by its being struck by the club-head at a point a little distance away from its centre. The impact of the club on the ball is of very short duration—a fraction of a millisecond—and the forces which give the ball its momentum are necessarily enormous. Because of this, and the flexibility of the shaft, the head twists if not struck at its centre, and thus causes the ball to spin. The point of contact between ball and club-head has only to be off centre by a small fraction of an inch for a noticeable effect to be produced. Hence the care necessary in the swing, so that the club-head travels in one plane and strikes the ball squarely. The golfer's head must be kept still to provide a pivot and the club raised slowly backwards so as to avoid setting it oscillating in a plane at right angles to the plane of swing. Jerked movements and 'pressing' can lead to forces not in the desired plane, and thus put the point of impact off the centre of the club-head.

In tennis, top spin on the ball can be of great value—indeed essential. It can bring a swift return ball to ground within the court, whereas without the spin it would travel well outside. A cricket ball, being heavier and travelling more slowly than a golf ball, drifts to a less extent because of spin, though drift can still be appreciable.

The Bernoulli effect is also responsible for the lift of an aeroplane wing. If an aerofoil be held in a current of air so that its plane is slightly inclined to the direction of flow, it is found that the velocity of the air is greater over the top than underneath. A region of low pressure thus develops over the upper surface and one of high pressure under the lower. This provides an upwards force. The speeding up of the air above the wing and its slowing down underneath is equivalent to the addition of a circulation round the wing to the otherwise uniform flow of air. The lift produced by an aerofoil is thus clearly related to the Magnus effect. This circulation is continuous with the vortex filaments which stream away from the tips of the wings. The circulation round the wing is known as a bound vortex since it remains attached to the wing.

The difference in velocity in fluid passing over an aerofoil is clearly shown in the photographs in Plates X (ii), (iii), and (iv). These were taken in a water-trough. Small pieces of metal foil were floated on the surface of the water to show its movement. They were photographed in a camera with the shutter permanently open in front of which revolved a disc in which a slot was cut. The film is thus exposed in the camera for a number of equal times. The velocity of the water is thus indicated by the length of the dashes produced by the pieces of foil. Over the top of the wing it is seen that the velocity is increased while underneath it is diminished. There will thus be an area of low pressure over the upper surface and an area of high pressure over the lower, giving the wing a lifting force. As the angle of attack of the wing is increased this difference in velocity increases, giving greater lift. If the angle of attack is too great, however, the smooth flow breaks up and eddies form over the upper surface, destroying the lift. The wing is then said to be stalled.

PLATE X (ii). *The flow round an aerofoil, showing the faster flow above than below.*

PLATE X (iii). *The same at a higher angle of attack, showing a much greater difference in the velocities above and below the foil.*

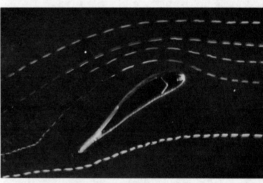

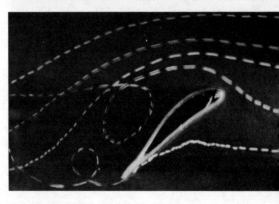

PLATE X (iv). *The same with an angle of attack past the critical angle, when it no longer behaves like a streamlined object.*

The aerofoil in Plates X (ii), (iii), *and* (iv) *may be regarded as an asymmetrical but streamlined shape.*

The photographs were produced by viewing five or six bright spots, floating on the surface of water, through a rotating shutter. The object protruded through the surface. Thus the velocity of the water is proportional to the length of the dashes.

The sail on a boat acts in very much the same manner as an aerofoil tipped up vertically. The lift of the aerofoil then becomes a horizontal force at right angles to the sail. An aerofoil also suffers drag, a force of resistance directed in the opposite direction to its motion. The resultant force on a sail will therefore not be quite at right angles to it, but will be deflected slightly backwards. When a boat is too close hauled, the force on the sail will possess very little component parallel to the direction of the boat. It may even be directed backwards. On the other hand, when the sail lies parallel to the direction of the wind as seen from the boat, there will be no force on it. The best position for the sail lies between these extremes. A simple calculation, treating the airflow as a jet impinging on the sail, is sometimes given which shows that the best position for the sail is obtained when its plane bisects the angle between the keel of the boat and the direction of the wind. The sail, however, is not a simple plane and the treatment neglects the flow of air round the sail. That eddies are streaming away from the rear edge of a sail too close hauled is often indicated by its continual vibration. Practical advice is sometimes given in the form 'sail with the burgee over the peak'. It does not pay to haul a sail too close in and thus set it at too large an angle to the wind, in an effort to get more power from it.

The lift on an aerofoil acts in front of the mid-point of the section. Its line of action lies roughly one-third from the front to the back edge. This can be verified in a simple manner with a sheet of paper. If a sheet of paper is launched into the air its leading edge rises and the paper climbs steeply for a short distance and is then brought to rest. It then descends in the opposite direction, what was the trailing edge now leading. The whole process is then repeated. The new leading edge rises, the paper climbs steeply, is brought to rest and then glides down once again in the original direction. This fluttering fall continues until the paper reaches the ground. The tendency of the leading edge to rise when the paper is first launched can be overcome by adding weights to the front. The simplest way of doing this is to fold the leading edge back, the process being repeated until sufficient weight has accumulated in front so that the paper glides down steadily when it is launched. When it has been adjusted in this way it will be found that the sheet will balance on a ruler placed about a third of the way back from the leading edge. For an object to glide steadily through the air without altering its angle of attack, its centre of gravity should coincide with the centre of lift.

Most objects which are thrown, such as a discus or a javelin, are projected with a spin and this profoundly modifies their behaviour. Just as a hoop bowling along the ground does not fall over as it would do if it were not rotating, so a spinning body sailing through the air has different properties to one which does not rotate. These properties are in addition to the effect on the airflow which we have already considered in the Magnus effect. The flights of a boomerang or a simple cardboard disc spun out of the fingers are determined by their spin combined with the aerodynamic forces. A discussion of the behaviour of such projectiles, however, must be postponed until after we have studied the rotation of rigid bodies.

As has already been mentioned in connection with the aerofoil, objects travelling through fluids experience resistance to their motion, known as drag. It can vary greatly according to the shape of the object and it arises from three different causes. The first of these is viscosity and it is the dominant cause of resistance when the motion is very slow or the moving object is very small—or, of course, when the fluid through which the motion takes place is very viscous, a case which has less practical importance. All fluids, however, are viscous to a greater or lesser extent; that is to say, the movement of one layer of fluid is affected by the movement of its neighbours. If we blow across the surface of water in a cup, at first only the top layer moves, but if the blowing is continued the top layer exerts a force on the layer immediately below it and sets it in motion, and that layer, in turn, exerts a force on the layer below it, and so on. The movement is thus communicated to the whole volume of water. When a body moves through a fluid it carries the layers which are in contact with its surfaces along with it, and since these layers exert forces on neighbouring layers, setting them in motion, they must themselves experience a reaction in the opposite direction. Since the layers in contact are carried along by the moving body this reaction is communicated to the body itself and constitutes a resistance to its motion. It increases directly as the velocity of the body. For common objects moving through air or water, however, viscous drag forms only a small part of the resistance to movement.

For an object which is completely immersed in a fluid, like a fish or a submarine in water, or a bird flying through the air, the most important cause of resistance is turbulence—the generation of eddies in the wake of the body. The effect was first investigated by Osborne Reynolds in 1883. He injected a fine stream of coloured water into the centre of a tube down which a stream of clear water flowed. For very slow rates of flow the coloured water formed a thread along the axis of the tube. The flow of the water along the tube was steady and the paths of the water particles—the streamlines—were parallel to the length of the tube. At a certain speed, however, the stream became turbulent and then the tube was filled with eddies. The thread of coloured water broke up. It rapidly became diffused by the eddies throughout the whole tube and was no longer visible.

At very low speeds the streamlines of a fluid flowing past an object are smooth continuous curves, but as the speed is increased eddies form behind the object and at a somewhat higher speed are carried away by the stream. When the body moves through the fluid the energy which the eddies contain is derived from the movement of the body, and the formation of a column of eddies in its wake dissipates its energy.

The production of eddies is greatly influenced by the shape of the body moving through the fluid. A flat plate moved at right angles to its plane creates vigorous eddies, but bodies which are rounded in front and tapered behind produce less vigorous and less frequent eddies at the same speed. This streamline shape, therefore, allows much greater ease of movement through a fluid, and it is remarkable how it has been evolved in the course of geological time in the larger creatures which fly through the air or swim through water. It is interesting that the smaller insects are not so streamlined as the larger animals—presumably because the resistance they experience to motion is less predominantly due to turbulence. This is perhaps an indication of how sensitive the process of evolution has been to the factors which increase the efficiency of an organism. The streamlined shape has been adopted for many man-made articles also, particularly for rapidly moving vehicles such as aeroplanes and motor-cars. The smooth flow of fluid past a streamlined body is shown in Plate X (v), and the turbulent flow past one which is not so shaped, in Plate X (vi). To produce the eddies absorbs energy from the body moving through the fluid and thus leads to a resistance to motion. The eddies form behind the body and then drift away downstream. They rotate alternately in a clockwise and anticlockwise direction. The main eddy behind the body in Plate X (vi) rotates anticlockwise. It will be followed by another eddy rotating in the opposite direction.

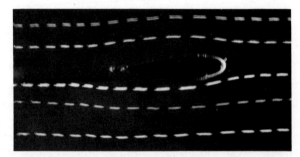

PLATE X (v). *The streamlines of the flow around a symmetrical 'streamlined' object.*

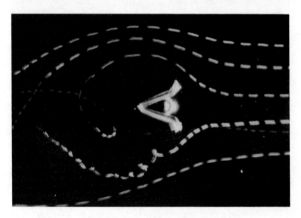

PLATE X (vi). *The flow round a symmetrical but unstreamlined shape, causing eddies in its wake.*

There are, however, some cases when it is desirable to increase the resistance to motion, rather than diminish it. The oar is a case in point. The blade of an oar, in the form of a plane at right angles to the direction of motion, is about the least streamlined shape possible. The function of the oar, however, is not to move through the water when a force is exerted upon it. It should remain as nearly as possible fixed. The size of the eddies which form behind it varies with the force applied to it and indicates to the coach the effort being made by various members of his crew!

The third source of resistance to movement arises from the generation of waves. In the case of passage through water this only occurs at the surface, so that it affects ships but not submarines or fish. For ships, however, it is the most important cause of resistance. There are two sets of waves constituting the wake of a ship.[1] One consists of waves tailing behind and travelling forwards in the same direction and with the same velocity as the ship. They extend backwards for half the distance the ship has travelled, the amplitude gradually diminishing the further one goes behind the vessel. The other set of waves forms the familiar arrow-head with its point at the ship's bows. It is a curious fact that, in deep water and for moderate velocities, the angle of the arrow-head is always the same irrespective of the speed of the ship. It is always, in fact, 39°. The waves of which it is composed are inclined to the line of the arrow-head, crossing it at an angle of $35\frac{1}{4}°$.

Although there is no surface on which waves can form, objects moving through the air can give rise to sound waves, the production of which will lead to resistance, but at speeds well below the speed of sound (750 miles per hour at ground-level) not much energy is lost in this way compared with the losses from turbulence. As the speed of sound is approached and exceeded, however, these conditions change. Shock waves are set up which account for a large loss of energy. It is the resistance arising from this cause which constitutes what has been called the 'sound barrier'. The lost energy becomes apparent over a wide area in the form of supersonic bangs. The term sound barrier suggests that once it is passed resistance will diminish. This is not the case, however. Resistance continues to increase as the speed is increased, but not at such a sharp rate as it does as the velocity of sound is being passed.

[1] R. A. R. Tricker, *Bores, Breakers, Waves, and Wakes*, chap. 17.

CHAPTER XI

Movement in Water

As we have just seen, the basic principle that action equals reaction, or Newton's third law of motion, applies just as much in water as on land. The forward thrust for movement is obtained by propelling water backwards. The simplest such action to appreciate is when the water is expelled in the form of a jet. The squid and octopus, when moving rapidly, fill their mantle cavities with water and squirt it vigorously backwards through a siphon or tube. In a less active way, the pulsations of a jellyfish direct water away from its bell, giving another example of jet propulsion.

Most fish derive their thrust from a side-to-side movement of the tail or caudal fin. Being pliable, the tip of the fin lags behind the root so that an inclined surface is presented to the water. The deep body, dorsal fin above, and anal fin beneath, resist lateral movement of the body in the same way as the keel of a yacht. Thus the animal slips forwards as the inclined tail fin presses sideways, and water in this region is moved backwards and slightly sideways. The flexible flippers worn by swimmers and frogmen work on the same principle (Fig. XI (1)).

FIG. XI (1).

Longer fish such as eels show distinct waves running down the body. Waves can be seen in the bodies of shorter fish but are much less marked. Wave motion demands a large number of elements, each moving slightly out of phase with the adjacent one. The segmental muscles making up most of the weight of fishes form such a system. When the cycle of one element is slightly ahead of the one behind it, the wave will run rearwards. With the single caudal fin, a single inclined plane is presented to the water, but in the case of the longer fishes there is often a whole series of them. Where there are several wave-lengths along the body, the keel-like stabilising effect will be unnecessary, the side thrust from one element cancelling with the opposite thrust from that element half a wave-length ahead. However, the deep body supplemented with dorsal and ventral fins is still important to minimise the spillage of water from the high pressure on one side to the low pressure on the other

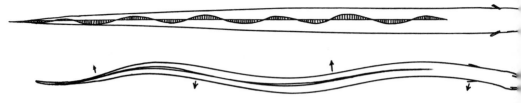

FIG. XI (2).

(Above) *Ventral view of* Electrophorus electricus, *the electric eel. A wave motion is generated by means of the ventral fin. Some of the muscles homologous with the main swimming ones of the fish are here used to form the electric organ.*
(Below) *Dorsal aspect of Conger.*

—the same effect as the wing-tip vortex of the bird, to be mentioned in the next chapter.

Flatfish swim with a marked undulation, and in the bony flatfish such as the sole, plaice, and dab, anatomically it is a side-to-side wave, for these fish lie on their sides. The other class of flatfish, relatives of the sharks, such as skates and rays, execute an anatomically up-and-down wave, having developed different muscles.

Fishes with higher numbers of wave-lengths to their body lengths are the African Gymnarchus and the South American electric eel. These fishes keep their bodies straight and only throw their fins into undulations (Fig. XI (2)). They can move forwards or backwards by running the wave from head to tail, or vice versa. Another fish which derives most of its power from its dorsal fin is the sea-horse, where there are several small waves in the length of the fin.

Besides caudal, dorsal, and anal fins which are on the midline, there are four others, the paired pectoral and pelvic fins. Those of most bony fish have narrow bases and can be rotated on their axes through large angles. Their prime function is manoeuvring, and in this capacity they can also be rotated outwards as brakes. A stationary stickleback can often be seen to be fanning its pectoral fins in such a way as to produce lift. The dogfish, which is denser than the sea-water in which it lives, uses its pectoral fins as short wings to give lift in forward motion. This fish has a caudal fin with more area beneath the end of the back-bone than above it. In a simple side-to-side beat, therefore, there must be a down thrust on the water as well as a backward one. The vertical thrust must be reduced in faster swimming.

Very little effort is needed to move slowly through water, but it increases rapidly as speed builds up. Ships are in the unfortunate position where they stir up the surface of the sea into a wake of waves, and this uses a lot of energy. Thus, although on a calm day it is possible to move a large ship by simply standing on its mooring warps, Table XI (I) shows that it took an extra 1,500 horse power to increase the speed of the particular ship from 15·2 knots to about 16 knots.

TABLE XI (I)

Horse Power Developed by a Diesel Vessel at various Speeds

Speed (knots)	11·5	14·0	15·2	15·9
Brake horse power	2,628	4,945	6,365	7,785

Wave resistance is affected very greatly by small changes in the velocity and shape of the ship. Various systems of waves are set up by a ship moving through water, the bow and stern particularly being responsible for marked trains of waves. At some speeds these interfere destructively and the ship requires less force to drive it forward. At other speeds the two wave trains augment each other and the ship experiences increased resistance, so that the relationship between resistance and speed is not a simple one. The resistance is also changed in shallow water.

Submarines are better off as they do not agitate the surface and their resistance laws are akin to those operating on fishes. Here again, however, it is not possible to relate speed and resistance by any simple formula, and though the relation is a much more favourable one for rapid travel, it is still much more economical not to be in a hurry. Fig. XI (3) shows the relation between velocity and towing force for a model whale, with its fins set so that it travelled on the surface for the upper line, and submerged for the lower line.

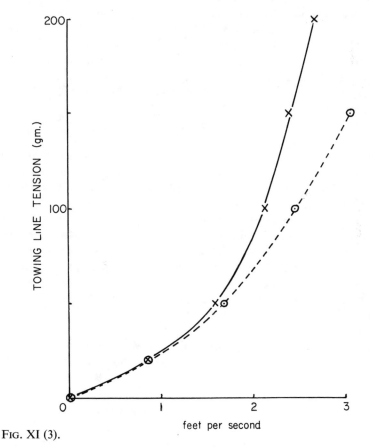

FIG. XI (3).

The relation between speed and towing force of a 20″ model Sperm Whale

x = at surface

o = well submerged

Regardless of the speed of travel, the resistance to forward motion is decreased by streamlining. The symmetrical shape in Plate X (v) is typical of the dorsal view of many fishes. The smooth flow, and lack of eddies, reduces resistance to that of skin friction. The skin friction is caused by the viscosity of the water. A boundary layer is dragged along with the object, and between it and the undisturbed water there is a velocity gradient which takes energy to maintain it. It is because the body is more nearly streamlined that the crawl-stroke in swimming is so much more economical than the breast-stroke. In the latter, when the legs are brought forward the thighs present a surface to the water not altogether unlike that of the unstreamlined body in Plate X (vi). In the crawl the legs remain stretched out behind. The propulsive power derived from the legs, however, is limited by the lack of flexibility in the ankle and the small area of the feet. The mode of operation, however, is the same as that of the fish's tail and the effectiveness of the legs can be increased enormously by wearing flexible flippers.

Some fish are exceptions to streamlining. One, the angler fish, has an almost circular body, half of which is mouth, and a grotesquely small tail for propulsion. However, this animal adopts a passive existence, dangling a rod-and-line-like structure in front of its mouth, with which it lures its prey. A second is the globe fish, almost spherical in shape and covered with stiff projecting spines, but since it is so well armed, rapid swimming must be unnecessary. Flatfish are, of course, well streamlined, but their narrow dimension is vertical and not horizontal.

A feature of the water habitat is the great change of pressure with depth. The same pressure change is experienced in diving 30 feet in water as occurs in diving from the top of the atmosphere to sea-level. This pressure, about 15 pounds per square inch, is about three times what the lungs can exert. The pressure gradient can be felt on the eardrums in an ordinary swimming-pool. Fish counteract this pressure gradient to maintain equilibrium at a chosen depth. Some possess an air sac in the abdominal cavity called the swim bladder. In herring, salmon, carp, and freshwater catfish and their relatives, it has a direct connection with the pharynx, and hence with the mouth, so that an air bubble can be swallowed when the fish is on the surface, or expelled at any time. However, the bladders of many fish are not connected to the mouth, making direct air exchange impossible. The walls of swim bladders are well supplied with blood capillaries, giving them a structure similar to that of a lung or gill, and these areas are probably concerned with interchange of gases between blood and swim bladder. Thus by gaseous exchange from the blood, or by direct flow of air, the pressure in the swim bladder is controlled.

Imagine a fish to be perfectly poised. It is in equilibrium at such a level that the overall density is equal to that of the surrounding water. If it dives, the water pressure increases, compressing the swim bladder. The fish must increase the pressure in its swim bladder in order to regain its former overall volume. Conversely, on rising, the pressure must be decreased. Until the adjustment is completed, muscular effort will have to be expended in beating the fins to maintain depth.

It will be seen that this equilibrium is an unstable one. The slightest dive compresses the swim bladder, increases the density of the fish, and causes it to sink faster. Similarly, the slightest rise begins an upwards acceleration. This instability becomes acute in fish compelled to surface rapidly from great depth in a trawl net. If they were netted at 100 fathoms, they would be decompressed 20 atmospheres in coming to the surface, a process lasting about five minutes. This causes the swim bladders to swell to many times their former volume, sometimes blowing out of the fish's mouth. The trawl net becomes more and more buoyant as it reaches the surface, and a good catch is indicated if the cod end of the net rises a few feet out of the water on surfacing.

The fairground toy called the cartesian diver may be a more familiar example of this instability. This toy is a small hollow vessel sometimes painted to look like some mythical animal. Its lower extremity is an open tube connecting with the internal hollow. Thus, the airlock inside can be altered in volume by changing the pressure on the surrounding water, usually by screwing the bottle-top. Screwing up causes the diver to sink to the bottom, and unscrewing to rise to the top, but constant adjustment is necessary to maintain an intermediate level.

Sense organs must be present to detect the pressure changes. Large changes would doubtless be recorded by general stretch receptors in the tissues near the swim bladder, but a more sensitive method is to be expected for fine monitoring of this depth balancing. Most 'coarse' fish, and freshwater catfish, have two short chains of ossicles connecting the swim bladder to the internal ear apparatus. They are thought to be connected with transmission of sound vibrations, and it may be that they can also transmit steady changes in the volume of the swim bladder.

Water animals are confronted with other problems of sensation, some arising from the similarity in density between protoplasm and water. The water buoys up the whole body, as anyone who has allowed a bath to empty round himself will appreciate. With pressures being exerted over wider areas, the skin will not be in a position to record such useful postural information as it can in a land animal where pressures are more concentrated. This may account for the greater prominence of the otolith (Fig. IV (4)) in fishes. Being much denser than water, it exerts a force on the cells of the macula on which it lies.

This lack of density difference between the surroundings and the flesh creates hearing difficulties also. A sense cell lying in a medium of its own density will be moved bodily by a sound vibration, since the wave-length of useful sounds is many times the length of the cell. To activate it, its opposite ends must move relative to each other, and this will happen at an interface between materials of different densities. The boundary between body tissue and swim bladder is one which could give the fish a sense of hearing, and in some fish, as already mentioned, there is a transmission line to the ear. The boundary of the otolith is another suitable site.

Another organ which seems to be concerned with small water movements is the lateral line organ. This is a minute canal running along each flank, communicating with the surface through small pores. In the canal are small gelatinous cupolae over groups of sense cells, very like those of the ampullae of semicircular canals (Fig. XVI (1)).

The fish Gymnarchus may use its lateral line system in a special kind of electrical detection method. Some of its body muscles, no longer required for swimming, have retained their ability to generate resting potentials and action potentials. It can depolarise all the resting potentials on one side of each cell, leaving those on the other surface. As these cells are in column the resulting voltage is the accumulation of all those in series. The electric field from this battery spreads through the water with lines of current flow resembling the well-known field round a magnet. Anything entering this field with a different specific resistance to that of water will distort the line patterns. It is conceivable that such distortions could be detected by the lateral line, since it is long and contains many sense cells. Other evidence that this system is useful to the fish is that it lives in muddy waters, where the eyes would be of little use, and that it steps up its frequency of discharge if a new object is introduced into its aquarium. Also, this idea of a low-voltage navigation aid allows of a hypothesis for the development of more powerful electric organs by natural selection. The stunning capabilities of the latter could hardly evolve in one step, and an organ not powerful enough to kill would confer no advantage on its owner if it could not be used for something else like navigation and object location during its development.

The brain, the co-ordinating centre of the sensory information, shows interesting variations correlated with the habitat of the fish. From experiments on the brains of animals, the functions of the major brain areas are known. It might be expected that areas of the brain concerned with certain faculties would be enlarged where this faculty played a large part in the life of the animal (Fig. IV (9)).

Of other nervous activity associated with movement, perhaps the most amazing are the powers of navigation of some fishes. Pacific salmon which spawn in Lake Cultus, on a tributary of the Fraser River in Canada, swim out to sea where they remain for three years. They then return, and the Canadian Fisheries Board have shown that they all go up the same river. Not only this, they take the correct turnings where tributaries flow in, so that eventually they arrive back at Lake Cultus. In marking experiments, not one was found in any of the other tributaries. It is postulated that this amazing feat is achieved with the aid of the chemical sense, the fish tasting the differences between the waters. The idea is an attractive one since the senses of smell and taste are so sensitive, and the area of brain devoted to the sense of smell is proportionately large in primitive vertebrates such as fish. Thus, the salmon might home on the west coast of America, which would need little accuracy, and then swim along the coast until meeting water with the correct taste. Of course, the remembering of this sensation for three years is notable, but in man certain experiences are often recalled from some time past if a smell associated with the event is encountered again.

The story of the eel found in British freshwater habitats is equally remarkable. The spawning grounds were traced to the Atlantic side of the West Indies. The fry are transported largely by the Gulf Stream, but this gives the adults an even longer swim to the spawning grounds. No doubt such a migration would have the effect of weeding out the unfit individuals and keeping the species healthy, but the means is a very curious one. It has been suggested, however, that the European eel never returns to spawn, but that the supply of elvers is maintained by a breeding stock in the Sargasso Sea.

A third case is the movement of the cod population which spawns north of the Lofoten Islands just inside the Arctic Circle.[1] These populations migrate over a distance of some 700 miles. Some interesting detective work on the age of fish correlated with the times of capture, depth, and current showed that the fry move north to north of Bear Island and to Spitzbergen in their first season, while another population moves round the coast to the north of Russia. Then, each winter, each age group penetrates further south in the direction of the spawning grounds, returning north in the summer. Eventually, when they are mature, their swim southwards in the winter takes them to their spawning grounds. Although this may sound a complicated migration, there may well be a very simple explanation. In the summer months, when it is light, the fish are in the surface layers of water feeding on the plankton there. They must drift with the water then, for they have no reference points for navigation. In winter, when it is dark, they sink to the bottom, and orientate themselves to swim against the current, which is possible through the sense of touch. They will thus retrace their summer path at a different depth. As the fish grow older, they would be expected to be stronger, and hence appear further and further south.

The orientation to lie facing upstream is very strong in some fish. Sticklebacks and trout, for example, maintain their station so accurately that it is difficult to see their presence. In these cases, it is done mainly visually. The apparatus in Fig. XI (4) enables this phenomenon to be studied. It consists of an annular trough of water formed by placing a cylindrical glass pneumatic trough in the middle of a larger one. The bottom and sides are marked with a prominent pattern of lines drawn on paper stuck on the outside. The fish, for example a stickleback, is placed in water between the two troughs. The whole is mounted on a turntable. On rotating the trough, the water at first remains stationary but the fish maintains station opposite one of the marks, swimming into what, to it, appears to be a current of water flowing past. After the rotation has been continued for some time the water eventually rotates with the trough and the fish no longer points itself in a given direction 'upstream'. When the trough is stopped the water continues to flow for some time and the fish immediately swings round in the opposite direction to that which it maintained at first to face the new direction of the 'current'.

This apparatus also enables one to investigate the rate of swimming of small fish. The sudden darts by which one recognises them in their natural environments suggest high speeds. Sir James Gray, experimenting on larger fish, found that 9-inch trout did not exceed 5 miles per hour. However, their acceleration was remarkable, rising to 4g, which means that the parts of the body are pushed forwards with a force four times their own weights. The

[1] G. C. Trout, 'The Bear Island Cod Migrations and Movement'. *Fishery Investigations*, Series II, xxi, No. 6, 1957.

darting effect noticed by the angler is doubtless the flash of light reflected from the side of the body when the swimming wave passes down it, combined maybe with a confusion of acceleration with velocity. One of the record-holders is the dolphin—a mammal not a fish—which can sustain 20 knots. Such speeds have been recorded owing to the habit of swimming in company with ships. It is, however, possible that they supplement their own efforts by swimming near the crest of a wave generated by the ship, when the water will be travelling forwards.

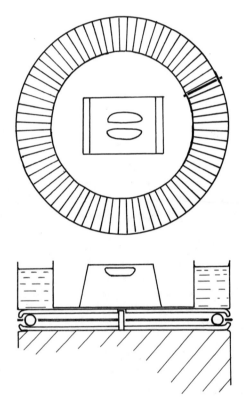

FIG. XI (4). *Plan and elevation of water trough for study of fish swimming. The ball-race is constructed from record-player turntables, the ball-bearings being separated by a wooden spacer. The water circuit is the space in between the two circular troughs which lie on marked card. The inner trough is held down by a large weight.*

CHAPTER XII

Bird Flight

IT is clear that most birds are very well adapted for fast movement through air. The general shape is streamlined, which means that energy will not be wasted in stirring the air into eddies, and the body feathers enhance the effect by lying in the direction of the airflow. The wings and tail are virtually airproof, and the legs are tucked up or trailed in flight. Internally, there are marked adaptations for flight, but here the bird betrays its landbound ancestry, for the structures are moulded out of the usual vertebrate parts (Plate IX (i)). The back-bone, composed of vertebrae, runs from the skull into the tail, but owing to the great strength needed in the wing region, the separate vertebrae there are fused to form a rigid column. Ribs and sternum are present, although the sternum is enormously enlarged to accommodate the attachment of the large flight muscles of the breast. When on land, the weight of the bird is normally carried on the two hind limbs although some of the best flyers, like the shearwater, have their legs set so far back that they cannot stand up on them. The joints in the hind limbs are not quite the same as those of other vertebrates. As with them, the hip joints are ball and socket ones, the knee joints are simple hinges, and there is a single bone, the femur, between them. The next bone, however, is thought to be a fusion of the shinbone with the proximal ankle-bones, making the next joint equivalent in position to the middle of our feet. It bends in the same sense as the mammalian ankle. The next element, which may be very long, as in waders, usually bears four toes. The feet are modified for the various modes of life, being webbed in swimmers, clawed in climbers and birds of prey. Webbed feet help as airbrakes during landing, and sometimes act as water skis. The puffin uses its webbed feet to supplement the tail surface in normal flight.

The fore limb has the normal ball and socket shoulder joint, and the humerus separates it from the simple hinge joint at the elbow. Next come the radius and ulna, side by side, and the wrist and finger-bones are modified from the normal five-finger plan, although zoologists recognise homologies even here. The thumb is separate enough to be raised in flight, but the other digits are all inside the outline of the wing.

Many of the bones are hollow. It is easy to appreciate that for a given weight of material, greater rigidity is derived from hollow cylindrical, rather than solid rod, construction. In some cases the cylinder is augmented by diagonal internal struts. In some cases the hollows are air sacs.

The main flight muscles are the pectoralis major and minor muscles, Fig. XII (1). The major is attached to the lower part of the keel of the sternum and inserts on the lower side of the humerus. It is responsible for the downbeat of the wings. The upstroke is powered mainly by the pectoralis minor which lies beneath the pectoralis major, but since the air pressure aids

FIG. XII (1). *The position of the wing skeleton and the main flight muscles in a bird. Only the right pectoralis major is shown. The two smaller muscles, left and right pectoralis minor, act on the dorsal surface of the humerus via long tendons.*

the upstroke, it does not have to produce as much power as the larger antagonistic muscle. The pectoralis minor muscle ends on a long tendon which passes through a hole between the three shoulder bones to insert on the top of the humerus. This is, therefore, an animal pulley system. Other smaller muscles control the rotation of the humerus on its own axis, and thus increase or decrease the angle of attack of the wing to the airstream. In the wing itself are smaller muscles which control its shape.

The leading edge of the wing, between shoulder and wrist, is formed by a fold of skin pulled into a curve by the extension of the elbow joint. Small feathers in this region help to give the wing an aerofoil cross-section. The main wing area is formed by large feathers, the primaries, attached to the flesh covering the equivalent of the hand, and the secondaries, somewhat smaller feathers, attached in the arm region. As the wing closes and opens, they are kept evenly spaced by an elastic ligament joining their shafts at their points of insertion into the skin. The spreading and folding of the wing is thus controlled by the same muscles that extend and flex the arm, and there is no separate control for each feather.

The lift for flight is derived from the airflow over the special shape of the wing (Fig. XII (2)). It is most simply understood for gliding flight, while

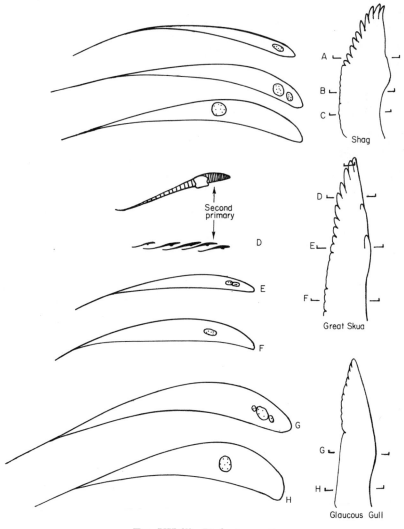

FIG. XII (2). *Bird wing sections.*

flapping flight is an extension of the principles of gliding where the airflow is speeded up by the movement of the wings. If a symmetrical streamlined shape is placed in a wind tunnel, the airflow is parted by the leading edge, and the flow round both sides is the same. It speeds up as it passes the widest parts and slows down again as the section tapers towards the trailing edge. If an asymmetrical shape is substituted, such as an aerofoil section, with a pronounced hump on the upper surface, airflow speeds up more over the hump than over the lower surface which may be slightly concave. These flow patterns have been illustrated in Plates X (ii to v) using water flow. The crux of the matter of obtaining lift from such flow lies in the Bernoulli mechanism, discussed in Chapter X, producing lower pressure where the airflow is faster. The aerofoil section must therefore have lower pressure on the upper surface than on the under surface, and this difference gives the upwards lift. A series of manometers let into an aerofoil section placed in an air stream give a distribution of pressure as shown in Fig. XII (3). The resultant of the pressures over the whole wing can be considered to act through one point called the centre of lift.

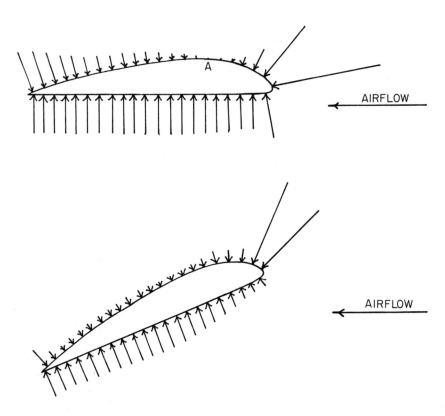

FIG. XII (3). *Arrows to show the pressure on an aerofoil at two different angles of attack. The length of the arrow is proportional to the pressure difference from the point A.*

By increasing the angle of attack of the wing to the airflow, the path round the upper surface of the wing taken by the streamlines is lengthened, and lift increases. This holds until the angle of attack reaches about 15°. Then the aerofoil loses its streamlined property, and a confusion of eddies breaks out on the upper surface. The low pressure formerly present disappears, leaving only the small contribution to the lift from the under surface. This condition is called a stall, and the bird or aeroplane falls until it has regained an angle of attack allowing streamlined flow. In designs where the tail is well aft of the wings, recovery is rapid, for air pressure on the tail quickly brings the nose down. The loss of speed associated with a stall is also quickly restored in the resulting dive. As lift decreases with decreasing speed, the angle of attack of the wings must be increased to enable the lift to equal the weight of the bird or aeroplane. The stall, therefore, occurs at a definite airspeed for any flying object, its stalling speed.

Birds landing into a head wind can often be seen to glide down and stall on to the ground from a height of a few inches. If there is little wind, the resulting flapping landing obscures this. In normal flight stalling is rare, but displaying wood-pigeons often take a steep flapping climb, and then glide upwards until they stall.

When landing, the lower the stalling speed, the greater the safety. As the angle of attack increases with reducing airspeed, the stall can be put off by the use of 'slots', which are foils erected just above the leading edge of the wings. Some aircraft are fitted with them, and birds have a similar device in their thumb, already mentioned. The thumb bears a couple of feathers and although it covers only a little of the leading edge it is present over the forward projecting wrist, where the stall breaks out first. This slot mechanism is normally inconspicuous but is seen on some photographs of landing birds, e.g. Plate XII (i)(3).

Lift can be supplemented by the lowering of flaps under the trailing edge. The nearest equivalents possessed by birds are webbed feet and tails which can be fanned out. No doubt these also act as simple air brakes.

Gliding is a process of continual but gradual sinking through the air immediately around. Only by losing height in this way can energy be obtained for forward movement. The forwards force needed to maintain speed is very much less than the weight of the craft—in man-made gliders, of the order of one-thirtieth. The glider must point downwards enough for the lift reaction to possess a sufficient forwards component (Fig. XII (4)). In flight of a steady velocity, this force balances the one of drag. Thus the less the drag, the shallower the gliding angle and the greater the distance which can be covered for a given drop in height.

Apart from the gliding flight of the albatross, shearwaters and fulmars, which are restricted to a few feet above sea-level, it is only when the air is rising faster than a bird sinks that it can stay up indefinitely and gain altitude. Such rising air is found in bubbles and columns which have been heated by the ground on hot days. Upcurrents also occur when a wind blows on to a cliff or hill-side, and a third type, called wave lift by pilots, is produced when wind blows over hills, and rises and falls in a manner analogous to the undulations in a shallow brook with a stony bed. In the atmosphere, such waves extend well above the normal concerns of birds, and gliders have been able to rise to great heights in them. The highest thermal lift produces thunder clouds which can rise to some 40,000 feet or more.

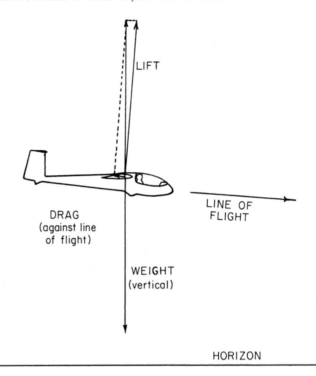

FIG. XII (4). *Forces acting on a glider.*

When man is gliding he receives a lifting sensation when he enters rising air, if he comes across it fairly suddenly. However, after the initial acceleration the only signal that he is changing height can come from the escape of air from the middle ear into the mouth via the eustachian tube (Fig. IV (3)), which is often called ear popping. This is not a very sensitive method, for the effect only takes place every hundred feet or more, and the visible recession of the ground suffers from similar drawbacks as a sensitive altimeter. It will be remembered that the senses are unreliable in the similar situation of an enclosed lift where there are no fixed height marks. When man succeeds in gaining height, he usually relies on an instrument called a variometer, which works on a principle like that of the pressure release from the middle ear, but has a much more sensitive way of detecting the outflow of air.

The same problem confronts soaring birds and it is not understood how they solve it. One possibility is for there to be very sensitive pressure or airflow receptors in the ear. It is known that birds can hear very low frequencies, such as radiate from very distant explosions, much better than man. The cochlea of the ear (Fig. IV (3)) is the part responsible for sensitivity to sound. Different pitches of note are received at different depths down the cochlea spiral, the high frequencies at the middle ear while the low ones penetrate towards the apex of the spiral. Now the apex of the bird's cochlea contains a sensitive structure not present in mammals, and it is conceivable that this might be developed by soaring birds to detect the very low rate of pressure change on climbing and sinking. Alternatively, an ear-popping mechanism might be used, or another possibility is that air could be detected flowing into or out of the air sacs in the hollow humerus bones. The reservoir of air here is much larger than that in the middle ear, so the problem of detecting inflow and outflow will not be so great. Lastly, it is possible that their high acuity of vision might enable birds to detect the recession or approach of the ground visually.

Another puzzle was, for a long time, the gliding flight of those birds like the albatross, shearwater, and fulmar. Its secret lies in the different wind speeds in the lowest 50 feet of the atmosphere. Owing to the friction between the air and the surface over which it is blowing, the wind is slower near the ground than it is above. In other words, there is a wind gradient. Imagine the bird at the top of this gradient. If it glides downwind, as it loses height it will be meeting the air relatively faster. Thus when it nears the surface it can have built up a fairly high airspeed. At this point it must wheel round and climb. Then it will be going through the wind gradient in the opposite direction, and again be encountering air at a higher relative speed. By this method it could never travel directly upwind, but it could reach at an angle to the wind direction. Under certain circumstances, fulmars and their relatives use the equivalent of hill lift by flying along the side of a wave, a few inches above the surface. During the generation of ocean waves by wind, the wind travels faster than the waves, so that lift should be available either on the windward side or in an eddy on the lee side which could develop according to the Jeffry theory.[1] When fully developed, however, these waves travel at much the same velocity as the wind which gives rise to them. The birds would become more dependent on the wheeling flight in the wind gradient. Waves which have travelled out of the storm area may well be moving faster than the wind above them, or in a different direction. Further, on reaching shallow water, waves slow down. The soaring possibilities under these conditions will depend on the relative velocities of wind and waves.

In flapping flight, two distinct wing cycles are used, one in slow flight when taking off and landing in still air, and the other when flying rapidly. The former demands more violent flapping of the wings than the latter. The cycle for slow flight is shown in Plate XII (i) and in Fig. XII (5) for a tawny owl and pigeon respectively.

Starting with the wings extended above the body, they are beaten powerfully downwards and forwards, at a high angle of attack to the airflow. The thumb feather, or bastard wing, may be raised to give the slot effect. A similar safeguard against stalling may be derived from separation of the primary feathers.

The raising of the wings in slow flapping flight is accomplished by rotation at the shoulder universal joint so that the upper surface of the wing is seen

[1] R. A. R. Tricker, *Bores, Breakers, Waves, and Wakes*, p. 145, 1964.

PLATE XII (i). *The wing cycle of a slowly flying bird (tawny owl). The photographs were taken on separate flights but are numbered according to the normal sequence. Note the slot provided by the thumb feather visible half-way along the leading edge of the wing in the third photograph.*

(1)

(2)

(4)

(5)

(6)

(7)

(8)

in a side view of the bird. The wings swing forwards and upwards so as to obscure the head momentarily. A slight flexion ensues, and then there is a violent flick in which the wrists move the primary feathers outwards, upwards, and backwards. The primaries are travelling so rapidly that they part, and each acts as a miniature wing, thus giving lift on the upstroke. The wings then approach each other over the back, and in some cases meet with a loud clapping noise. They are now ready to repeat the cycle.

It will be recalled that the upstroke muscles, the pectoralis minors, are much smaller than the downstroke ones. This active upstroke uses them a great deal, and it is not surprising that frequent take-off and landing, with little time for recovery in between, is very tiring for the bird.

In rapid flying, the downbeat is the power stroke, and there is a little forward component in it. During the upstroke the angle of attack only changes a little, and there is no extreme movement as before. The pressure of the air raises the wings, and very little or no muscular effort is called for. This wing cycle can be maintained for long periods since the enormous pectoralis major muscle is concerned with supplying most of the power. As before, the whole wing is not in the same phase of the cycle at any instant, the tip lagging behind the wrist in the vertical plane, Fig. XII (6).

A number of other factors help to determine the flight characteristics of the wing of a bird. One of these is the wing-tip vortex. Since there is higher pressure beneath the wing than above it, air will flow upwards round the tip of the wing. As the wing moves on, a column of rotating air called a vortex is generated. In certain atmospheric conditions, vortices can be seen streaming from the wing-tips of aircraft as transient vapour trails. A blunt-ended wing has a relatively large terminal vortex, for the broader tip allows more air to spill upwards. A long narrow wing-tip loses less. Many birds with blunt-ended wings achieve a compromise by separating the terminal primaries into a series of narrow-tipped wings. Birds whose wings are long and narrow have a tip composed of only one or two primary feathers.

Another factor is the aerofoil section. Some of these are shown in Fig. XII (2), for three birds, the shag, great skua, and glaucous gull. The measurements were made in still air, and during flight there will be some variation, especially at the trailing edge. It is of interest that the primary feathers near the tip have an aerofoil section themselves, and, when separated, will thus be more effective in providing lift than simple laminae. The long thin trailing edge of the sections is provided by the extremities of the primaries or secondaries. The area of the section occupied by flesh and bone is relatively small, the rest being made up of series of upper and lower covert feathers.

The most potent part of the wing section for providing lift is the curved upper surface, as we have seen in Fig. XII (3). Moreover, the effectiveness of any part has much to do with the section thickness and the curvature at that point, so that some areas of the upper surface contribute more to supporting the bird or aircraft than others. Measures of the 'wing loading' expressed as $\dfrac{\text{total weight}}{\text{wing area}}$ ignore this variation across the section, but nevertheless provide some information of interest.

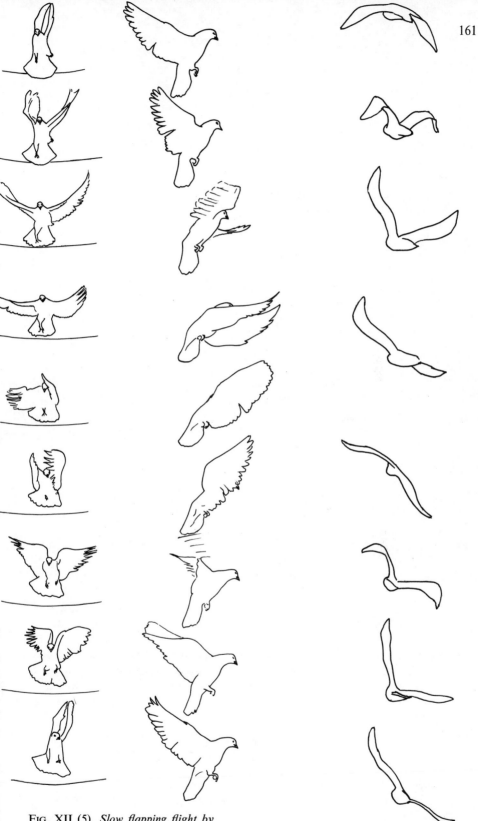

FIG. XII (5). *Slow flapping flight by a pigeon. The bird approaching the observer is performing an S-turn, hence the asymmetry of legs and wings in the drawings.*

FIG. XII (6). *Oblique views of Great Skua flying rapidly.*

TABLE XII (I)

*List of Approximate Wing Loadings of a Number of
Loaded Aircraft and Individual Birds*

Type	Loading in gm. cm.$^{-2}$
over 300 m.p.h.	
Britannia	48·3
Stratofortress	44·5
Viscount	36
Sabre	33
Comet	26
under 300 m.p.h.	
D.C.3 (Dakota)	14·7
Anson	13·2
under 200 m.p.h.	
Auster A.O.P.6	6·6
Chipmunk	6·1
Helicopters (rotor loadings)	
S.55	50
Brantley 305	42
Brantley 2B	33
Gliders	
EoN Olympia	2·07
EoN Baby	2·00
EoN Primary	1·36
Birds	
Puffin	2·45
Shag	1·16
Great Skua	0·98
Manx Shearwater	0·86
Oyster Catcher	0·79
Tawny Owl	0·39
Storm Petrel	0·31

Since lift is proportional to the square of the velocity, it is to be expected that the faster flyers will be designed to carry higher wing loadings. This, however, acts against the demands of safety by increasing the stalling speed. The helicopters might appear to be exceptions to the argument since they have comparable carrying capacity and speed to the Anson and Auster, but are able to sustain higher loading values owing to the very much higher speed of the actual rotors. Sometimes a 'disc loading' is given which is

$$\frac{\text{area swept out by one rotor per revolution}}{\text{total weight}}.$$

Such a value is of course a lot lower, and sounds safer.

The man-made gliders overlap with the sample of birds, and the speeds of the two groups are comparable. Of the gliders, the first has the highest wing loading and performance and the third has the lowest. The wings of this model are very broad-tipped and must create the biggest vortex.

The puffin, with the highest value for the wing loading of the birds given here, has very small wings and a very rapid wing-beat. It apparently has a very high stalling speed, for when taking off from cliffs it prefers to drop steeply, using potential energy to gain airspeed. Puffins landing and taking off give the impression of being near the limits of safety, but their wings may well be a compromise, for they are also said to be used in underwater swimming. The shag also appears to have difficulty in taking off. So does the Manx shear-water, but this is because the legs are set very far back, and it cannot stand up. The last five examples given have an apparently much more effortless flight. The Manx shearwater and storm petrel use the same methods of gliding as the albatross already described. The low value for the tawny owl must enable it to glide very slowly, and hence silently, and it should be able to carry heavy prey without a high stalling speed.

The aspect ratio is often quoted as having great significance. This value is the number of times the length of the aerofoil at the wing-root goes into the span. The long thin wing with high aspect ratio is associated with a fast penetrating glide, and is seen in gulls, albatrosses and their relatives and high-performance sailplanes. The long wing will have more of the strip near the leading edge which is more potent in providing lift, and can have a smaller area than a low aspect ratio wing supporting the same load. The drag due to skin friction is proportional to the area and the square of the velocity, so economies in area become very important in rapid flight. A limit to the span is set by the stresses in the wing-root and the necessity of fitting a strong enough spar inside the aerofoil section. Birds with low aspect ratios are those which soar passively in thermal upcurrents, those which carry prey, and those which fly slowly. Examples are buzzards, vultures, eagles, owls, and herons.

The lift required by a bird, being a function of area and span, allows the smaller ones to have relatively smaller wings, for the weight of the body is proportional to the cube of the length. The golden eagle and the goldcrest, when drawn in silhouette and scaled to be of equal span, will be seen to have very different relative body sizes, although their wing aspect ratios are much the same.

Birds such as swallows, which manœuvre adroitly at high speed, subject themselves to considerable strains during cornering. Gravity accelerates objects falling freely at the rate of 32 feet per second per second, and an acceleration of twice this requires a force of $2g$ on each unit of mass, or twice the normal weight. A swallow flying at 40 miles per hour in a circle of radius 60 feet is subject to this acceleration and must provide twice the lift that it does in normal flight. If a bird is turning without sideslip in a horizontal plane, the angle of bank gives a direct indication of the g stress, the relation being that drawn in Fig. XII (7) (see also Appendix I).

The following, then, influence the shape of wings: airborne weight, wing span, wing area, tip shape, shape of aerofoil section, spar strength, speed of flight, loads carried, and manœuvrability.

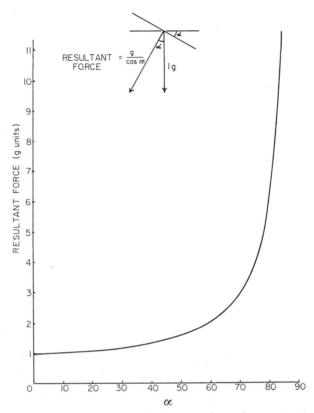

$$\text{RESULTANT FORCE} = \frac{g}{\cos \alpha}$$

FIG. XII (7). *The forces acting on a bird or aeroplane when turning in a horizontal circle at different angles of bank, without sideslip.*

Birds are not the only animals to have developed the power of flight. Invertebrate animals are poorly represented among the flyers, but the insects are a highly successful group. The smallest species have wing spans of less than half a millimetre, and at this scale it is viscosity which plays the dominant role in movement through the air. Streamlining is of less importance, and the wings of some of these specimens resemble garden rakes which, scaled up, would be most unairworthy. If the viscosity were also scaled up to provide the same flow conditions for a 2-inch model, something about ten times as viscous as golden syrup would be needed. These small insects are really rowing themselves through the air. At the other end of the scale, the Atlas moth of the East, with a wing span of 9 inches, has a very penetrating glide, and its aerodynamics is more akin to that of birds and aircraft.

Vertebrate flying animals are very varied. The flying fish is capable of gliding after a take-off run where its tail is still in the water beating. It is said that these flights last for only one or two seconds, although much longer ones may result from the use of rising air over the surface of the waves. The amphibia are represented by a gliding frog called Racophorus, whose flying surfaces are its large webbed feet. However, its gliding angle is poor, and its performance is little more than an extended parachute drop. Reptiles have only one flying representative left, *Draco volans*, a lizard, said to have a performance similar to that of Racophorus. However, the pterodactyls of the

Jurassic and Cretaceous were reptiles, and undoubtedly successful flyers (Plate XII (ii) (B)). Their small breast-bones suggest that there was no anchorage for powerful wing muscles and that they were primarily gliders. The main difference between these and birds is that the pterodactyl's wing was a membrane stretched from an enormously enlarged little finger to the hind-leg region. They may have perished for the same reason as the dinosaurs of their time, but it is hard to imagine that healing would have been possible had the membrane ever become torn.

(B)

PLATE XII (ii). *Casts of fossils:* (left), *Archaeopteryx;* (right), *Pterodactyl.*

The flying exponents of the mammals, the bats, also use a membranous wing, but it is spread over four compartments since all the fingers form part of the supporting structure. The flying squirrel is well adapted with a skin stretching from hand to foot, and ordinary squirrels have little fear of jumping off any tree.

The birds themselves originated from reptile stock, the earliest known representative being Archaeopteryx. This animal had feathers, yet there were prominent claws on small fingers of the fore limbs, there was a long reptilian tail, and the jaws were set with teeth (Plate XII (ii) (A)).

This chapter can hardly close without some mention of spiders, some of which have taken to flying using their own aircraft. Flying spiders pay out a long thread of silk, and when this is long enough, take to the air on it. They are at the mercy of upcurrents, and aerial trawling has caught them at great heights. They may not be altogether without control, however, for on one occasion a spider was reported to have rolled up its thread in mid-air. No doubt this kind of flying is a mechanism for the dispersal of the species, and judging by the quantity of gossamer in the air on certain days is commonly used. Fabre, the celebrated French entomologist of last century, became fascinated by these spiders, and was delighted to see them escape out of his window on their threads of silk.

CHAPTER XIII

Rotation

T HE movement which we have considered so far has been limited to simple translation. Its study is usually known as particle dynamics and it takes no account of rotation. When rigid bodies of finite size, however, are acted on by forces, they are not only moved bodily from place to place but in general they suffer rotation also. We must now take account of this freedom to rotate.

It is possible to develop the theory of rotational movement by considering the mechanics of a number of particles linked rigidly together. Before considering this possibility, however, it will help towards an understanding of the principles if the subject is first approached from the point of view of an experimental inquiry. Just as the dynamics of particles was evolved on the basis of certain experimental observations, so it is possible to have the dynamics of rigid bodies based similarly upon experiment also. How the results to which direct observation leads can then be made to follow from existing particle dynamics can be investigated later.

In approaching the rotation of rigid bodies experimentally, the development of the mechanics of particles, which has already been studied, can be of great assistance. In rotational motion we are concerned with angular velocities instead of velocities of translation. They can be measured in degrees per second or radians per second, or, indeed, in terms of any arbitrary unit of angle per unit of time. Similarly, angular acceleration is the rate of change of angular velocity. Thus when angular velocity is measured in degrees per second, angular acceleration would be measured in degrees per second per second, and so on. The symbol commonly used for angular velocity is ω, and for angular acceleration we will employ $\dot{\omega}$ (pronounced omega dot). The angle turned through is usually written θ. Sometimes the angular velocity, which is the rate of change of angle, is written $\dot{\theta}$ and then angular acceleration becomes $\ddot{\theta}$ (theta double dot).

For simplicity, to start with we will confine our attention to bodies which are constrained so as to rotate about a fixed axis, such as a flywheel, the axle of which is mounted in bearings, or a beam pivoted at a certain point. The analogy which the movements of bodies thus constrained present with those of linear motion of particles is immediately suggestive. In the first place, if such a body is set rotating about its fixed axis, it will continue to rotate after the force which set it in motion has ceased to act, just as a particle which has been set in motion will continue to move when not acted on by a force. By making the surfaces in contact with the particle as smooth as possible, the movement continues nearly uniformly. Similarly by improving the bearings of the rotating body, its rotation continues nearly uniformly. It is, in fact, easier to improve the bearings of the rotating body than it is to make the surfaces sufficiently smooth in the case of the particle. When a turning force

166

is applied to the body capable of rotating, its angular velocity is increased or decreased according to the direction of the turning force, in a similar manner to the change in velocity produced in a moving particle by an impressed force. Our immediate object in studying rotational motion must be to make this analogy more definite.

We must first consider the nature of what we have so far spoken of as a turning force. When a body is pivoted so that it can turn about an axis, a force will only tend to turn it if its line of action does not pass through the axis. The turning effect will increase as the force is applied further from the axis, and the product of the force and the distance of its line of action from the axis can be used as a measure of the turning effect. It is known as the moment of the force about the axis. Actually two forces are involved in turning a body since the pivot exerts a second force. This prevents the body moving as a whole and we shall see that it is equal and opposite to the applied force. Since it passes through the pivot it does not have the same line of action as the applied force. Two such equal and opposite forces acting along parallel lines at a distance apart are known as a couple. The moment of the couple is defined to be the product of the magnitude of one of the forces and the perpendicular distance between their lines of action.

In many ways rotational motion is easier to deal with than translational motion. In the first place friction can be reduced to negligible proportions very easily, by mounting the body under examination on a point bearing. A glass tube sealed off at one end makes a suitable bearing to rest upon the point, or a hole drilled in brass or steel can be similarly employed. A beam so mounted and set rotating will continue to turn for a very long time, especially if it is fairly massive, though even a light aluminium girder will continue to rotate very nearly uniformly for many rotations. Using uniform beams made from U-shaped aluminium girder, rotational replicas of some of the experiments performed for linear motion with the trolleys, described in Chapters II and VI, can be carried out.

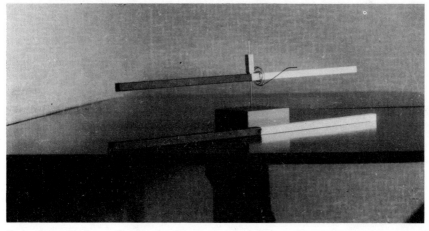

PLATE XIII (i). *A small girder pivoted on a steel point so as to turn freely. One end has been coloured black and the other white. It carries a small spring and on top is fitted another pivot upon which can be placed a second beam at present lying on the table.*

Plate XJII (i) is from a photograph of such an apparatus. The beams are about 2 feet in length and are cut from square-section aluminium girder of side about ½ inch. The photograph shows one girder mounted on the pivot. One end has been coloured black and the other white to enable them to be distinguished. Inserted into a small piece of wood, attached to the mid-point of the girder, is a second pointed pivot on which can be mounted a second girder. A light steel spring is attached to the lower beam and this can be arranged to press on the upper one to enable one to exert a turning force on the other.

Plate XIII (ii) shows an exactly similar beam to the lower one mounted above it on the pivot. The two can turn quite independently of each other. It

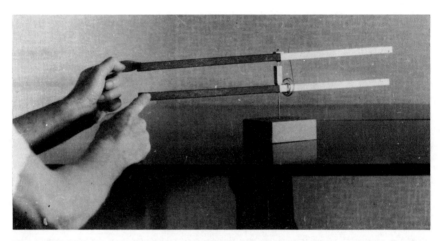

PLATE XIII (ii). *The second beam has been mounted on the pivot carried by the first. The two beams can rotate independently of each other. The spring has been set so that a force is exerted between the two beams.*

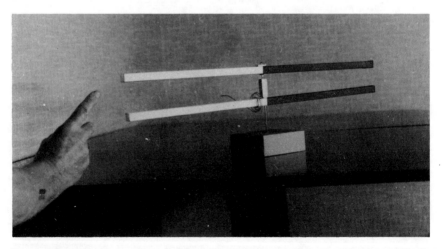

PLATE XIII (iii). *The two beams, when released, rotate in opposite directions with the same angular speed. They come into line again when each has made a half rotation as in this photograph.*

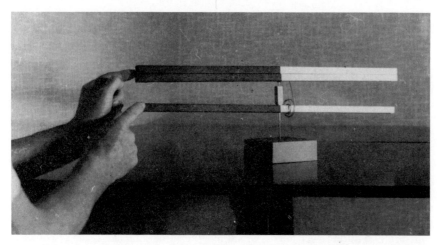

PLATE XIII (iv). *In this experiment the upper beam possesses twice the mass of the lower. They are started, as before, one above the other.*

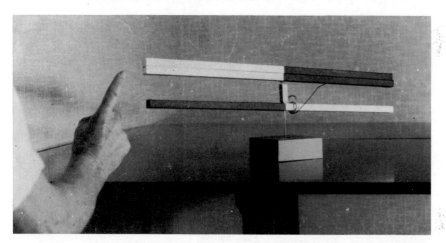

PLATE XIII (v). *Only half the angular velocity is generated in the upper beam of double mass as is given to the lower beam. When the upper beam has completed half a revolution the lower one has made one complete rotation.*

is worth while, in cutting the girders, to take some trouble to make them of as nearly the same length as possible since the experiments to be carried out are capable of considerable accuracy. The photograph shows the two beams held one above the other with the spring set so that each exerts a force upon the other. When the beams are released, by removing the fingers from each at the same moment, and in such a manner as not to impart any rotation to the system, it will be found that both beams start to move, one in a clockwise and the other in a counter-clockwise direction. It will be found that they move with equal and opposite angular velocities, the beams again coming into line after each has made half a turn, as in the photograph of Plate XIII (iii).

This result is entirely analogous to that which was obtained for linear movement with the trolleys. When each had been adjusted to be of the same weight as the other and one exerted a force upon the other, each moved in the opposite direction to the other and at the same speed. The system which possessed no linear momentum to begin with continued to possess no resultant linear momentum after the action had taken place. The result was the same whether the large boy pulled the small one or vice versa. Exactly similar results can be obtained for the rotational movement of the two equal beams. It does not matter whether the spring is attached to the lower or upper beam, and it is the same whether a strong spring is used or only a weak one. The experiment suggests that there may be something corresponding to linear momentum in the case of rotational movement.

This view is supported by the results of varying the experiment so as to double the mass of the upper beam. Plate XIII (iv) shows the arrangement. Another beam, identical to the other already used, has been attached to the upper beam so that the two move as one. The system is started as before and when released the lower beam, which has the same dimensions as previously, turns through two revolutions for each one turned through by the upper double beam. Plate XIII (v) shows the position after the upper double beam has completed half a revolution. In the same time the lower one has completed a whole rotation. The angular velocity generated in the lower beam is thus twice that generated in the upper. This again accords with the results of the trolley experiments in the case of linear motion. It suggests that we might try defining angular momentum by the product of the mass of the body and its angular velocity, just as linear momentum is the product of the mass and the linear velocity. The following experiment, however, shows that this will not do.

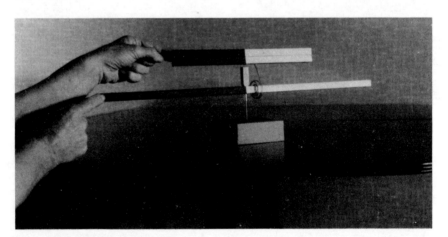

PLATE XIII (vi). *In this experiment the upper beam possesses the same mass as the lower, but it has been divided into two and the two halves mounted together so that the length has been reduced to one half that of the lower beam.*

For this experiment we divide a beam, of the same length as one of the original beams, into two equal parts, and attach them to each other as in the photograph of Plate XIII (vi). This gives us an upper beam of the same mass as the lower but of only half the length. Now when the system is released the shorter upper double beam turns through four rotations for every one performed by the lower. Plate XIII (vii) shows the position of the beams when the upper one has made one complete turn. The lower one has completed a quarter turn only. Plate XIII (viii) was taken when the lower beam had made half a turn. The upper one appears lined up as at the beginning but it has made two rotations in the interval. If the upper beam has only half the mass of the lower one as well as being reduced to one half of the length, it rotates even more easily. It will be found that the upper beam makes one complete rotation while the lower one makes only one eighth of a complete turn. The two beams are again in line with their original position when the lower one has made half a complete turn, by which time the upper one will have completed four rotations. Such an experiment is illustrated in Plate XIII (ix).

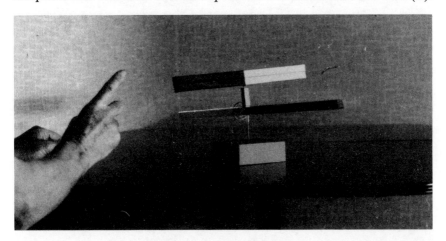

PLATE XIII (vii). *When the upper beam has completed one revolution the lower has made only one quarter of a turn.*

PLATE XIII (viii). *By the time the lower beam has made one half a revolution the upper one has made two complete turns and the beams are again in line with their position at the start.*

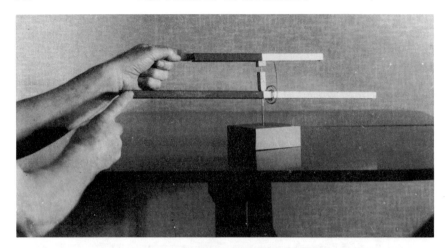

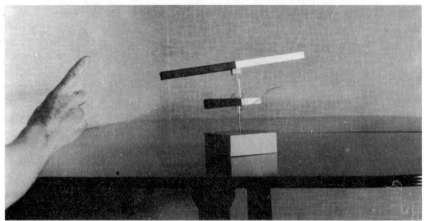

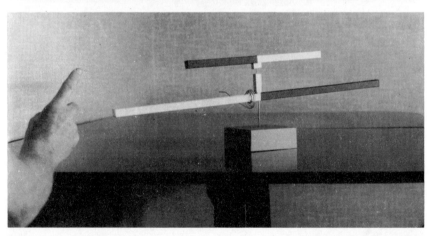

PLATE XIII (ix). *If the mass of the upper beam as well as its length is divided by two,
then when it has made one complete revolution the lower beam turns only through an
eighth of a turn. By the time the lower beam has made half a turn and come into line
with its original position the upper one has completed four whole turns.*

These experiments show that it is insufficient to employ simply the mass of the object in defining angular momentum. The first and second experiments show that it will be proportional to the mass so long as the length of the body remains unaltered, but we must use a quantity that will also depend upon the distribution of mass as well as on its magnitude, when this distribution is altered. Bodies which have their mass concentrated near the axis of rotation are easier to set turning than those in which the same mass is distributed further from the axis.

To deal with this problem we can turn once again to linear motion for suggestions as to how to proceed. In the case of linear motion it was the movement of a body acted on by a force which it seemed reasonable to assume constant, that provided the key to the question. With linear motion it was the force derived from gravity—the weight of the body—which produced a constant acceleration in the body acted on. A constant force generated a constant acceleration, and from this fact measures of both force and mass were derived. In the case of rotation, the corresponding question would be—does a constant couple generate a constant angular acceleration?

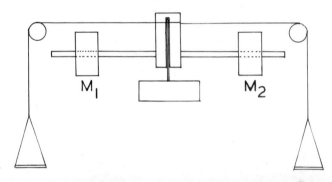

G. XIII (1).

PLATE XIII (x). *The apparatus for the investigation of the rotation of a body the distribution of whose mass can be varied.*

We can investigate this question by means of the apparatus of Plate XIII (x), of which Fig. XIII (1) is a diagram. Essentially it consists of a beam made of two brass rods screwed into a centre block, along which slide two brass weights M_1 and M_2, thus allowing the distribution of mass of the apparatus to be varied. The centre block has been drilled so that the whole can be mounted on a steel point on which it can turn freely. Cotton threads are wound round the centre block and pass over pulleys, and from these scale pans are suspended. By placing equal weights in the pans a couple can be exerted on the pivoted system so that it is set into rotation. We know from our previous experience that, provided the acceleration of the weights is small compared with the acceleration of gravity, a constant force will be exerted by the threads. The threads are wound up, the beams released, and at the same time a ciné film is taken of the beams from above. The film is exposed at 64 frames per second to secure good definition of the moving apparatus, and this also provides a large number of readings from which the angular velocity can be estimated. After development the resulting film is projected frame by frame and the position of the beam measured on a scale graduated in degrees. Although individual readings can be made to only about a quarter of a degree, the very large number of readings which the film provides still enables the experiment to achieve considerable accuracy, limited only by the steadiness of the speed of the camera, which is quite good. The angular velocity can be estimated by subtraction. For example, by subtracting the reading on the first frame from that on the ninth, the angle turned through in $\frac{8}{64}$ second can be estimated. By subtracting the reading on the second frame from that on the tenth, the angular velocity $\frac{1}{64}$ of a second later can be estimated, and so on. Angular velocities measured in this way provided the graphs of Figs. XIII (2) and XIII (3), that of Fig. XIII (2) showing the angular velocity

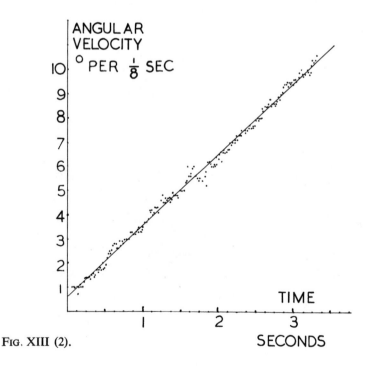

FIG. XIII (2).

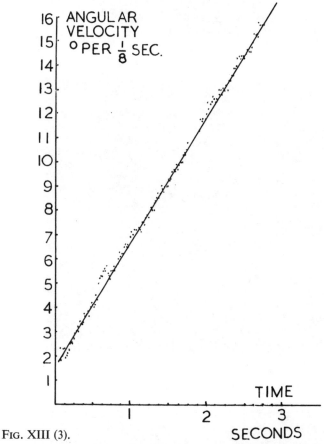

ANGULAR
VELOCITY
° PER ⅛ SEC.

TIME

FIG. XIII (3).   SECONDS

with the masses on the beam far from the axis and Fig. XIII (3) with the
masses closer in. Photographs from the ciné film showing the masses in
the extended and contracted positions are reproduced in Plate XIII (xi). The
positions at intervals of every 12 frames are shown in the superimposed
photographs of Plate XIII (xii). The graphs show that the angular velocity
increases uniformly with time. In other words, the beam has been given a
constant angular acceleration. This is true whether the masses are fastened
close in to the axis of rotation or further out. When the masses are fastened
close in, the apparatus is easier to rotate and the couple generates a greater
angular acceleration than it does when the masses are attached further out.

We can therefore proceed as with linear motion. The moment of inertia of
a body is a quantity similar to mass in linear motion measuring the difficulty
in setting the body rotating. We can define it as the time taken by a standard
couple to generate a standard angular velocity, in a similar manner to the
definition of mass in linear motion. Taking for the purpose of our measurements the standard couple to be that which is applied by the weights in the
scale pans in the above experiments, and the standard angular velocity to be
$10°$ per eighth second, we see that with the masses in the extended position on
the beam, the moment of inertia is about 3·33 seconds per unit couple per unit

angular velocity, while when the masses are in the contracted position the moment of inertia is 1·96 in the same units.

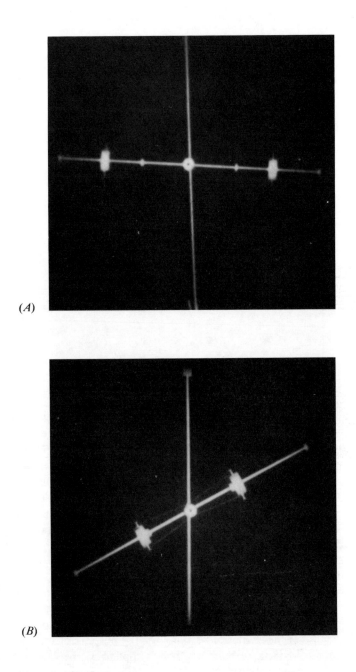

(A)

(B)

PLATE XIII (xi). *Photographs from a ciné film showing the weights on the beam in the extended and contracted positions. The film was taken from above to enable the angles through which the beam turns to be recorded.*

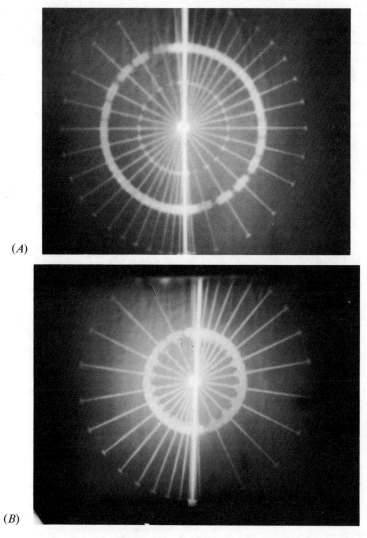

(A)

(B)

PLATE XIII (xii). *Photographs from the ciné film superimposed to show the angular acceleration of the beam in the extended and contracted positions respectively. Every twelfth frame is reproduced.*

We could, if we wish, proceed further as with linear motion and define a scale for couples by means of the acceleration they produce in a standard body. It is, however, convenient to measure the couple from the forces applied and their distance apart, the forces being measured as with linear movement. This requires a further experiment to show that the angular acceleration of a body is still proportional to the couple if measured in this way. Once we know that a constant couple produces a constant acceleration, however, our timing procedure can be very much simplified. We no longer need to take a ciné photograph of the movement. We can if we wish simply take the time for which the couple acts and then count the number of revolutions made by the beam per second after the couple has ceased to act and the beam rotates freely, and divide the second by the first to obtain the angular acceleration. Alternatively, we can allow the couple to act for a given number of revolutions, that is through say an angle θ, and measure the time for the beam to turn through this angle. If the angular acceleration, ω, is constant

$$\theta = \frac{\omega t^2}{2} \qquad \ldots 1$$

just as the distance is given by $s = \frac{1}{2}at^2$ in linear motion,

or

$$\omega = \frac{2\theta}{t^2}.$$

The results of an experiment carried out in this way are recorded graphically in Fig. XIII (4).

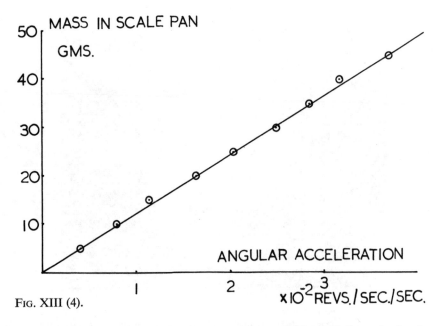

FIG. XIII (4).

We thus arrive at the relation between the couple C, applied to a body, the moment of inertia, I, of the body and its angular acceleration ω:

$$C = I\omega.$$

This relation is completely analogous to the equation

$$F = Ma$$

which we have already obtained connecting the force, F, acting on a body of mass, M, and the linear acceleration which ensues. Just as the second equation is in reality a definition of force and mass, as we have seen, our present treatment would suggest that the first equation is similarly a definition of what is meant quantitatively by the term moment of inertia. We shall see later, however, that the first equation can be deduced from the second together with Newton's third law of motion, and that the moment of inertia can be calculated in terms of the masses of the various parts of the body and their distribution.

To complete our experimental study of moments of inertia, however, we will investigate how they vary with the distribution of mass. For this purpose we can again employ the apparatus with the sliding weights. We allow our standard couple to act for a measured time, T, during which it turns the body through a given number of rotations. This gives us the angular acceleration ω from equation 1 and hence the moment of inertia from

$$I = \frac{C}{\omega}.$$

By measuring the moment of inertia with the weights in various positions we are able to plot the graph of Fig. XIII (5). In this graph the moment of inertia is plotted against the square of the distance of the masses from the axis. The graph is clearly a straight line. It does not pass through the origin, however, for two reasons. Firstly, the beams themselves together with the central cylinder will possess a certain moment of inertia which will not vary with the position of the weights, and secondly, even if the weights could be moved so that their centres of gravity lay on the axis of rotation, they would still possess a finite moment of inertia since we cannot treat the sliding masses as simple particles. As the masses are moved outwards from the axis, the moment of inertia increases by a quantity proportional to the square of the distance of the masses from the axis. The result is consistent with the moment of inertia depending upon the square of the distance of the mass from the axis, a result already suggested by the experiment with the beams, one of which was cut into two and the two halves mounted together. It will be remembered that it made four revolutions to the one of the lower beam against which it reacted.

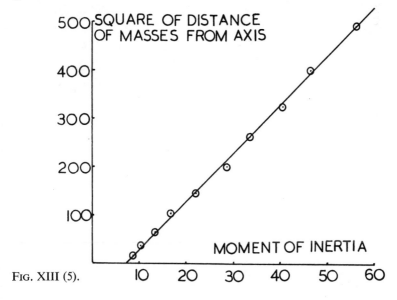

FIG. XIII (5).

We might also set up an experiment to show that the moment of inertia of a body is proportional to its mass so long as its linear dimensions are unaltered, but it is hardly necessary to do this. We have only to imagine two pieces of apparatus like the weighted beam mounted vertically one above the other so as to rotate about the same axis. If both systems are the same and we place identical weights in the scale pans, then both beams will rotate so as to keep pace with each other. They could, therefore, be joined together so as to form one body acted on by a couple double the size of that used for one beam only. The acceleration of the double beam acted on by the double couple will be the same as that of the single beam acted on by the single couple. The double beam must, therefore, possess double the moment of inertia of the single beam.

CHAPTER XIV

The Conservation of Angular Momentum

IN the mechanics of a rotating body its moment of inertia plays the same role as does its mass in the case of linear motion, angular acceleration replaces linear acceleration, and couples replace forces. Just as we can define linear momentum to be the product of the body's mass and its linear velocity, so it is possible to define an analogous angular momentum as the product of the moment of inertia and the angular velocity, or in symbols, $I\omega$. The importance of linear momentum was that it was conserved in any system not acted on by an external force, and we saw that the law of the conservation of momentum was the most fundamental of the observational data in the science of mechanics. A similar law has been found to apply to angular momentum, and experimental evidence supporting this must now be considered.

We have already met some of it in the experiments with the rotating beams acting upon each other by means of the spring. In these experiments the system always started from rest and thus possessed no angular momentum initially. Interaction between the beams always generated equal and opposite angular momenta in the two beams so that the total in the system remained at its original value, namely, nothing. When the two beams were identical and so possessed equal moments of inertia, the angular velocities generated in them were equal and opposite and so, therefore, were the angular momenta. When the mass of the upper beam was doubled without diminishing its length, by attaching another similar beam to it, the angular velocity it acquired was half that generated in the lower beam. The moment of inertia of the double beam being double that of a single one, upper and lower beams were again given equal and opposite angular momenta. When a single beam was cut into two and the two halves fastened together to give a beam with the original mass but with half the length, it acquired four times the angular velocity that was generated in the lower beam. Since moment of inertia varies as the square of the length, the divided beam will possess only a quarter the moment of inertia of the lower beam. When the two react together we see that once again equal and opposite angular momenta will be generated. The same continued to be the case when the upper beam had not only half the length but also half the mass of the lower beam.

The law of the conservation of angular momentum, analogous to the conservation of linear momentum which has already been discussed, is one of the most important principles in rotational mechanics. It has many important applications, some of which we shall be considering in later chapters. There is, however, one important difference between the conservation of angular momentum and the similar law of the conservation of linear momentum, to which we must now draw attention. Unlike its counterpart in linear motion —mass—which is constant for any body in the everyday world, moment of inertia can be varied. It depends not only upon the mass of the body but also upon how the mass is distributed. By concentrating the mass near the axis of rotation, the moment of inertia can be reduced. By removing the mass to places remote from the axis of rotation it can be increased. The angular momentum of a body is the product of its moment of inertia and its angular velocity—$I\omega$. If, in the absence of an externally applied couple, the angular momentum remains constant, it follows that when the moment of inertia, I, is altered the angular velocity, ω, must change in the opposite direction so as to maintain the product constant. The angular *velocity* possessed by an isolated system can therefore be altered without the action of an external couple. If we wish to speed up the rate at which a body is rotating, all that is necessary for us to do is to decrease its moment of inertia. This we can do by bringing its mass in nearer the axis. To slow the body up we must increase the moment of inertia by redistributing the mass further from the axis.

It is a simple matter to demonstrate this possibility using the apparatus with the weights sliding on the rotating beams of Plate XIII (x). The scale pans are removed so that the beam can be rotated freely and it is easy to arrange that the weights can be pulled into the contracted position by means of rubber bands. The weights are held in the extended position by means of cotton threads which can be released by removing a simple and sensitive central catch. The apparatus is set rotating and the catch is removed. The weights are brought into the contracted position with the result that there is a sudden and striking speeding up of the rotation.

The apparatus is capable of giving good quantitative results. We have already determined the moments of inertia of the apparatus with the weights in the extended and contracted positions. We have, therefore, only to measure the initial and final angular velocities in order to verify the conservation of angular momentum in this case. These two angular velocities can be determined roughly, if we wish, by counting revolutions, but for accurate results it is better to record successive positions of the beam by means of the ciné camera. The superimposed photographs of Plate XIV (i) show the angles turned through in the interval between 12 frames of the film before and after contraction. To obtain the full accuracy of which the film is capable, however, it is better to measure each frame as before and plot the results graphically. The result of doing this is shown in Fig. XIV (1). From the graph we see that the angular velocity is slowly decreasing all the time on account of friction at the bearing, but immediately before the contraction took place it was 206° per second whereas after the contraction had taken place it was 348° per second. The value found for the moment of inertia in the extended position was 3·33 seconds per unit couple per unit angular velocity, so that the initial angular momentum was

$$3\cdot33 \times 206 = 686 \text{ units.}$$

The value for the moment of inertia in the contracted position was 1·96 in the same units. The final angular momentum after the contraction had taken place was therefore

$$1\cdot96 \times 348 = 682 \text{ units.}$$

The agreement between the values before and after the contraction is better than 1 per cent.

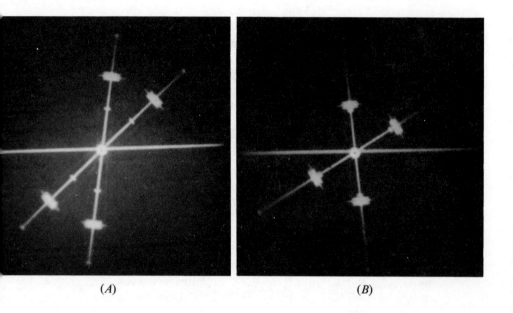

(A)   (B)

PLATE XIV (i). *Two superimposed photographs from the ciné film.*
(A) *The angle turned through by the beam with the weights in the extended position, immediately before contraction.*
(B) *The angle turned through by the beam with the weights in the contracted position, immediately after the contraction had taken place.*
In both cases the time interval is that between 12 frames of the film.

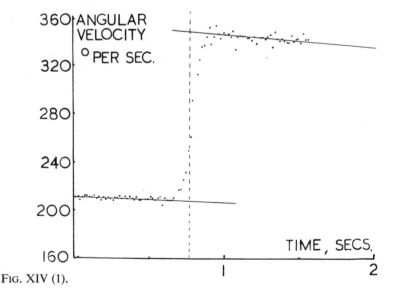

FIG. XIV (1).

The experiments with the rotating beams showed how angular momentum of one beam can be generated at the expense of generating an equal and opposite angular momentum in the other. If one of the beams had possessed angular momentum initially, the interaction would either have augmented what it had originally, or diminished it, according to the direction in which the fresh momentum which was generated took place. It thus becomes possible to transfer angular momentum from one part of a system to another, a fact which is of great practical importance. When a system is isolated the total angular momentum which it possesses remains unaltered, but its distribution among the various members of the system can be changed, through the action of the members on each other.

There is an important respect in which rotational motion appears to differ from translational motion. However the linear momentum of a system may be distributed throughout the system and changed by the action of internal forces, nothing will alter the motion of the centre of gravity except an external force. When a body rotates through 360° it arrives back in its original position. Suppose a member of a system to be set rotating through the action of internal forces. The remainder of the system will be given an angular momentum equal and opposite to that generated in the member which has been set rotating. If the member is then brought to rest, again by means of internal forces, after it has turned through 360° relative to the rest of the system, the angular momentum in the member and in the system as a whole will neutralise each other and the system will again be stationary. However, the system as a whole will have turned through a definite angle in the process. It is thus possible to turn a system round in space by means of internal forces alone. This fact has also important practical applications.

An experiment to demonstrate this can be arranged using the rotating beams. Plate XIV (ii) is a photograph of the apparatus. The lower beam carries pivots at each end on which two smaller beams can rotate. The one on the left acts merely as a counterpoise. That on the right is set rotating by means of a rubber band. Fig. XIV (2) shows how this may be done without deflecting the apparatus as a whole. The small beam is held at right angles to the lower one by means of a piece of cotton thread. When this is burnt with a match the rubber band sets the small beam rotating on its pivot, in a counter-clockwise direction. As soon as this occurs the lower beam starts to rotate in the clockwise direction. The system as a whole possessed no angular momentum to start with, and the small beam having been set in motion by means of internal forces only, no angular momentum can be generated in the whole by the process. Equal and opposite angular momenta are generated together.

As the small beam rotates it unwinds a piece of string which is attached to it and the lower beam, and then starts to wind it up in the opposite direction. When this process is completed the small beam is brought to rest relative to the lower beam. Its angular momentum is destroyed—by internal forces as when it was created. The result is that the whole system is again brought to rest, the angular momentum in the small beam just neutralising that which was generated in the rest of the system initially. While the rotations were going on, however, the system as a whole turned about the central pivot. The result of the process is thus to turn the system and this was accomplished through the action of internal forces alone.

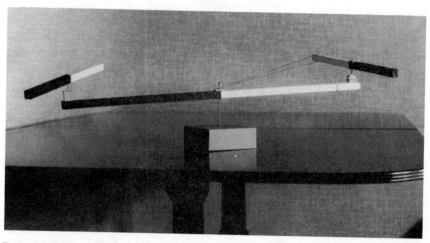

PLATE XIV (ii). *An experiment to demonstrate the transfer of angular momentum. The large beam carries two smaller beams each of which is mounted on a point pivot and is free to rotate. The one on the right-hand side is set rotating by forces internal to the system by means of the rubber band attached to it at the far end. The near end is held in place by a cotton thread which can be burnt. As it turns the small beam first unwinds and then winds up a piece of string which finally stops its rotation. While the small beam is rotating the system as a whole turns about its pivot. Its motion ceases as soon as the small beam is stopped by the string.*

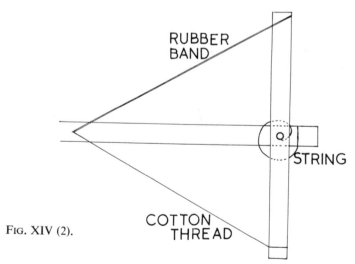

RUBBER
BAND

Q

STRING

FIG. XIV (2).

COTTON
THREAD

Apart from numerous applications to be considered later in the book, this completes the experimental study of the dynamics of rotation which we propose to make. It will suffice to provide a basis for understanding what happens in most of the problems of rotational movement met with in every-day life. We have seen that rotations can be treated in a manner analogous to those appropriate in the case of linear motion. Mass in linear motion is replaced by moment of inertia in rotational movement, and force by couple. Moment of inertia, however, is not a constant quantity as mass is in everyday life. It can be varied at will. This gives a measure of control over rotation without dependence upon an external couple which, in an isolated system, we do not possess over the motion of the centre of gravity in a straight line. We will conclude this chapter by considering two simple theoretical examples, the results of which are of importance for the understanding of some of the common phenomena of rotation and which will also indicate how the results which we have obtained by direct experiment may be derived from Newton's laws of motion.

Let us consider the motion of two particles of masses M_1 and M_2 (Fig. XIV (3)) connected by a light rod and acted upon by a couple composed of two equal and opposite forces, F, applied to the two masses respectively. To simplify matters we will consider the forces to be very large and to act for a very short time, t, so that the bar does not move appreciably while they are acting. This enables us to neglect the forces exerted by the bar on the masses, since these will be at right angles to the direction of the forces, F, which will be the direction of the initial motions. Suppose that the bar starts to turn about some point, P, distant x_1, from M_1, and x_2 from M_2. If ω radians per second is the angular velocity with which it turns, the velocity of M_1 will be $x_1\omega$ and of M_2 will be $x_2\omega$. These velocities will have been generated in time t by constant forces, so that the accelerations of the two masses will be $x_1\omega/t$ and $x_2\omega/t$ respectively.

Thus
$$F = \frac{M_1 x_1 \omega}{t} = \frac{M_2 x_2 \omega}{t} \qquad \dots 1$$

The couple acting is
$$C = F(x_1 + x_2)$$

$$= (M_1 x_1^2 + M_2 x_2^2)\frac{\omega}{t}$$

$$= (M_1 x_1^2 + M_2 x_2^2)\dot{\omega}$$

where $\dot{\omega}$ is the angular acceleration.

Comparing this with the general relation,

$$C = I\omega,$$

we see that the moment of inertia I of the system about P is

$$I = M_1 x_1^2 + M_2 x_2^2$$

and secondly, from equation 1,

$$\frac{x_1}{x_2} = \frac{M_2}{M_1}$$

and thus the system rotates about its centre of gravity, which is not set in motion by the couple.

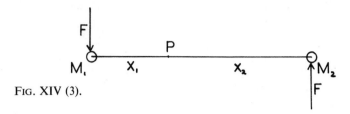

FIG. XIV (3).

As a second example let us consider the motion produced by a single force, F, acting at the centre of gravity of the same system of two masses, as in Fig. XIV (4).

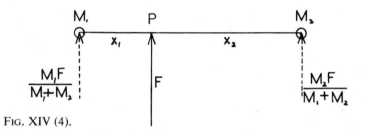

FIG. XIV (4).

Since the resultant of two parallel forces, P and Q, is a force which is parallel to them and of magnitude $P + Q$, and which acts along a line which divides the distance between P and Q in the ratio P/Q, we may replace the force F in Fig. XIV (4) by two forces of magnitude $M_1 F/(M_1 + M_2)$ acting on M_1, and $M_2 F/(M_1 + M_2)$ acting on M_2. The acceleration of M_1 will therefore be $F/(M_1 + M_2)$, and this will also be the acceleration of M_2. The system thus moves parallel to itself without rotation, with an acceleration which is the same as though the force F acted upon the total mass of the system concentrated at the centre of gravity.

This result is in agreement with common experience. If a rod carrying two bodies is balanced on the finger at its centre of gravity, it can be moved about freely by simply moving the finger, without causing it to turn.

These results are perfectly general and apply to any system of bodies connected rigidly together. When a couple is applied to such a system it causes it to rotate about its centre of gravity, which remains stationary. If the system is acted on by a force applied at its centre of gravity, then no rotation is produced. Motion is entirely translational and the system behaves as though all its mass was concentrated at its centre of gravity.

If a force is applied to the system at some point other than its centre of gravity, this is equivalent to applying a force at the centre of gravity equal and parallel to the original force, together with a couple. Suppose that the force F in Fig. XIV (5) is applied at some point such as A. At the centre of gravity, P, let us introduce two equal and opposite forces each equal to F. They will neutralise each other and cannot affect the motion of the body. The force F, acting at A, and the force acting in the opposite direction at P form a couple

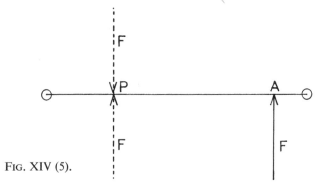

FIG. XIV (5).

whose moment is $F.AP$. We are then left with the remaining force F at P. The movement of the system will thus be the same as it would be under the action of a couple of moment $F.AP$, together with a force F acting at the centre of gravity. The couple will cause the system to rotate without moving the centre of gravity, while the force F at the centre of gravity will cause the system to move with a simple translational motion, as though all the mass was concentrated at the centre of gravity and the body moved without rotation. Problems of rotation and translation can thus be disentangled from each other and considered separately.

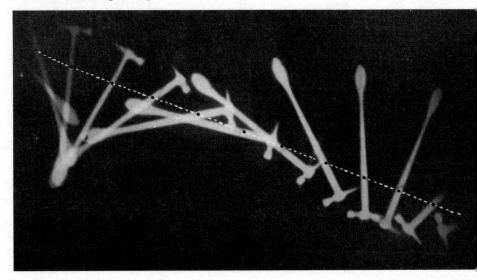

PLATE XIV (iii). *The flight of a hammer seen from above. Its centre of gravity moves in a straight line.*

As an example of these principles we may consider the movement of a body, such as a hammer, when it is thrown through the air. After it has left the hand the only forces acting on it are the weights of the various parts. The resultant of these passes through the centre of gravity and therefore causes no angular acceleration. The centre of gravity of the hammer moves through the air like a particle. It follows the familiar parabolic path. Since there is no angular acceleration, any rotation imparted to the hammer when it is thrown will continue uniformly. Plate XIV (iii) is a photograph obtained by superimposing frames from a ciné film taken of a hammer in flight. It was taken from directly overhead so that the path of the centre of gravity of the hammer appears as a straight line. It is indicated in the photograph by the dotted line.

The same principles apply, of course, to a human being jumping through the air. His centre of gravity, once he has left the ground, follows the same trajectory as would a particle which has been projected with the same velocity and at the same angle to the horizontal. Like the centre of gravity of the hammer, it will also follow the familiar parabola. Nothing the person can do by moving limbs or trunk in the air can alter the inexorable progress of his centre of gravity along this parabolic path. Such movements can alter the position of parts of the body relative to the centre of gravity. By throwing the head backwards, the jumper may obtain the impression that he hangs momentarily in the air, but it is only the head which is held stationary in these circumstances. Some other part of the body has to move forward more rapidly to compensate.

This is shown in the tracings reproduced in Fig. XIV (6) and taken from a ciné film at equal intervals of time. Figs. XIV (6) (A) and (B) are of different performers each trying to demonstrate 'hanging' in the air. In Fig. XIV (6) (A) the effect is small. The body is held more or less erect throughout the leap and what effect there is, is achieved by bringing the arms forward between the second and fourth positions. Successive positions of the performer's head are indicated by the rectangles underneath the tracing. There is a slight retardation between these positions, which is, of course, compensated by an accelerated movement between positions four and six, when the arms are brought back again. In Fig. XIV (6) (B), the hanging is obtained by arching the body, thus throwing the head backwards. The arms move steadily backwards throughout and thus contribute a slight constant forward motion of the rest of the body relative to the centre of gravity. The arching of the back contributes a more pronounced hanging effect to the movement of the head, as can be seen by its slowing up in its forward motion between positions two and three. Steady forward motion is resumed once the arching is completed. In both cases the centre of gravity of the body, which will be at about waist-level, follows the familiar parabolic path. (*Figs. XIV* (6) (*A*) *and* (*B*) *overleaf.*)

Fig. XIV (6) (A).

Fig. XIV (6) (B).

CHAPTER XV

More Advanced Problems in the Physics of Balance

WE return, in this chapter, to some further considerations of the problems presented by balance. In Chapter III we were concerned with the balancing of objects in stable equilibrium and the problems they presented were in statics. Dynamical considerations entered into the question of balancing the rod on the finger and in connection with the two kinds of bicycle, all of which involved the principles of linear motion. We must now turn to cases where the dynamics of rotation plays the dominant role.

We get immediately to the heart of the matter if we consider how it is possible for a man to balance himself on a tight-rope. The base on which the body rests is reduced to a line. Not only is it impossible to obtain a restoring couple from the feet to rectify a displacement when balance has been disturbed laterally, but it is also impossible to move the point of support so as to bring it underneath the centre of gravity. Unless we can obtain some means of restoring the position once a small displacement has been experienced, the balance will be unstable. Any small deflection caused by stray vibration, a puff of wind, or involuntary muscular movement will grow larger and larger until we finally fall off the rope altogether.

If we rule out the method of simply holding on to a support, as being *ultra vires* in tight-rope walking, there are two ways of achieving stability which have been employed in such acts. One is virtually holding on to an invisible support, namely the air. The performer carries a sun-shade which he moves in a direction at right angles to the rope and well above it, at head-level. The resistance of the air to the movement of the sun-shade provides a restoring force sufficient to maintain balance, given a little practice. There is nothing very novel in this.

From the present point of view, to enable us to understand the mechanism of normal balance, however, it is the second method which is the more important. In this method the tight-rope walker carries a balancing pole. It is held horizontally at about waist height, so that the centre of gravity of the performer, together with his pole, remains above the rope all the time—at about the same height, in fact, as that of the centre of gravity of the performer in the absence of the pole. The act is easier if the pole is weighted at the ends. Balance is maintained by employing the principles of rotational dynamics and it is obtained as follows.

Fig. XV (1) will help in the description of the process. The tight-rope walker is represented by HR, standing on the rope at R. His balancing pole, P_1P_2, is held horizontally. Suppose now that he suffers a displacement to one side and starts to fall over, as in the second diagram of Fig. XV (1). As soon as he becomes aware of this he can restore his position by swinging the pole downwards on the side towards which he is falling. In the case indicated by the figure, this would generate a clockwise angular momentum in the pole and an equal and opposite angular momentum must therefore be generated in the rest of the system. This counter-clockwise angular momentum is taken up by the walker, whose position is thereby restored. By means of a small degree of over-compensation the pole can be got back to its original horizontal position, so that the initial state of affairs before the fall commenced is completely restored.

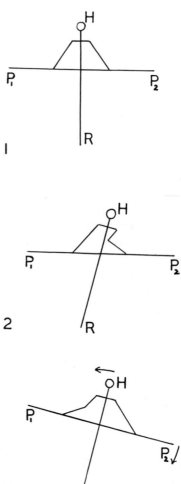

FIG. XV (1).   3

A model of a tight-rope walker which displays the principle of the operation can be constructed without difficulty. A photograph of one is reproduced in Plate XV (i). The vertical beam represents the performer and the horizontal one, which is pivoted at the centre, is his balancing pole. A rubber band on the right-hand side provides the muscle whereby the pole can be moved. The latter is held in a displaced position by means of a cotton thread attached to the other end. The tight-rope is a piece of wire passing loosely through a hole in the foot of the upright piece of wood. The model is propped in an inclined position tilted towards the left, as in Plate XV (i) (A). The cotton is burnt by a match flame and the balancing rod released. The pole moves downwards on the left while the model as a whole falls over to the right; towards the opposite side, that is, to that of the original tilt.

(A)

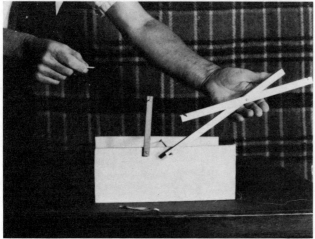

(B)

PLATE XV (i). *Model tight-rope walker. The nearly upright rod in Plate (A) represents the walker. He is leaning over to the left and is prevented from falling by the strut. The rod is pivoted at its lower end, the pivot representing the rope. Another rod pivoted freely at its centre is attached to the first and represents the walker's balancing pole. A stretched elastic band on the right-hand side provides the walker with muscles with which to move the pole. When the cotton is burnt the pole will rotate swiftly in an anti-clockwise direction. The system as a whole possesses no angular momentum to start with, so that the walker must rotate in a clockwise direction to compensate the angular momentum he has given to the pole. He thus falls over to the right as in Plate (B). With less violent motion of the pole a living walker can thus maintain balance.*

Since it is on the angular momentum generated in the balancing pole that the restoring couple depends, control will be easier the greater the moment of inertia of the pole. Its weight should, therefore, be concentrated as near to the ends as possible. The moment of inertia can be increased by adding weights, if necessary, to the ends. The method of balance is the same whether the rope is taut or slack. In the case of a slack rope the feet are also free to move as well as the upper part of the body, but the same correcting movement with the pole will still restore the body to the vertical position, though both feet and head move to accomplish it.

The most famous performer on the tight-rope was a man who made his appearances under the name of Blondin. His real name was Jean François Gravelet and he was born in 1824. He first crossed Niagara on a tight-rope on the 30th June 1859. In September he crossed at night and stood on his head in the middle of the rope silhouetted against fireworks. On one occasion he carried his manager across on his back. He used a 40-foot balancing pole for the purpose. It is of interest that contemporary drawings all show his pole as tapering towards the ends. It is at the ends, of course, that the weight is most effective, and the reason for having the pole tapered is not at all clear. Blondin completed a life of seventy-three years, exposed to the extremest hazards, and died quietly in his bed at the house to which he retired in Ealing.

PLATE XV (ii). *Blondin crossing Niagara Falls. Photo reproduced by kind permission of the Gernsheim Collection and Hulton Picture Library.*

There is no great virtue in being able to walk the tight-rope, but just to stand and take a few steps on a rope a few feet off the ground is by no means difficult. The movement which is required in the pole to restore balance is entirely natural. When leaning towards one side it is almost instinctive to lower the pole on that side to make contact with the ground, to save oneself from falling. This is exactly the direction in which the pole must be moved to keep oneself upright. A few minutes' practice is sufficient to ensure that balance is restored before the pole actually touches the ground.

PLATE XV (iii) (A). *It is not a difficult matter to balance on a rope with the help of a balancing pole. The one used here is about 12 feet long and carries a 9-pound weight at each end.*

PLATE XV (iii) (B). *Balance can also be maintained by holding the weights in the hands. It is more difficult than with the pole, since the moment of inertia is reduced by bringing the weights closer in.*

The difficulty of the task can be adjusted by altering the weights attached to the end of the pole. When these are fairly heavy—say 9 pounds at each end of a 12-foot pole—the task is comparatively easy. If the weights are then removed, it will be found that it is necessary, at least at first, to thresh about with the pole much more rapidly to keep on the rope. The pole itself can then be dispensed with and the weights carried in the hands, the arms being extended horizontally from the shoulders. Finally, the weights can be discarded altogether. Balance then has to be maintained by means of the arms and the upper part of the body alone. This method is part of the reflex mechanism by means of which we maintain balance when walking, especially if we are passing along a narrow path or on the edge of the pavement, where balance by steering, as with a bicycle, is not possible. If balance is at all difficult we instinctively extend the arms horizontally from the shoulders and thus increase their moment of inertia about a horizontal axis running fore and aft. This converts them into a more effective balancing organ against lateral displacements.

PLATE XV (iii) (C). *Without the weights the arms and upper part of the body have to be employed to maintain balance.*

PLATE XV (iii) (D). *Balance can also be maintained by getting a purchase on the air by means of an umbrella.*

Another act which imposes problems of balance as severe as, if not more severe than, those presented by the tight-rope is the riding of a monocycle. We have seen already that when riding an ordinary bicycle the maintenance of lateral balance is achieved by steering a course which always keeps the line joining the points of contact of the wheels with the ground, underneath the centre of gravity. Our experience with the bicycle in which the wheels were mounted side by side, instead of in the usual tandem fashion, shows that fore and aft balance can be maintained by adjusting the speed, again to keep the line joining the points of contact of the wheels with the ground always underneath the centre of gravity. The monocycle presents both these problems simultaneously and at the same time raises a third. The third problem is how the machine is to be steered. In the ordinary tandem bicycle leverage for the purpose of steering is obtained from the fact that the two wheels are at some distance apart, and thus provide a wheel-base from which a turning couple can be exerted. With a monocycle, however, there is no wheel-base and thus no means of obtaining the normal purchase with which to steer.

Steering requires rotation about a vertical axis through the centre of gravity. Initially machine and rider together possess no angular momentum about such a vertical axis. Apart from the effect of precession of the wheel, which will be dealt with later, the cycle can be rotated in one direction, therefore, only at the expense of turning some other part of the system in the other. Again the upper part of the body and the arms have to be called into play. Their effectiveness can be increased if the arms are extended horizontally from the shoulders and also by holding weights in the hands, as in the case of the tight-rope. As we saw when dealing with the rotating beams mounted on the point pivot, a body can be made to rotate in space without the help of an externally applied couple, by the process of turning part of it through 360°. The original attitude of the body as a whole is unaltered in this way, but it is turned through a certain angle in the operation. This can be illustrated by experiments with a rotating stool. Sitting on such a stool it is possible to turn oneself by waving the arms around vigorously. Again the process is easier if weights are held in the hands and easier still if a pole is swung round with a weight at the end, both of which mechanisms increase the moment of inertia of the part which is turned. It would be possible to turn a spacecraft round in space in a similar manner without the use of rocket jets which eject valuable matter which has to be carried aloft for the purpose. Turning a wheel inside the craft would accomplish the same rotation. It could not, of course, alter any angular momentum possessed by the craft as a whole, but once this had been disposed of by means of external jets, subsequent reorientations could be accomplished entirely by means of internal movements.

A problem involving these principles is that which is presented by the proverbial ability of a cat always to land on its feet if dropped upside down. To accomplish this feat, which is usually easily within the animal's compass, several factors are made use of. Fig. XV (2) contains tracings made from a film at equal intervals of time (approximately $\frac{1}{20}$ second apart) showing eight positions of a cat during its descent. An important part of the technique appears to be the turning inside out of a U-shaped position of the body,

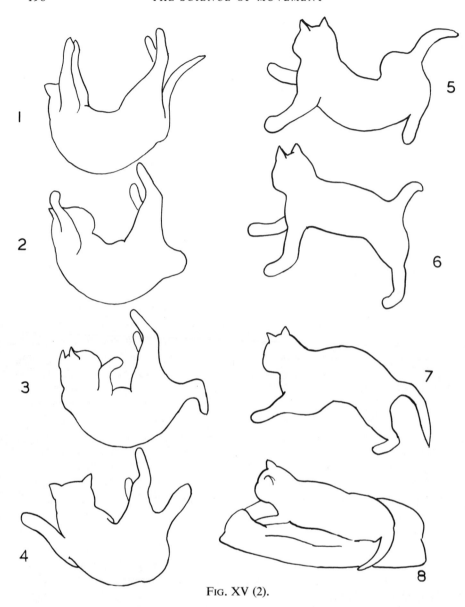

FIG. XV (2).

indicated diagrammatically in Fig. XV (3). The animal starts with its back on the outside of the U. As viewed from above, front and rear ends of the body are turned in opposite directions, thus putting the back on the inside of the U. This manœuvre involves little overall rotation of the animal as a whole. A simple straightening of the trunk then restores the animal to the right way up. This part of the process occupies the period between positions 3 to 5 in Fig. XV (2).

In practice, precedence is given to the fore part of the body, which is righted first. As a preliminary to accomplishing this, the front paws are drawn in and made to lie near the axis about which rotation is to take place, thus diminishing the moment of inertia of the front end, which is to be rotated. The hind limbs are left extended until the front half has been practically righted. If the height through which the animal drops is insufficient it may land the right way up in front but with its hindquarters only partly round. Once the fore part is righted, the haunches are then swung round. During this process the fore limbs are again extended so that the moment of inertia of the front half is increased and its orientation is not again upset. The rotation of the rear half is also assisted by a vigorous rotation of the tail. Even with an animal as flexible as a cat, the U-shaped position is not completely attained, so besides the equal and opposite rotations of the two ends there is also a component rotation about a horizontal axis which has to be accomplished. This is mainly effected by rotation of the tail. Although the U-shaped position does not eliminate the horizontal rotation entirely, it does so reduce it that it is brought more within the limits of what can be done by swinging the tail around—the alternate extension and contraction of the limbs, increasing first the moment of inertia of the hindquarters and reducing that of the fore, followed by the reverse process, and the rotation of the fore and hind parts separately also plays an important part.

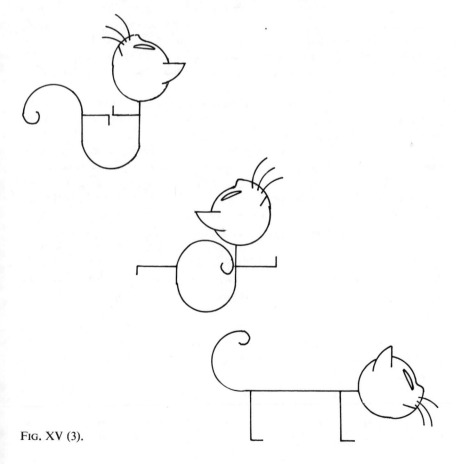

FIG. XV (3).

CHAPTER XVI

More Advanced Problems in the Biology of Balance: Rotational Co-ordination

IN Chapter IV on the ability of an animal to maintain its posture in space, the only forces considered were those acting steadily in one direction. Certain phenomena, such as dizziness, cannot be explained by the performance of the organs considered there. Dizziness, resulting from prolonged rotation, is a somewhat abnormal sensation. Just as the knee-jerk reflex is an apparently useless action, but results from an unusual situation, so the feeling of dizziness can be traced to a sense organ which normally provides information useful for co-ordination.

An experiment throwing light on dizziness results from sitting a blind-folded person on a revolving stool. The stool must run freely, and make little noise or vibration, so that the senses of touch and hearing are not available to supplement the organs perceiving rotation. Ear plugs can also help to achieve this. A seat mounted on a ball-race is thus necessary, and a convenient one can be made from two record-player turntables separated by large ball-bearings. The ball-bearings are held apart by a wooden spacer (see turntable in Fig. XI (4)). Further, blindfolding must be so effective that the subject cannot perceive direction from general brightness.

Thus isolated, if the stool is turned through an angle of, say, 90° and then stopped, the subject records what has happened accurately, and the same applies to a turn in the reverse direction. For the next stage, the subject should indicate with a finger which way he thinks he is turning, and point upright if he thinks he has stopped. Thus no clues can be given away indicating the position of the recorder and operator. A prolonged rotation is then administered, after a rapid acceleration. As before, the subject indicates the direction of movement correctly but may begin to have doubts after about 20 seconds. He is then slowed down slightly, but continues rotating in the same direction. The subject will most probably claim that he has stopped. Then the true stopping is made to follow, and the reaction of the subject is invariably to indicate that he is moving in the opposite direction. The same kind of result may be obtained by driving blindfolded passengers in circles in a car at constant speed on an area of tarmac.

The subject is interpreting acceleration in one direction as movement in that direction, a similar state of affairs to the linear motion in the enclosed lift already considered in Chapter IV.

We must go to the ear for an explanation again, and this time to the semi-circular canals (Fig. IV (3) and Plate XVI (i)). These form a continuous circuit in conjunction with the utriculus. An outer space is filled with a fluid called perilymph, while an inner membranous labyrinth is filled with endo-lymph. The three semicircular canals of each ear, placed roughly at right

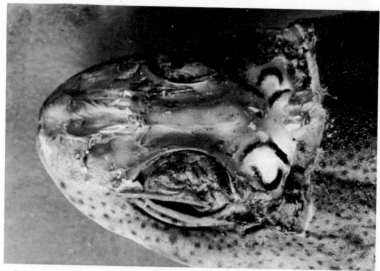

PLATE XVI (i). *Dissection of the head of a dogfish to show the semicircular canals, two vertical and one horizontal on each side, which have been injected with ink. Both endo- and peri-lymphatic ducts are stained. Photographed by M. E. Howard.*

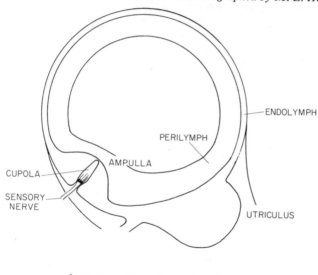

FIG. XVI (1). *Diagram showing the proportions of one semicircular canal (human).*

angles, each bear a swelling called the ampulla (Fig. XVI (1)). Inside this, lying in the endolymph circuit, is a swing-door-like structure or cupola, at the base of which are cells sensitive to the bending of the cupola. Movement of the fluid in the canal will deflect the cupola and stimulate the sense cells and their sensory nerves. Activity in the auditory nerve has been picked up during artificial cupola deflection.

Models are useful to explain the working of this system. One such was a large trough filled with water, representing the endolymph, while the cupola was represented by an elastic vane dipping into the water. For operation it was placed on the revolving stool previously occupied by the blindfolded subject. Small and short deflections to either side are indicated truly by the vane. To imitate dizziness, the trough is turned for a time. Eventually the water catches up with the trough, and the elasticity of the vane causes it to return to the central position. However, the real motion is still being maintained steadily. On stopping the apparatus, the water carries on, deflecting the vane until the current slows enough for the vane's elasticity to centralise itself again.

Although this model can be adjusted to give response times similar to those of human dizziness, there are objections to the way in which it functions. The first is that the canal containing the endolymph is less than a millimetre across in section, and since the viscosity of the fluid is close to that of water, it is impossible to imagine flow continuing for the period of dizziness, which is often about 20 seconds. Secondly, fluid emerging from the semicircular canal into the utriculus would fan out and lose its energy of movement. Thirdly, the best microscope preparations of sections through the ampulla show that the cupola moves in swing-door fashion and must present an almost complete blockage to endolymph flow. Thus the model described has too large an inertia factor, and too small a viscous one.

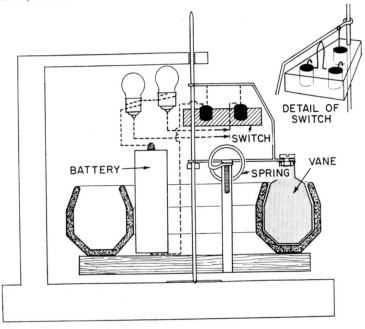

FIG. XVI (2). *Model of semicircular canal made from a flower ring, here seen in section. Reproduced by kind permission of the* School Science Review (*vol. 42, p. 518*).

Fig. XVI (2) depicts a model where the vane presents the observed blockage, and the endolymph is represented by oil of a suitable viscosity. A calculation taking into account the mass of the fluid, and the elasticity of the vane, demands a liquid of viscosity near that of a fairly thick grade of motor oil for the model shown, which had a diameter of about 8 inches. The calculation also gives the time of afterflow in a canal the size of those in the ear, to be less than 1 second. That is, in less than a second after starting a fairly rapid rotation, the endolymph is revolving with the canal.

Let us follow the new model through the treatment given to the blindfolded person. A deflection of the vane is caused by short rotations in either direction, and this operates the switch on one or other of the lights, representing nerve activity. When a prolonged rotation is started, the inertia of the oil moves the vane to one side, and this happens in a fraction of a second. After this the oil is moving with the canal. During the ensuing steady rotation, the slight elasticity of the vane, which fills the section, pushes the fluid very slowly back round the canal. After about 20 seconds, it will have returned to its central position and the 'nerve activity' will be switched off. This is equivalent to the first phase of dizziness where rotation is still continuing. When the rotation is stopped, the inertia of the oil causes an overshoot, again damped down by the viscosity in under a second, and there follows a recovery period in the same manner as before. This model suffers from the crudity of having only two nerve fibres, and it is not able to signal strength of stimulus. However, it is sufficient to indicate the physical actions in the canal.

Some of the nerve reflexes arising from the semicircular canals are concerned with maintaining balance during angular rotation. The muscles must be controlled in order to place the limbs appropriately to maintain stance. Other reflexes using the sensory information from the semicircular canals are concerned with the control of the eyes, and are responsible for the visual abnormalities experienced in dizziness. When the head turns round, the eyes do not follow, staring directly outwards, but move in a series of jerks. They fix on an object, follow it round smoothly, and then flick forward to find another object which is followed round in its turn. This activity, called the nystagmus reflex, involves the co-ordination of the tension in the six eye muscles moving each eyeball. We have already seen how the tension in muscles is controlled, but if both eyes are to be kept looking at the same object, all twelve muscles must be co-ordinated to a remarkable degree. It is hardly surprising that the eye muscle motor units are so small, allowing accurate gradation of tension.

When the cupola in one canal is deflected, the nystagmus flicks occur in the opposite direction, the analysis of the relatively simple sensory nerve message being composed into rapidly changing motor messages by the brain. During a prolonged rotation the cupola will have time to push the endolymph back round the canal and cease its sensory message when it has recovered the central position. Then the eyes will cease their nystagmus flicking and the subject will see objects streaking past, being no longer able to fix on them. Also at this stage some balance control is lost. When the rotation finally stops, the cupola is deflected and nystagmus flicks start again, this time in the opposite direction. Since the objects are stationary, they appear to be moving steadily and then flicking back alternately. Also, the postural muscles are being commanded to make corrections for non-existent rotation, and staggering is the result.

If the head is allowed to nod forwards so that the chin is on the chest, and one becomes dizzy by rotating about the vertical as before, on stopping, the eyes perform a nystagmus reflex as if objects were rotating clockwise or anticlockwise in front of the face. Before trying this, one should be sure to clear away obstructions, because it is such an unfamiliar situation that staggering is more extreme. Very little of this treatment induces a feeling like sea-sickness. Since there are three semicircular canals lying in different planes in the ear, it is possible to explain this case of rotatory nystagmus, as well as that arising from the simple rotations dealt with first. As the three lie in planes almost at right angles to each other, one or a combination of them will be in a position to react to any rotation. The importance of any one canal in any specified rotation can be worked out using vectors, and this vector analysis is another remarkable action which must be performed by the brain.

Sea-sickness, which can only be mentioned briefly, no doubt is a compli-cated subject involving individual psychology as well as simple physical laws. The root of it must be the conflicting reports from different sense organs, such as the semicircular canals recording what is usually interpreted as rotation when none in fact is occurring. In a ship, if one is down below, the horizon may appear through a port-hole at quite unexpected times, and may be moving when one expected it to be stationary at the end of one of its apparent oscillations. The problem of gaining sea-legs is no doubt one of living with those conflicting reports long enough to learn how to sort them out and expect unconsciously what is coming next.

A more lowly animal, the housefly, and its relatives with two wings, have solved the problem of detecting rotation in an entirely different way. They use the principle of the gyroscope. This is described in Chapter XIX, but since it has important implications for balance, it will be dealt with here, the theory of gyroscopic motion being left until later.

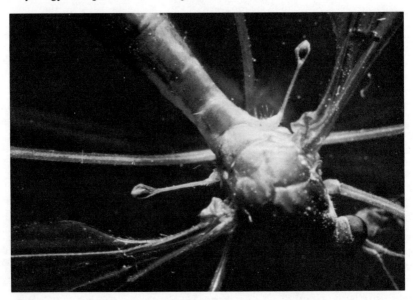

PLATE XVI (ii). *The halteres of a crane-fly.*

No known animal has evolved structures which can rotate like a wheel, but the fly is able to make use of the gyroscopic forces generated during a recipro-cating movement. Most insects have four wings, but in place of the rear pair the fly and its relatives have small club-like projections called halteres (Plate XVI (ii)). The skeleton of an insect is its exterior skin. That of the halteres is very thin in a number of small slightly domed areas, and to each of these is attached a small hair rooted in a sense cell. If the haltere is strained, the domes will alter their curvature, and this will be detected by the sense cells underneath. The domed small areas are slightly elongated and will deform most easily in response to forces across their width. Since there are several batteries of these sense cells, each with the elongation in different directions, the fly should be able to appreciate the direction of the resultant stress on the haltere.

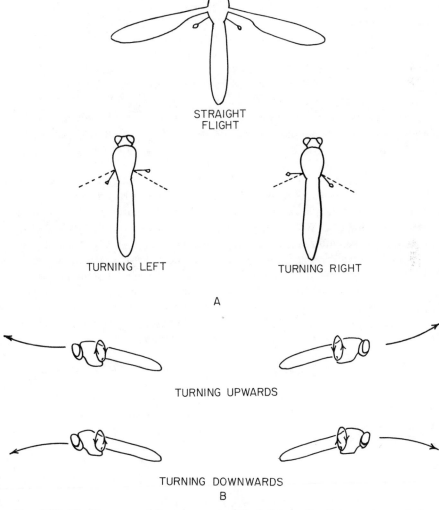

FIG. XVI (3). *Diagrams of the movement of the halteres of a dipterous insect during various manœuvres.*

In ordinary straight flight, the halteres beat up and down on the same line with respect to the body. When the insect turns, a gyroscopic force will be produced. Using the convention that an axis of rotation points in the direction a right-handed corkscrew would move, as the left haltere travels upwards it is equivalent to rotation about a horizontal axis pointing forwards. When it travels downwards it is equivalent to a rotation about a horizontal axis pointing backwards. The opposite holds for the right haltere. When the insect turns towards the right, it applies a couple to the halteres about an axis pointing downwards. When a couple is applied to a gyroscope the axis of spin tends to set towards the axis of the applied couple. Thus when the left haltere is moving upwards while the insect is turning to the right, the axis of spin of the haltere will be deflected downwards from its original horizontal forward direction. Hence as the haltere moves upwards its head will be carried forwards. When the haltere is on its down beat, its axis of spin points backwards and the effect of the couple applied when the insect turns to the right will be to deflect this downwards. Thus the head of the haltere also travels forwards as it descends. This is in the same direction as when it was moving upwards. Hence, as the insect turns to the right, the head of the left haltere tends to move forward of the plane in which it normally oscillates. Similarly, the head of the right haltere will tend to move backwards and the organs can provide the insect with a turn indicator (Fig. XVI (3) (A)).

Since a fly without its halteres is unable to control its direction, it seems certain that there is enough force to distort the batteries of sense cells, and that the nervous system is able to analyse the signals and control the wing beating appropriately. It will be noted that the movement of the halteres is in the same direction as that in which the insect started to turn, but the mass of the halteres is insufficient to provide the fly with much turning couple.

In pulling out of a dive, or starting a climb, the halteres will generate a rotatory motion (Fig. XVI (3) (B)). Take the left haltere as the fly's body tilts upwards. As the haltere moves upwards the axis of spin points forwards. The axis of the applied couple points outwards to the right side. The haltere must therefore strain forwards. During its downbeat, the axis of spin is reversed, and it will strain backwards. Thus the motion will be elliptical and differs distinctly from the response to turning left or right.

A turn about the third axis, that is a roll, will have no gyroscopic effect, for the axis of spin is then the same as the axis of the couple.

CHAPTER XVII

Work, Energy, and Perpetual Motion

THE terms work and energy are employed in everyday speech, but in mechanics they are given special definitions. While they retain a certain part of their everyday meaning, when used in mechanics they do not keep it all, and it is important to realise that arguments based upon the looser use of the terms in common language can be misleading. In mechanics a force is said to do work only when its point of application is moved in the direction in which the force acts, and the amount of work performed is defined to be the product of the force and the distance the point of application moves in this direction. Thus, though we may exert a very large force in holding up a heavy chest, for example, and may easily exhaust ourselves if we keep it up for long, we perform no work in the mechanical sense, unless we actually lift the chest into a higher position. If we lift a pound weight 1 foot we perform 1 foot pound weight of work (often abbreviated to 1 foot pound); when a force of 1 poundal displaces its point of application 1 foot in the direction in which it is acting, 1 foot poundal of work is performed, or when a force of 1 newton similarly displaces its point of application a distance of 1 metre, work equal to a newton metre is performed. The newton metre is given the name joule.

An engine which performs work at the rate of 1 joule per second is said to work at the rate of 1 watt. If it does 1,000 joules per second it works at the rate of a kilowatt. In the British system an engine which works at the rate of 550 foot pounds per second is said to be of 1 horse-power. Power is simply rate of working.

The energy possessed by a body is a measure of the work it is capable of doing. Thus a body may possess energy by virtue of the fact that it is moving. To bring it to rest a force must be applied to it, and in bringing it to rest the force will be moved backwards. It will have work performed against it. Suppose a body of mass M is moving with velocity V; how much work can it perform against some force, F, which brings it to rest? The force, F, will generate a retardation equal to F/M, which will, therefore, destroy the velocity V in VM/F seconds. During the period in which the velocity is decreasing, its average value will be $V/2$ (it starts with the value V and decreases uniformly to nothing). The body will, therefore, travel a distance

$$\frac{V}{2} \cdot \frac{VM}{F}$$

in being brought to rest. The work done against the force, F, will be the product of this force and the distance moved. It is, therefore,

$$\frac{1}{2}MV^2.$$

207

This is the work the body can do by virtue of its movement. It is called its kinetic energy. It is the same whatever the force which brings the body to rest.

A body may also possess energy by virtue of the fact that it is in an elevated position. The work it can do when it is lowered to some standard position—usually taken to be the surface of the earth, though, since it is only differences which are of any interest, this is unimportant—is called its potential energy. If a body of mass M is lowered through a height H, the work which its weight, Mg, performs will be MgH. This is, therefore, the value of the potential energy of the body.

Suppose a body falls freely from rest at a height H. Initially it is stationary and possesses no kinetic energy. Its potential energy is MgH. Suppose at the end of its fall it has acquired a velocity V. This velocity will have been generated by the acceleration, g, of gravity in a time V/g. During its fall its average velocity will have been $V/2$ and, therefore, the distance through which it falls will be

$$\frac{V}{2} \cdot \frac{V}{g}$$

so that,

$$\frac{V^2}{2g} = H.$$

Multiplying both sides by Mg, we have

$$\frac{1}{2}MV^2 = MgH.$$

The left-hand side is the kinetic energy which the body possesses at the end of its fall, when its potential energy has all disappeared. The right-hand side is the potential energy with which the body started. The total energy of the body has remained constant. It has simply been converted from the potential to the kinetic form. This is a simple particular instance of a general principle known as the conservation of energy, than which probably no other principle of science is more important to us. The principle is that energy cannot be created or destroyed but can only be converted from one kind to another. Work cannot be obtained for nothing but only at the price of the consumption of energy of one kind and its conversion to another. This principle only became obvious when various varieties of energy had been recognised. When the falling body is finally stopped at the end of its fall, by impact with the ground, most of its energy is converted into heat, another form of energy. Some may be transformed into the energy of sound also.

The basis of the principle of the conservation of energy was laid in the course of the sixteenth and seventeenth centuries through attempts to obtain perpetual motion—that is, through attempts to obtain work for nothing. All these proved fruitless, though sporadic effort lingered on to a much later date and they even crop up from time to time today.

Before it was known that liquids always find their own level it was thought that work might be obtained by connecting a wide vessel to a narrower one, either at the bottom or at the top in a siphon. The siphon with unequal limbs, shown in Plate XVII (i) (A), was designed by a man called Leupold in 1607, to work in this way. He thought that the greater weight of the water in the

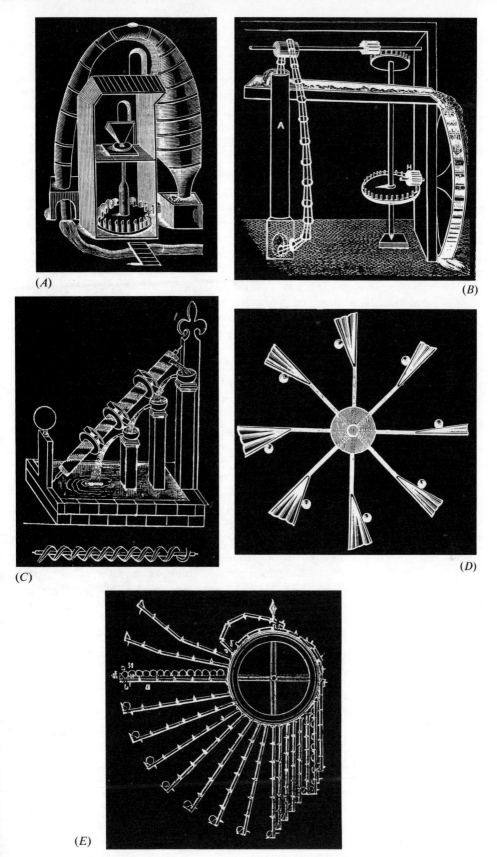

PLATE XVII (i). *Historical devices for securing perpetual motion.*

wide limb would draw up water from the stream into the narrow limb and deliver it at a greater height than that at which it started. Corn could be ground by a mill operated by the water on its return. In 1618 Robert Fludd produced the design for the water wheel driven by water pumped up by its own system of buckets and chain (Plate XVII (i) (B)). Needless to say, it would not work even if modern gearing were to be substituted for the gears of oak and ash which were all that were available to him. Bishop Wilkins (1614–72), Bishop of Chester, and one of the founder members of the Royal Society, tried many devices but found them useless. One of his machines was the Archimedean screw turned by its own water, shown in Plate XVII (i) (C). Another device he tried was an inclined plane up which an iron ball was caused to run by a magnet at the top. Near the top the plane had a hole in it, through which the ball was supposed to fall and so return to its original position. Towards the end Wilkins suspected that perpetual motion was impossible. A Marquis of Worcester wrote a book in 1659 called *A Century of Invention*, for which he received an honour from Charles I. In it he described a wheel worked by weights to function perpetually. Many variations on the idea were proposed later. The basic idea was to arrange weights to be at a distance from the axle on one side of the wheel and close to it on the other, so that a turning moment would result. One such wheel is illustrated in Plate XVII (i) (E). The similar device shown in Plate XVII (i) (D) and worked by mercury in bellows comes from the *Gentleman's Magazine* of 1772. In 1770 a man called Orfyreus gave an account of an 'Automaton' which was said to have gone for eight days in the castle of the Duchy of Cassel, without attention. The inside of the machine, however, was shrouded from view and, as the inventor broke it up in disgust after being offered a paltry 80,000 crowns for his invention, the secret has unfortunately perished with him!

The long line of failures led, in the end, to the belief that perpetual motion was impossible in principle and that the various forms of energy which could be recognised must be equivalent. The view was supported by the idea that the behaviour of matter could be explained on the basis of atoms—particles which moved about and to which considerations similar to those we arrived at in the study of the potential and kinetic energy of a falling body would apply. The matter was not finally clinched until the middle of the nineteenth century by men like Helmholtz, Clausius, Joule, and Kelvin. Joule measured the conversion factor for the transformation of mechanical energy into heat. His measurement is usually known as that of the mechanical equivalent of heat, but actually it was of the heat equivalent of mechanical work, which is a good deal simpler to deal with. Joule employed the energy supplied by falling weights lowered on strings like clock weights, to stir water in a calorimeter, and measured the rise in temperature produced. He could thus measure the energy supplied by the weights in falling and the heat developed in the calorimeter. His experiments gave the result that it required the expenditure of about 4·2 joules of work to produce 1 calorie of heat.

The reverse process of the conversion of heat into mechanical work takes place in various forms of engines. In the internal combustion engine the heat produced by the combustion of the fuel causes gas to expand in a cylinder and drive the piston forwards. The conversion of heat into work, however, is never complete and some of it is always wasted. The ratio of the work got out of a machine to the heat put in measures its efficiency. There is always a great deal of waste heat and practical efficiencies are very low. The best that can be achieved with ordinary engines is from 30 to 40 per cent. Efficiencies as low as 4 or 5 per cent, however, are by no means uncommon. More energy is wasted than can be converted to useful ends. Animal muscles are essentially engines which convert chemical energy into mechanical work. The work they perform may take the form of lifting the body against gravity or of propelling it forward against resistance, or it may be used internally in driving the blood round the arteries and veins, or in moving food along the alimentary canal.

When a series of bodies is lifted the work performed is determined by the height to which the centre of gravity of the whole is raised and by the total weight of the system. If a mass M_1 pounds is raised to a height H_1 feet, and a mass M_2 pounds to a height H_2 feet, the total work performed will be

$$M_1H_1 + M_2H_2 \text{ foot pounds.}$$

Fig. XVII (1).

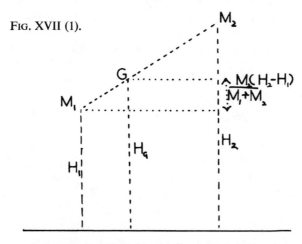

The centre of gravity, G, will divide the line M_1M_2 in the ratio of M_1 to M_2. The height to which the centre of gravity will be raised will therefore be

$$H_G = H_1 + \frac{M_2(H_2 - H_1)}{M_1 + M_2}$$
$$= \frac{M_1H_1 + M_2H_2}{M_1 + M_2}.$$

The total work performed is therefore:

$$M_1H_1 + M_2H_2 = (M_1 + M_2)H_G.$$

That is to say, it is the same as in raising a mass equal to the total mass moved, through the height by which the centre of gravity is raised. The result can be extended to any number of masses and from this it follows that the work which must be done to lift a body (as opposed to a particle) will be given by the product of the weight of the body and the height through which its centre of gravity is raised.

CHAPTER XVIII

The Dynamics of Athletics I: Movement in a Straight Line

IN this and the next two chapters advantage will be taken of a consideration of various athletic activities to illustrate the principles of dynamics. A knowledge of the principles of dynamics has contributed much to the achievement of modern athletes. Here, however, we shall look at the same field rather from the point of view of appreciating the importance and wide application of the science. Both understanding and ability to apply it, of course, work together and benefit each other. We shall not, however, be concerned to discuss the finer subtleties of athletic performances but shall rather concentrate on the principles upon which they must be based. We will first investigate one or two cases where the generation and conservation of linear momentum plays the dominant role. Cases where angular momentum is the more important will be considered in Chapter XIX. In most athletic events it is not possible to separate the two completely, however, and both will usually be found to play some part.

The athletic activity which, even in the modern age of the motor-car, none can avoid entirely is that of walking. In ordinary unhurried walking the legs swing from the knees and hips more or less as a pendulum. The time of a stride is determined by the natural period of the leg. For a man of average build the time for a complete swing forwards and backwards of the leg held stiffly is about $1\frac{1}{3}$ seconds. When walking, however, each foot strikes the ground about once every second. This is only a little longer than the natural period of the lower half of the leg swinging from the knee. When walking the leg is flexed at the knee which moves much less than does the foot.

As already discussed more fully in Chapter IX, the time of swing of a pendulum is proportional to the square root of its length, so that the number of strides made per second by a man will be inversely proportional to the square root of the length of his leg—or to the square root of his height, if leg length is a constant fraction of height. The length of his stride, on the other hand, will vary directly as his height, so that his rate of walking might be expected to be proportional to the square root of his height. It is no doubt because length of leg determines the speed of walking that foals, which in the wild state would have to keep up with their parents, are born with abnormally long legs.

It is a great mistake to suppose that to keep the body moving forward at a uniform speed requires considerable drive from the legs. Unless walking against a strong head wind the force required is very small—of the order of the weight of 1 ounce. The only force which the body requires to keep it moving forward is that which is necessary to overcome the resistance of the air. At walking speeds this is quite negligible and it may be in any direction according to the direction of any light wind which may be blowing. The effort required in walking is employed solely in swinging the legs and if these are allowed to oscillate at their natural rate the process absorbs little energy. As has been mentioned before, it becomes a good deal more tiring to walk for any length of time at a speed markedly different from one's natural pace, and this is even more true of dawdling than of walking quickly. As far as possible changes of speed are effected by alterations in the length of stride, the legs still being allowed to swing naturally.

Even in sprinting, great muscular drive is not required to maintain the body's uniform velocity. A 10-second 100 yards corresponds to an average speed of about 20 miles per hour, and air resistance at such a speed, though appreciable, is not large. The experiment can be performed of running over the long trolley to test this assertion. Even though the trolley is made as light as possible, and one runs over it steadily quite fast, it is not propelled appreciably backwards, as it would be if the legs had to provide a large drive to keep the body moving forward. At high speeds some drive is, of course, required, and what is necessary has to be provided by the legs, but the forces required are small compared to those ordinarily exerted by the legs, which are, of course, of the same order of magnitude as the body weight. The main problem presented by running fast is how to move the legs sufficiently quickly so that they may remain underneath and support the body, the energy which is used being spent internally in the muscles.

In running, the length of the stride is increased, compared with walking, by a leap in which the body is out of contact with the ground for a short time. The number of strides taken per second is also increased. The speed of a sprint differs from that of an ordinary walk by about a factor of six. Very roughly this is achieved by increasing the length of stride three times and taking twice as many of them per second.

While there is no contact with the ground during the leap, the centre of gravity of the body will describe a parabolic path, which means that whatever the runner may do it is bound to rise and fall. This will absorb energy, since the muscles do not recover the kinetic energy with which the body lands and with which they supplied it at take-off. The angle of projection should be such as to give maximum range for the force applied. Since, for economy of effort, the force applied will not greatly exceed body weight, the optimum angle of projection will be low (Appendix VI). There will be nothing to be gained from a bouncing gait with great leaps in the air.

The increase in the number of strides taken per second will also call for the expenditure of extra energy. The rate of swing of the legs has to be increased by muscular effort. The leg in contact with the ground is kept fairly straight. Its function is to support the weight of the body and to project it in the next leap. When the foot first makes contact with the ground, the centre of gravity of the body will be descending, and this motion has to be reversed. One way of achieving this would be to maintain the leg rigid and allow the forward momentum of the body to carry it up and over the foot. This would not only slow the body down but, what is more important, it would not provide the flexure of the leg necessary for the taking of the next stride. The knee is therefore flexed slightly, the downward motion of the centre of gravity is slowed up and finally reversed, ready for the succeeding leap. The main effort required of this leg is to provide a vertical force to transfer momentum to the body in this direction. Since muscles cannot do this instantaneously, the effort is bound to be distributed over much of the period in which the foot is in contact with the ground. Before the centre of gravity passes over the foot which is on the ground, any vertical force derived from it would, of course, tend to turn the body backwards. After the centre of gravity has passed over the foot, such a force would turn it forwards. Such rotations can easily be absorbed by movements in parts of the body or limbs—in arm movement, for example.

Apart from the vertical force required to project the body upwards in its next leap, the only other force which the so-called 'leg drive' is required to supply is the small horizontal force to overcome the resistance of the air. Horizontal momentum may also be given to the leg itself in the spring, to help to carry it forward in readiness for the next stride, though thigh and abdominal muscles are responsible for this in the main. Any such momentum added to the leg by the spring must be reabsorbed by the ground when the foot next makes contact with the ground. Otherwise the body would be accelerated and overrun the feet.

A little caution is necessary in interpreting photographs of runners in action. They must be interpreted dynamically; the temptation is to look on them too much from the static point of view. For example, in the second, sixth, and tenth tracings in Fig. XVIII (1), the centre of gravity of the body lies well forward of the foot which is in contact with the ground, giving the impression of immense forward drive from this leg and consequent large acceleration. The body is not, in fact, being accelerated appreciably at all, but is moving forward uniformly. It is likely that all the drive has ceased from the leg in this position and that it is lagging behind merely because the body has got well beyond the point on the ground where the foot has been planted. The maximum effort from this leg is made near the positions of the fifth and ninth tracings, when it is almost underneath the body's centre of gravity.

As the body passes over the leg which is in contact with the ground in Fig. XVIII (1), the leg is rotating in a clockwise direction. This rotation continues after the leg has left the ground. The backward movement of the thigh is then stopped and the angular momentum is transferred to the lower leg. This transference of angular momentum helps to stop the thigh from rotating and to start it turning in the opposite direction. The foot is thereby carried high up, close in to the seat, where its motion is finally reversed. Another effect of this flexure of the knee is to reduce the moment of inertia of the whole leg about an axis through the hip joint, so that the muscles which are already carrying the thigh forwards are able to do this more easily (see also Plate IV (iii)). As the thigh continues to rotate into an almost horizontal position, the lower leg and foot commence to rotate in the counterclockwise direction like a flail, and when the thigh is brought to rest the transference of some of its angular momentum to the lower leg helps to bring it forward into the position where it next makes contact with the ground.

| I | 2 | 3 | 4 | 5 | 6 | 7 | 8 | 9 | 10 |

FIG. XVIII (1). *Successive positions of a runner at intervals of* $\frac{1}{16}$ *second.*

Successive positions of the right leg of the runner of Fig. XVIII (1) are traced in Fig. XVIII (2) (overleaf).

The movement of animals has to be effected by means of comparatively inefficient reciprocating motions, nature having so far failed to evolve a wheel, though the motion of the foot of a runner follows the motion of a point on the circumference of a wheel surprisingly closely. These reciprocating movements bring the mass of the limbs forwards first on one side and then on the other. They are equivalent to rotational oscillations in which angular momentum is generated first in one direction, then destroyed and finally regenerated in the opposite direction. We may consider these rotations broken down into components about three axes at right angles. The most important of these components takes place about a vertical axis. As the left leg, for example, is brought forward and the right falls back, the result is equivalent to a rotation of the lower part of the body in the clockwise direction as viewed from above. To achieve this, clockwise angular momentum has to be generated in the lower part. A little of this, as we have seen, may come from contact with the ground, but most of it is brought about through the action of the abdominal muscles which tend to generate an equal counter-clockwise angular momentum in the upper part of the body. Thus while the legs and hips rotate clockwise, the arms and shoulders rotate counter-clockwise. As a leg moves forward on one side, the arm on the same side moves backwards. Since the arms, not having to make contact with the ground, can be moved more freely than the legs, the arm movement can be made more effective by bringing the hands in across the chest. It is the rotation of the upper part of the body in counter-clockwise direction which is required to counteract the clockwise movement of the lower. This compensating movement of arms and legs is clearly shown in the tracings in Figs. XVIII (1), XVIII (2), and XVIII (3).

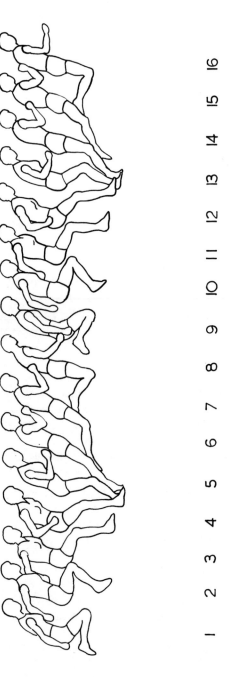

Fig. XVIII (2). *Successive positions of the right leg of the runner of* Fig. XVIII (1).

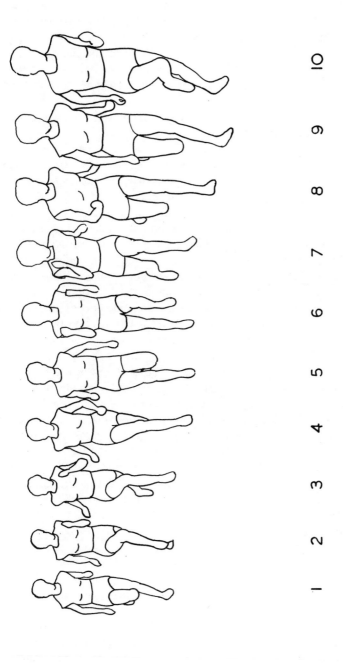

FIG. XVIII (3). *Positions of a runner seen from the front, at intervals of $\frac{1}{16}$ second. Each tracing has been displaced by a constant amount to the right to avoid overlapping. A foot is in contact with the ground in positions 4 and 5 and 9 and 10.*

Similar rotations take place also about horizontal axes. When the legs are being brought forward their centres of gravity are higher than when, in contact with the ground, they travel backwards. This is equivalent to a clockwise rotation about a horizontal axis running at right angles to the direction of travel of the body in Figs. XVIII (1) and XVIII (2). Unlike the rotation about the vertical axis, however, this rotation is constant and not reciprocating. It calls for no compensatory movement in the arms and shoulders. Indeed the arms partake in a precisely similar constant rotation in the same direction. When the arms are brought forward the hands are held higher than when going backwards so that this motion is also equivalent to a clockwise rotation. Indeed, just as the movement of the feet approximates to being circular so, often, does the motion of the hands.

The reason for this particular movement of the hands can be seen from a consideration of the rotations which take place about the other horizontal axis—that running fore and aft. The leg is raised and lowered on one side while the other leg moves in the opposite direction on the other. This is equivalent to an angular oscillation about the horizontal fore and aft axis. It entails the continual generation and obliteration of angular momentum. That part of this which cannot be obtained from the action of external forces arising from the contact of the feet with the ground can only be achieved by compensating oscillations in other parts of the body. The oscillatory angular momentum of the hips and legs is again compensated by opposite motion in the shoulders and arms. When the leg on one side moves upwards, the shoulder and arm on the same side move down (Fig. XVIII (3)). The movement of the hands is approximately circular to compensate the similar motion of the feet. If the arms are not flexed at the elbows but kept stiff, as in the fashion of military marching, the necessary upward and downward motion can only be achieved by means of an exaggerated swinging of the arms.

There is one other point about these compensating movements that is worth mentioning. The legs are longer and much more massive than the arms, and it might appear impossible for the movements to compensate each other. Complete compensation may not be necessary, since the feet are in contact with the ground and are able to generate momentum through the action of the ground on them. However, the moment of inertia of the arms can be increased by holding them away from the body. This will be effective for both the vertical and fore-and-aft horizontal axes. Were it necessary to compensate for the steady rotation of the legs about the other horizontal axis, the arms would have to be waved around in a more or less extended position, if their moment of inertia was similarly to be increased. This, however, it is unnecessary to do.

Another indication that the body requires little 'drive' in order to maintain it travelling forward at a constant velocity is provided by the fact that, after acceleration has ceased, it is held almost upright in running. Any force which tends to accelerate the body, such as F in Fig. XVIII (4), must arise between the feet and the ground and will tend to cause the body to rotate—in a counter-clockwise direction in the figure. This can only be counterbalanced if the body leans forward so that its weight provides a turning force in the opposite direction. If the body is maintained upright there can be no accelerating force acting without the runner falling over backwards.

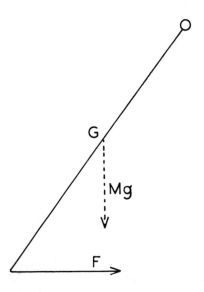

FIG. XVIII (4).

The state of affairs is different when the body is being accelerated. Then conditions are as indicated in Fig. XVIII (4) and the body has to be inclined forwards. This will happen at the start of a race. The greater the acceleration, the greater must be the inclination to the vertical. As the runner speeds up, the acceleration will decrease and ultimately it will vanish altogether. As this happens the runner must gradually straighten up so as to assume an erect posture when he attains his terminal velocity. There is no particular difficulty in accomplishing this—it is done by the ordinary mechanism of balance. During acceleration the runner's sensations are exactly the same as they would be if he were stationary and gravity acted at the angle at which his body has to be inclined (apart from an apparent increase in his weight which would not affect his balance and which he is unlikely to notice). If he leans at an angle which is greater than that required by his acceleration, he will feel himself falling forwards, and if he is inclined at too small an angle with the vertical he will seem to be falling backwards. He can adjust his inclination by the normal balancing movements—by the placing of his feet and the rotation of the upper part of his body—and he must do this continuously as his acceleration gradually changes.

Fig. XVIII (5) contains tracings of the positions of a runner, at equal intervals of time, during the start of a race. His acceleration can be judged from his position against the background which has been added to provide a scale. Initially his speed increases rapidly and his body is inclined forwards at a large angle to the vertical. By the time he has reached the sixth position he has practically attained his maximum velocity and his body has become vertical.

FIG. XVIII (5). *Successive positions of a runner at $\frac{1}{3}$ second intervals at the start of a race.*

The opposite sequence of events takes place when a runner slows up at the end of a race. The retarding force which slows him up is likewise developed by the action of the ground on his feet. It will possess a turning moment about the centre of gravity tending to make the runner fall on his face. To counteract this the runner has to lean backwards to allow his weight to generate an equal and opposite turning movement. Again, the change in inclination is brought about by the runner entirely instinctively, by the ordinary processes of balance.

Similarly when a runner proceeds along a curved track his body, if left to itself, would continue in a straight line. A force is necessary, directed towards the centre of curvature of the track, to cause it to move round the circle. This force must be supplied by the ground acting on the feet and tends to make the runner fall outwards. He must counteract this tendency by leaning inwards. It is for the same reason that a cyclist leans inwards on a turn and an aeroplane banks (Plate IV (iv)).

An event which involves the simplest principles of dynamics is weight-lifting. Twelve tracings of the positions taken up at the ends of equal intervals of time, in weight-lifting, are reproduced in Fig. XVIII (6). There are three stages. The first stage occupies the first four tracings and involves lifting the weight off the ground and getting it travelling upwards as fast as possible at chest height. Left to itself the weight would continue to travel upwards for a short time and this enables the lifter to lower himself quickly and so get underneath it. This process represents the second stage and occupies the next four pictures. The lifter has to get himself down more quickly than the weight falls and he is able to do this by virtue of the upwards initial motion he has imparted to the weight. The last stage is for the lifter to straighten himself, so that he finally stands erect with the weight at chin height. The whole process provides a simple example of the application of the principle of the conservation of linear momentum.

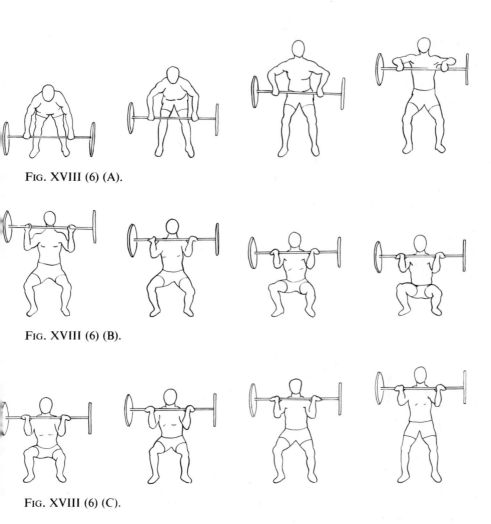

Fig. XVIII (6) (A).

Fig. XVIII (6) (B).

Fig. XVIII (6) (C).

Successive stages in weight-lifting.

The conservation of linear momentum also plays an important part in many throwing events of which the javelin will suffice for present considerations. Fig. XVIII (7) is from an example of this event. The thrower first develops as high a velocity in himself and the weapon as he can, by sprinting in the preliminary run-up. By this means the actual throw can add additional

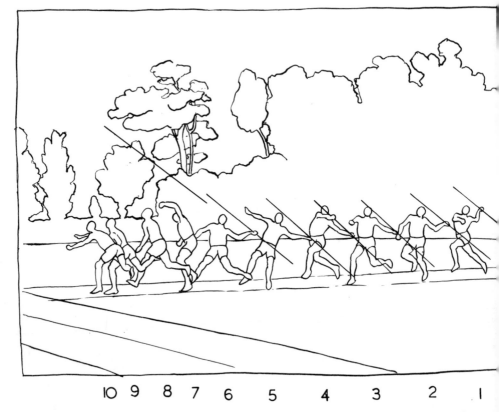

10 9 8 7 6 5 4 3 2 1

FIG. XVIII (7). *Successive positions in the throwing of a javelin ($\frac{1}{4}$ second interval).*

momentum to that already possessed by the javelin in the run. The requirements for a good position for sprinting, however, are not easy to combine
with what is necessary to obtain a good throw. The linear momentum of the
javelin attained during the sprint is not simply accepted as it stands. It is
augmented by transferring as much of the thrower's own forward velocity
as possible to the hand holding the instrument. In the third picture of
Fig. XVIII (7) the thrower turns his body so as to bring the javelin to
the rear. In the fourth picture the left foot upon which this left-handed
thrower will pivot is brought forward. The upper part of the body is thus
temporarily retarded. As the body pivots on the left foot in the fifth picture,
the upper part then accelerates forward, a movement which is aided by a
thrust from the leg leading to the next position. The body then rotates about
a more or less vertical axis through the right foot, and the trunk and arm
muscles project the javelin forwards in a flail-like movement. The javelin
having been delivered, the thrower has then to dissipate his own remaining
forward momentum without crossing the boundary. This he does by landing
on his left foot placed well forward of his centre of gravity, so that, although
his trunk leans forward, as a whole he is, in fact, leaning backwards. The

rotation of the trunk forwards helps to keep the centre of gravity back by inducing an opposite rotation about the left foot, which acts as the pivot, and which is kept in front of the centre of gravity in a series of hops until the remaining forward momentum has been disposed of. A similar sequence of events is shown in Fig. XVIII (8) in which the javelin is carried underarm in the run-up. This carriage, which is not now much favoured, gives a better sprinting position but necessitates a greater change in attitude preparatory to throwing.

Fig. XVIII (8). *Successive positions in the throwing of a javelin (underarm position)* (¼ *second interval*).

CHAPTER XIX

The Dynamics of Athletics II: Rotational Movement

WE must now turn to activities where rotational effects play the dominant role. The principles, which we have already elucidated, are exemplified most directly in the somersault. The body is given a certain amount of angular momentum in the initial spring. The subsequent angular velocity is controlled by the performer by variations in the moment of inertia. Let us take the backward somersault performed on the trampolin mattress and depicted in Fig. XIX (1) as an example.

Fifteen successive positions at equal intervals of time have been traced and the preliminary jump is recorded in addition to the somersault itself. The jump and the somersault, of course, both took place along the same vertical line, but in order to avoid the figures becoming confused because of super-position, each has been displaced horizontally the same distance from its predecessor.

There are two points of interest in connection with the preliminary jump, besides the gaining of height by storing up kinetic energy. At the conclusion of the jump the body is inclined forwards and it is straightened and thrown backwards while the feet are in contact with the mattress. In this way an initial angular momentum is imparted to the body in the direction in which it is ultimately to turn. The second point concerns the movement of the arms. These are also rotated during the preliminary jump, in the direction in which the somersault is to be made, thus storing up angular momentum for the turn. As soon as the somersault itself is commenced this rotation of the arms is stopped, so that the angular momentum is transferred from the arms to the body.

Furnished with this initial counter-clockwise angular momentum, the rest of the performance consists in the control of the angular velocity by adjust-ments in the moment of inertia, so that the turn is completed by the time the performer lands again on the mattress. In frames 10, 11, and 12 the body is contracted into a small compass. Its moment of inertia about an axis through the centre of gravity, perpendicular to the plane of the paper, is decreased. The angular momentum remaining constant, the angular velocity must, therefore, increase to compensate, and the performer turns over rapidly. In frames 13 and 14 the contraction is removed, thus slowing up the rate of turning, and this is further accentuated in frames 14 and 15, by the extension of the arms above the head. In this way the performer is able so to control his movement that he ensures, on the one hand, that he completes the turn by the time he lands and, on the other, that he does not turn too far and land on his back. The forward somersault of Fig. XIX (2) shows similar actions. The rotation is speeded up by an even closer contraction and is slowed down a little earlier by the full extension of the arms and legs. An expert performer

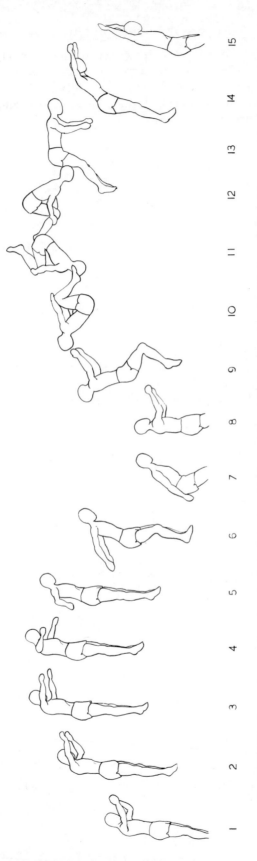

FIG. XIX (1). *Successive positions in a backward somersault. To avoid overlapping, each drawing has been displaced by a constant amount towards the right from its predecessor.*

on the trampolin is able to judge his initial rotation so nicely that he can dispense with the process of contraction altogether and perform the flat somersault shown in Fig. XIX (3). The slight adjustment of the moment of inertia by the crouching attitude in position 8 is all that is required to ensure that he lands on his feet.

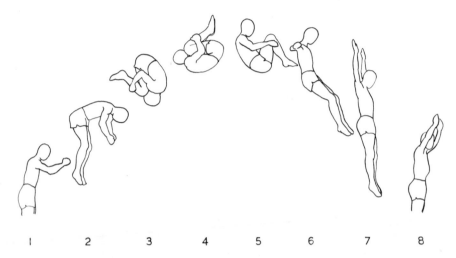

FIG. XIX (2). *Successive positions in a forward somersault.*

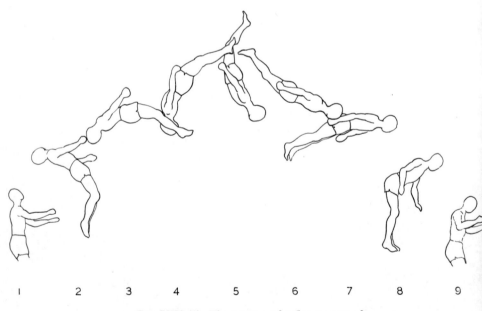

FIG. XIX (3). *The turning of a flat somersault.*

PLATES XIX (i) and (ii). *Forward somersault.*

The principle of varying the moment of inertia so as to change the speed of rotation is of wide application. It is employed by the dancer and the skater to obtain the spin in a pirouette. The turn is started with the arms and legs extended away from the axis of rotation, and as they are brought in towards it, the moment of inertia of the performer about the axis of rotation is reduced, giving an acceleration in the rate of spin. The diver controls the number of turns made in a somersault dive in the same way.

The moment of inertia of parts of the body may also be altered and thus one part made more difficult to turn than another. For example, by extending the arms horizontally from the shoulders the moment of inertia of the upper part of the diver about a vertical axis may be increased. If the legs and body are kept straight and the body twisted about the hips, the lower part will turn through a much greater angle in one direction than the upper part does in the other. Now if the arms are brought in to the side and the legs extended sideways and the twist undone, the upper part will turn through a larger angle than the lower. The legs may then be straightened so that the body will be straight as a whole once more, but it will have turned about the vertical axis in the air without the action of any externally applied couple.

In jumping, both in the high jump and the long jump, a number of problems present themselves for solution. Let us begin by considering the long jump. There is first a simple application of the law of the conservation of linear momentum, as in throwing the javelin. The long jumper endeavours to generate as large a linear momentum in his body as possible during the run-up, and this will continue to carry him forward while he is in the air. A good long jumper has, therefore, to be a good sprinter. In doing the long jump, however, he will not be able to utilise his highest sprinting speed. At his highest speed his legs are only just able to keep pace beneath his body and support its weight. They are not in a position to project the body upwards so as to keep it in the air for longer than the time of his normal stride. Nothing, therefore, appears likely to be gained by attempting to increase speed, as a result, for example, of a longer run-up. Some sacrifice of horizontal momentum is therefore required in order to obtain upwards velocity of projection. The jumper is bound to run below the top speed of which he is capable. At the same time a long jumper cannot afford to jump the highest of which he would be capable in a high jump, since this would throw away the bulk of the horizontal velocity which carries him forward while he is in the air. A long jump is, therefore, very much a matter of selecting the best compromise.

In choosing the angle at which to project the body in the jump, theory is of little help. The one thing which is certain is that the 45° angle for maximum range of the elementary mechanics textbooks has nothing to do with the case. This theory is worked out on the assumption that the velocity of projection remains constant as the angle of projection is varied, and this will manifestly not be the case in the long jump. It is obvious that as the angle of projection is increased the velocity of projection will decrease, since the body muscles have then to act against the pull of gravity. The lower angles of projection will, therefore, be favoured. In the long jump the law connecting the decrease in velocity of projection with increase in the angle cannot be predicted theoretically—the effect on the velocity in the approach run has also to be taken account of—and therefore the optimum angle of projection cannot be forecast. All that can be said is that it must be less than 45°. Since all long jumpers instinctively use a much smaller angle than 45°, this statement is not of much assistance. The problem could only be tackled experimentally. It is indeed possible, and even likely, that the optimum angle might vary from person to person. A value of something less than 30° would not be an improbable estimate with which to start. The angle of projection in the jump illustrated in Fig. XIX (4) appears to be about 27°, but it is difficult to measure because of the foreshortening and it can only be estimated roughly.

Like linear momentum, some vertical momentum is capable of being stored for a short time previous to the jump. Thus arms and the free leg can be accelerated upwards and will store momentum if this is done immediately before the jump. If this is done while the spring is being made with the jumping leg, however, the effect will be that this leg will operate against an increased load so that, in effect, the stored momentum will be obtained at the expense of what the jumping leg could provide. The contribution of these auxiliary movements is likely to be limited if not carefully co-ordinated with the principal spring.

The long jump also presents some interesting examples of the application of the conservation of angular momentum. Having decided on the optimum

FIG. XIX (4). *Successive positions in a long jump, using the hitch kick and arm movements.*

trajectory for his centre of gravity, the problem the long jumper then has to face is that of getting his heels as far forward as possible on landing, without entailing his having to sit down in the pit. Once he has projected himself in the jump, nothing the jumper can do in the air will alter the positions his centre of gravity will successively occupy in space. If the centre of gravity is moved forwards relative to the body, for example, by bending or movement of the limbs, this will be accomplished by moving the body backwards in space or vice versa. The body can also be rotated in space, in which case it will turn about the centre of gravity which will proceed as before, regardless of any of these changes.

At take-off the free leg will be somewhat in advance and the jumping leg behind the body. The jumper will wish to delay his landing as much as possible in order that his forward momentum may increase the length of his jump. He must, therefore, bring his legs forward while he is in the air. Four factors enter into this problem. There is first the question of any initial rotation imparted to the body at take-off. If the body is given any angular momentum when it is projected in the jump, this will remain with it throughout, although it can be redistributed among different parts and the rate of rotation can be varied. To get the feet forward at the end of the jump, backwards rotation is required and, if this were obtained by rotation of the body as a whole, this would indicate a 'pulling' action of the jumping foot to

produce it. It is probable that this would have to be purchased at the expense
of some forward momentum, but a small angular momentum could be made
to produce a large angular velocity by a suitable contraction of the body
during the jump, as in a somersault. It is doubtful if backwards angular
momentum provided at take-off would be of any value, however, since this
is in the opposite direction to what is required on landing. At that stage
forward angular momentum is desirable, to carry the centre of gravity up and
over the feet. Indeed, it is probable that some forward rotation would be
preferable to backward rotation at take-off. This could be absorbed and
counteracted during the flight by the limbs and so only become manifest when
limb motion ceases on landing.

FIG. XIX (5). *The same jump at twice the frequency to show arm and leg movements.*

The second and third factors which affect the attitude of the jumper on
landing are these movements of the legs and arms respectively, during the
jump. A popular method of jumping is that known as the 'hitch kick'
adopted in the jump of Fig. XIX (4). Arm and leg movement are shown more
clearly in Fig. XIX (5) where the interval between successive positions has
been halved. The jumper takes a pedalling-like step in the air. This communi-
cates forward angular momentum to the legs, and since this is initiated in the
air it will be obtained at the expense of a backwards rotation of the body. The
process is assisted by a similar rotation of the outstretched arms about the
shoulders. In both cases the rotation of the limbs is in the direction in

which the jumper wishes to turn on landing. When the limbs cease to turn their angular momentum is returned to the body, which is thus helped to turn forwards. The effect could be increased if the arms, instead of being brought to rest on landing, as is the common practice, were rotated vigorously in the reverse direction. It is, of course, impossible to reverse the rotation of the feet. If forward rotation is imparted at take-off, these limb movements would reduce its speed and could annul its effect in the air. The forward rotation would then not have the effect of shortening the jump by bringing the feet down prematurely and it would be available for righting the jumper when he landed. A so-called 'hanging' position in the air, in which the limbs are stretched out as far as possible, can also slow down the forward rotation by increasing the moment of inertia. There seems nothing to be said for the exaggerated arching of the back in this manœuvre, which contributes nothing to the effect. The term 'hang' is a misnomer. As we have seen, there can be no question of any 'hanging in the air' in any real sense.

The fourth factor which brings the feet forward for landing is the 'jacking' of the body towards the end of the jump. The trunk leans forward and the legs are brought up, the two rotations being in opposite directions. This is by far the most effective of the four processes, though it is not adopted markedly by the jumper in Figs. XIX (4) and (5). Whether he could have added an inch or so to his jump by doubling himself up more than he did is worth examining. On landing he had just sufficient forward angular momentum to rotate him forward so that he did not sit down but, as indeed is correct, he had little to spare. Had he turned forward very easily on landing with lots of angular momentum to spare, he obviously would have been in a position to have brought his feet further forward than he did. Had he 'jacked' himself more closely than he did, his feet would have been carried forward further than they were, but if he did nothing else about it he would not have had sufficient forward angular momentum to prevent his having to sit down, and his jump would have been spoiled. Yet his comparatively open attitude on landing indicates that there is a little slack to be taken up somewhere. One thing he might have done is to reverse his arms on landing. By doing this vigorously he could impart some additional forward angular momentum to his body, so that his feet could then be placed a little further forward. Had a little more forward angular momentum been obtained at take-off, his arm and leg movements being made as before, his feet could have been carried further forward without his having to sit down. Making the leg and arm movement more vigorous would achieve the same effect in bringing the feet forward, but would not contribute forward angular momentum after landing, since it would have been initiated in the air. Full advantage is required of each manœuvre.

The carrying out of a high jump is also of interest from the point of view of dynamics. The muscles involved in a high jump are capable, by their extension, of performing a certain amount of work, which can be converted into an equivalent quantity of kinetic energy in the body. This energy is capable of raising the centre of gravity of the body by a fixed amount. This is the brute force aspect of the problem of the high jump. It is not the whole of the matter, however, by any means. The upwards momentum given to the body in the take-off depends upon the way the spring is conducted, and in getting the jumper over the bar the effectiveness of the lift imparted to the centre of gravity is determined by the orientation of his body as he goes over the top.

It is quite possible theoretically for the centre of gravity to pass underneath the bar while the jumper himself passes over it, though it is doubtful if any jumper actually succeeds in doing this in practice. The degree to which he can approach it, however, plays a large part in determining the success of a jump.

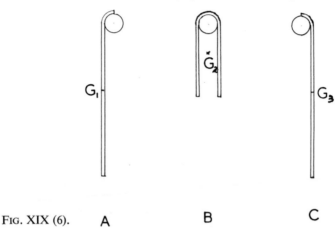

FIG. XIX (6).   A   B   C

Consider the piece of string being passed over a bar as in Fig. XIX (6). As the process commences, the centre of gravity of the string will be half-way down at G_1. When the string is half-way across the bar, the centre of gravity will be raised to its highest point, G_2. Thereafter it descends again and at G_3 it is at the same height as that at which it started. The string has been passed over the bar while its centre of gravity passes underneath. It is the ambition of all high jumpers to become like pieces of string!

Plates XIX (iii) and (iv) show two positions of a jumper performing a straddle jump, probably the most effective method in this respect. We notice the draped position in the first picture and the lowering of the arm as soon as it has crossed the bar, thus keeping the centre of gravity low and permitting other parts of the body to rise. The leading leg follows. Then there ensues the problem of getting the following leg safely over, and this is accomplished by the rotation given to the body on take-off, the angular momentum being transferred to the limb by straightening it. In the jump photographed, the performer evidently thought it advisable to speed the rotation up somewhat when he was just over the bar and therefore threw his right arm backwards.

In order to find the position of his centre of gravity he allowed himself to be strung up on a rope in two positions, in both of which he adopted the attitude, as far as possible, which he had when crossing the bar. Plates XIX (v) and (vi) show the result. In Plate XIX (vii) these two photographs have been superimposed in order to indicate the position of the centre of gravity. It lies outside the body and could well have passed through the bar, if not actually underneath it, in the jump.

PLATES XIX (iii) and (iv). *Two stages in the straddle high jump.*

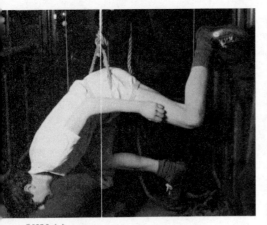

ₐTE XIX (v).

PLATE XIX (vi).

The centre of gravity of a body suspended from a single point of support must lie on a vertical line below the support. In this case, the high jumper shown in action in Plates XIX (iii) *and* (iv) *has been suspended twice, while in the approximate lay-out he maintains over the bar. Superposition of the photographs shows that the centre of gravity is outside the body, and will be very close to the bar, or maybe even coincident with it at the highest part of the jump.*

PLATE XIX (vii)

The scissors jumper in Fig. XIX (7) passes over the bar with her centre of gravity well above it. The scissors is a comparatively elementary style of jumping. Nevertheless, the example of Fig. XIX (7) shows attention to a number of points which improve the performance. The scissors is itself an improvement upon a jump in which both legs pass over the bar together. The legs themselves imitate very closely the action of the piece of string and their centre of gravity passes very close to, if not below, the bar. Upward momentum is stored in both arms and the free leg just before take-off, and the arms are lowered when the bar is being crossed and the leading leg as soon as possible after passing over the jump, in order to raise the rest of the body, and the other leg which has still to cross. The arms are lowered correctly as the body crosses the bar, and the free leg as soon as it has cleared. The trunk is bent forward and the head tucked in, both of which will tend to lower the centre of gravity of the upper part of the body and thus raise that of the lower, which might otherwise be in danger of coming into contact with the bar. However, the possibilities of the lay-out over the bar in the scissors jump are limited.

FIG. XIX (7). *A scissors jump.*

The scissors jump of Fig. XIX (7) may be compared with the Western roll of Fig. XIX (8). The jumper's centre of gravity still passes over the bar well above it, but it is lower than is the case with the scissors jump, by virtue of the fact that she lies on her side at her highest point. The arms are also lowered as soon as they are over the bar, thus lowering the centre of gravity—or to put it in a better way, raising some other part of the body not yet over the bar, since nothing which the jumper can do in the air will alter the position of

Fig. XIX (8). *The Western roll high jump.*

the centre of gravity of the body as a whole. In the Western roll the jumper takes off and lands on the same foot—it is in reality a hop.

Of the three jumps illustrated, the straddle approaches most nearly to the ideal of the piece of string. There are limitations, however, to the extent to which this sort of thing can be carried. It is possible to dive over the bar head first and, by pouring oneself over, imitate the string very closely. The difficulty and danger of the process lie in the landing, the arms not being sufficiently strong to take the impact, much of which would fall on the neck and shoulders. A jumper, therefore, who wishes to live to jump another day has to temper the method accordingly. The scissors jumper depicted lands easily on the feet; in the Western roll the landing is effected on both hands and one leg; and the same is true of the straddle.

In all three jumps the take-off is made from a position inclined backwards on the jumping leg while the free leg is being accelerated upwards, thus generating upwards momentum which helps to take the jumper over the bar. Only the scissors jumper appeared to use the arms to any extent in this way. While the free legs and arms are being accelerated upwards, the downwards pressure on the jumping leg is increased. As soon as the acceleration ceases, however, the upwards momentum carries the former members upwards and thus relieves the jumping leg, which has been flexed during these manœuvres.

The jumping leg is then straightened in the spring which is designed to carry the jumper over the bar.

In addition to upwards linear momentum these preliminary processes, performed while the jumping leg is still in contact with the ground, will also generate angular momentum. The principal rotation required is about a horizontal axis parallel to the bar and will be clockwise in Plates XIX (iii) and (iv) and Fig. XIX (8) and counter-clockwise in Fig. XIX (7), when viewed from the near end of the bar. With the scissors jump the free leg, being nearest the bar, will generate an angular momentum in the opposite direction tending to raise the near and lower the far side. This has to be counteracted in the spring. The crouched position over the bar will enhance the effect of the angular momentum generated, and it is doubtless to counter it after the jump has been performed that the arms are raised above the head finally so as to increase the moment of inertia—as in the case of the somersault. With the Western roll and the straddle, the free leg will generate angular momentum in the required direction, and this continues after the bar has been passed and leads to the landing being made with the head end down.

Rotation is also set up about a horizontal axis at right angles to the bar. With the scissors jump this leads to the backwards tilt of the body on landing which the raising of the arms has doubtless diminished. The rotation about this axis can also be seen in the Western roll and straddle jump. In these jumps there is also a small rotation about a vertical axis, though there is very little in the case of the scissors.

The centre of gravity is carried well above the bar in the last two jumps illustrated. They were carried out to demonstrate the techniques rather than to achieve maximum height. The bar might have been raised a little perhaps, without being knocked off, in each case. The lay-out over the bar afforded by the three styles may be compared from the figures and from the straddle jump in the photograph of Plates XIX (iii) and (iv).

While he is in the air and rotating, the jumper is carried over the bar by virtue of the linear momentum he possesses at right angles to it, which he derived from the approach run. A jumper must, therefore, run on a course sufficiently inclined to the bar for him to possess the necessary component of linear momentum at right angles to it. On the other hand, if the bar is approached at right angles, the jump will have to be commenced further out to give the free leg room to operate, and this will be awkward. On the other hand, by making the jump very obliquely, a longer time will be spent over the bar and thus the likelihood of its being knocked off will be increased, unless indeed this is compensated by a more rapid approach.

In the pole vault (Fig. XIX (9)) the linear momentum generated in the approach is converted into angular momentum when the pole makes contact with the ground, and this rotation about the point of contact carries the vaulter up. His linear velocity must be sufficient for his kinetic energy to equal the potential energy he will possess at the top of the vault, apart from the work his arms are able to perform during the ascent by bearing down on the pole and raising his body still further. At the top of the vault this downwards pressure of the arms on the pole, resulting in an equal and opposite force on the vaulter, does not pass through his centre of gravity. It therefore sets him rotating at the same time that his centre of gravity is raised. This rotation is in the opposite direction to that in which the body has been turning in the first half of the vault. It neutralises the initial rotation and finally reverses its direction so that the legs are lowered after they have passed over the bar and the head and shoulders, which have yet to get across, are raised. The rotation continues until the landing is made and slightly afterwards when it leads to the roll forward in the pit.

FIG. XIX (9). *Pole vault.*

CHAPTER XX

The Dynamics of Athletics III: Throwing

WE have already mentioned the throwing of the javelin in connection with the conservation of linear momentum. Any athletic event might have been taken in illustration of this principle, though the javelin with its freer approach shows it better than the others. We will now look briefly at the mechanics of throwing as a whole, to see some of the principles of dynamics in operation. To begin with, however, we will first discuss two preliminary phenomena, both of which have a direct bearing on the questions involved. They are the hitting of a ball with a bat and the cracking of a whip.

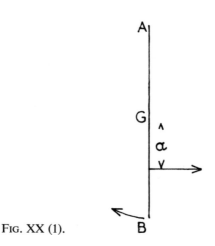

FIG. XX (1).

First let us consider the hitting of a ball. When the bat hits the ball or, what comes to the same thing, the ball strikes the bat, a force of reaction is exerted upon the bat at the point of impact. We have seen that any such force accelerates the body as a whole, as would the same force applied to the centre of gravity, and it causes the body to turn as would a couple whose moment equals the product of the force, F, and its distance from the centre of gravity, a (Fig. XX (1)). The acceleration of the centre of gravity will be the same as if all the mass of the body were concentrated there. The rate of rotation will be determined by the moment of inertia about an axis through the centre of gravity at right angles to the plane which contains both the force and the centre of gravity. There is a certain place where the force can be applied so that the combination of the movement of the centre of gravity and the rotation causes the body to turn about the end A. This point is known as the centre of percussion relative to A. In hitting a cricket ball the player endeavours to strike it so that it makes contact with the bat at its centre of percussion relative to the end held in the hands. If he does not succeed in doing this the shot stings, because the handle receives an impulsive force which his hands have to absorb. The mass of a cricket bat is fairly evenly distributed so that its moment of inertia about an axis through the centre of gravity is high. The rate of rotation is low and the centre of percussion is some distance below the centre of gravity. In the case of a golf club the mass is concentrated very largely in the head, and the centre of percussion will be closer to the centre of gravity. It is to obtain the same effect that the handle of a hammer is made of a lighter material than the head, so that the centre of percussion of the whole is close to where the nail is hit.

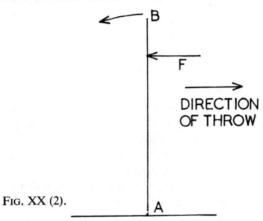

B

F

DIRECTION
OF THROW

FIG. XX (2).

A

Turning Fig. XX (1) upside down, as in Fig. XX (2), we obtain a diagram for the forces experienced by a man throwing an object to the right. The force, F, becomes the reaction from the projectile which is being accelerated. If this reaction is applied at the centre of percussion of the man relative to his feet, at A, then the ground will exert no horizontal force to counterbalance the force, F, which will simply rotate the man about his feet in a counter-clockwise direction, as indicated by the arrow at B. If the object is thrown from above the centre of percussion, the feet will tend to go to the right, in the same direction as the projectile, and the ground will exert a force on them to the left. If the object is thrown below the centre of percussion the feet will tend to go to the left, in the opposite direction to the missile, and the ground will exert a force to the right. Such rotations set up in the body by the reaction of the object being thrown have a bearing upon the positioning of the feet for throwing. When the object being thrown is light, however, such as a small stone, the momentum of the throwing arm itself becomes an important factor in the projection, and the body may suffer little reaction from the projectile being accelerated. It may even experience a force in the same direction as the acceleration—in the opposite direction to the force F in Fig. XX (2), that is to say.

This may be understood from a consideration of the cracking of a whip. This phenomenon is of interest also because it furnishes an everyday case where we come into contact with very high velocities—supersonic velocities in fact.

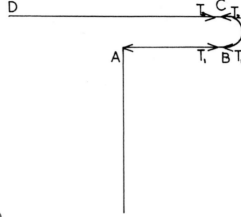

FIG. XX (3).

A whip is cracked by suddenly reversing the direction of travel of the end of the thong which is attached to the stock. A wave, like a wave in a linen line, travels down the thong, the direction of motion of the particles in the thong being reversed as they pass over it. The portion of the thong between B and C in Fig. XX (3) is thus undergoing this reversal of motion. This has to be brought about by the tensions in the thong itself, since no other force is available. The tensions in the neighbouring pieces exert forces T_1 and T_2 upon it, and these cause the necessary change in momentum of the piece of the thong between B and C. The tension T_1 is exerted by the piece of the thong lying between A and B, and it experiences an equal and opposite force. If this portion between A and B is moving at a steady velocity, the stock will exert an equal and opposite force on it at A. If it is being accelerated the stock must exert a greater force. Similarly, the force at C experienced by BC is provided by the piece of thong between C and D, which also is acted upon by an equal and opposite force, T_2. The magnitude of these tensions will be determined by the time taken by the particles of the thong to pass round the bend CB. The quicker they pass round, the greater must be the force which is exerted, in order to reverse their direction of motion in the shorter time. The force, T_2, acts on the end of the thong, CD, and will accelerate it, since there can be no counterbalancing force at the other end. This acceleration will cause the speed at which the particles arrive at C to increase, and, therefore, also the speed with which they pass round CB. The forces, T_1 and T_2, will therefore tend to increase all the time. Further, T_2 is acting upon the ever-decreasing mass left in CD. Speed, therefore, builds up and the result is heard finally in the supersonic bang, which is the cracking of the whip.

The human body is not sufficiently flexible for it to act like the thong of a whip completely, yet nevertheless, just as the piece of string provided a useful guide for the performance of the high jump, so phenomena resembling the cracking of a whip play an important part in the final stages in bowling and throwing, when the wrist, hand and fingers, which are comparatively weakly endowed with muscles, come into play. The projectile is not simply pushed forwards, but momentum stored in the arm is transferred to it. The difference is often exemplified by the throwing of young children, boys taking instinctively to the whip-like action which girls seem to have some difficulty in acquiring. If the arms and hands are to work in this way they must be stopped from the body outwards. The body muscles act first, but having imparted momentum to the arm they play less part in the final stages. They may even have to act in the reverse direction on the arm at the end, which would account for the tendency to lean backwards when throwing (see for example positions 5 and 6 in the tracings of the javelin throw in Fig. XVIII (7) and positions 7 and 8 in Fig. XVIII (8)).

In Chapter VIII we discussed some of the questions which arise when we wish to throw an object as far as possible and have seen that it is rarely true that the angle of projection should be as high as 45° with the horizontal. One reason for this is that when it is being thrown, a ball or other projectile is acted upon, not only by the forces applied to it by the thrower, but also by its weight. The aim in throwing is to exert as large a force as possible on the object for as long a time as possible, which means in practice for as long a distance as possible. When we throw at a very steep angle, not only does the weight of the body act against the propulsive force exerted, but the distance over which the force can be exerted is also diminished. The result of both these effects is that at high angles of throwing the velocity of projection must be lower than that which can be attained at low angles. If the velocity of projection remained constant, then the angle of projection to obtain maximum range will be 45°. If, however, the velocity of projection is greater for lower angles, then the angle for maximum range will be less than 45° to the horizontal.

The curves showing the angle of projection for maximum range given in Appendix VI (Fig. A.VI (4)) were worked out on the basis that the projection was by a catapult which always exerted the same force over a constant distance, like the catapult used to project the tennis ball in Plate VIII (iv). When a man throws a ball, he himself moves forward as a rule, to add some further momentum to the throw. Because of this and the limitations of his reach, the force producing a low trajectory is able to act for a longer time than one leading to a high trajectory. The effect of this is illustrated by Curve II in Fig. A.VI (4).

Fig. XX (4) gives tracings of a shot put by a girl student and Fig. XX (5) the positions of the shot at intervals of $\frac{1}{16}$ second. The shot left the hand at the point P, and it is obvious that almost all the acceleration it acquired took place between O and P, over a distance of some 5 feet. The velocity of projection was about 30 feet per second. If the force accelerating the shot is assumed to be constant throughout the distance over which it acted, this means that it would amount to between three and four times the weight of the shot. Curve II of Fig. A.VI (4) gives for the angle of projection for maximum range the value of 33°, which is about the angle at which the shot was projected. This was no doubt arrived at as a result of experience.

The fact that little acceleration was given to the shot before the point O does not necessarily mean that the movements of the thrower previously were wasted. They can serve to secure a good stance and balance for the put and, more importantly, can store momentum in the putter's body. Some of this momentum can then be transferred to the shot—mainly by the direct push of the muscles but partly by the whip-like action of the body and arm. The whip-snapping action of the arm is shown more obviously in positions 8, 9, and 10 of the javelin throw of Fig. XVIII (8).

FIG. XX (4). *Positions in putting the shot at ¼ second intervals.*

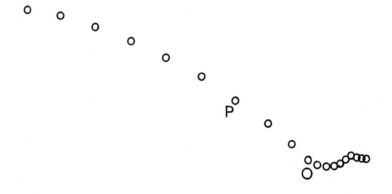

FIG. XX (5). *Positions of the shot put of* Fig. XX (4) *at ¹⁄₁₆ second intervals.*

FIG. XX (6).

Throwing a discus.

$\frac{1}{5}$ second intervals.

(A)

(B)

The velocity of projection given to a discus is obtained by the rotation of the body about a vertical axis, the missile being held more or less at arm's length in the process. Fig. XX (6) gives tracings of this event. An analysis of the acceleration and projection of the discus, similar to that of the shot, could be carried out. The flights of both javelin and discus, however, are much more affected by aerodynamic forces and the effect of spin than is that of the shot, the consideration of which is thus comparatively simple.

The flight of most projectiles is affected very markedly by any spin which may be imparted to them. The Magnus effect, which is often of very great importance, as for example in the flight of a ball, has already been considered. We must now very briefly take account of some of the other effects to which spin can lead.

Angular velocities are vector quantities and can be represented by straight lines, in both magnitude and direction. The length of the straight line represents the magnitude of the angular velocity, and its direction is that of the axis about which the rotation takes place. The convention is adopted that if the rotation occurs about the axis of X in Fig. XX (7) and is in the direction which moves OY towards the position OZ, then the angular velocity is positive and is represented by a line drawn from O towards X, as indicated by the arrow in the figure. It corresponds to the motion of a right-handed corkscrew, OY being drawn into the paper.

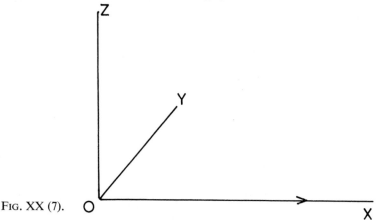

FIG. XX (7).

Angular velocities, being vector quantities, are compounded by the parallelogram law. If a body possesses two angular velocities simultaneously, represented by the lines OA and OB in Fig. XX (8), then it will move as though it possessed the single angular velocity represented by the line OC, which is the diagonal of the parallelogram formed by OA and OB. The proof of this is very simple, but to avoid making the text laboured it will be placed in Appendix V. We will proceed to discuss one or two examples.

When a top like a gyroscope is set rotating about its axle and is supported on a point at one end, with its axis horizontal, as in Fig. XX (9), the axis rotates continuously in the horizontal plane. This movement is known as precession and it arises as follows, from the action of the weight of the apparatus and the reaction of the support.

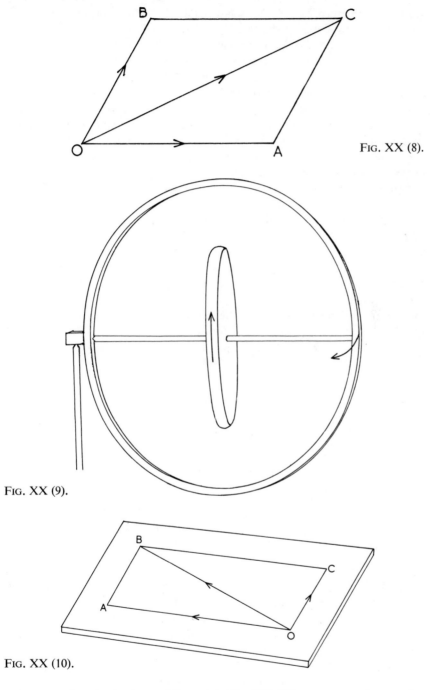

FIG. XX (8).

FIG. XX (9).

FIG. XX (10).

Suppose that the horizontal line, *OA*, Fig. XX (10), represents the angular velocity of the top at a certain instant. A short time later it will be represented by the line *OB*, lying in the same horizontal plane as *OA*. To change the angular momentum from *OA* to *OB* requires the addition of the angular velocity represented by OC. Now the weight of the top will tend to turn it about a horizontal axis in the direction of OC, and in each short interval of time it will generate a certain angular velocity about this direction, which is at right angles to the axis of spin of the top. The vector representing the angular velocity of the top, once set going, will therefore continue to rotate in the horizontal plane at a uniform speed.

As an example of the effect of spin on the flight of a projectile let us experiment with a small cardboard disc, such as used to be employed to close the tops of milk bottles. If it is held between the first finger and thumb of the left hand and pressed forward with the first finger of the right hand, it is easy to project the disc and, at the same time, impart a rapid spin to it. Suppose that it is projected forwards with its plane horizontal or inclined slightly upwards, as in Fig. XX (11). When a sheet of paper was launched into the air we saw that the resultant upward thrust which the air exerted upon it acted in front of the centre. It tended to tip the paper up in front. In the case of the disc which is spinning rapidly, this tendency to tip the front upwards results in a precession of the axis of spin. In Fig. XX (11) OS represents the angular velocity of spin of the disc, and OT the small angular velocity generated by the thrust of the air in a short interval of time. Thus at the end of the interval the axis of spin will have moved from the position OS to OR. The result is that the disc will rotate about its direction of flight, as would a right-handed corkscrew being screwed along the path.

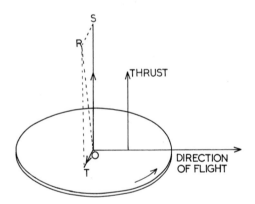

FIG. XX (11).

Another simple example is that of the boomerang. The simplest boomerang to make for purposes of experiment is a cross cut out of thin card, such as a postcard. If this is placed on a book with one arm projecting over the edge, as in Fig. XX (12), it can be struck smartly with a pencil or flicked by the finger and so set rotating about a vertical axis at the same time as it is projected forwards.

If the spin is anti-clockwise viewed from above, as will be the case when the boomerang is projected by a right-handed person, then the arms of the cross on the right-hand side, where rotation carries them forward, will meet the air at a greater velocity than do the arms on the left-hand side, where the spin carries them backwards. The lift is therefore greater on the right-hand side than it is on the left and, were it not for the spin, would rotate the cross about the direction of flight, lifting the right-hand side and lowering the left. Because of the spin, however, the effect of this difference in lift is to tilt the axis of spin so as to raise the front of the boomerang and lower the back. In Fig. XX (13) *OT* represents the angular velocity given the boomerang in a short time by the greater lift on the near wing. Combined with the angular velocity of the spin, *OS*, this gives a resultant spin represented by *OR*. The projectile, therefore, rises in the air until it loses its forwards momentum and then glides back along a similar path to that which it took on the outwards journey.

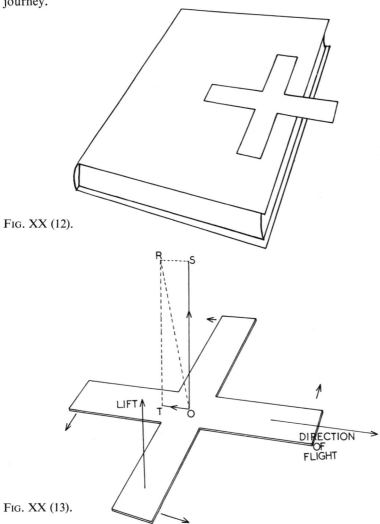

FIG. XX (12).

FIG. XX (13).

A very slight twist imparted to the blades so as to increase their lift when spinning, like a four-bladed propeller, helps the performance of the model, as we would expect. If the twist is too great, however, the rise will occur too quickly and the performance will be less good. The original boomerang of the

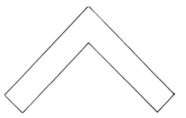

FIG. XX (14).

Australian aborigines consisted roughly of a half cross as in Fig. XX (14). This can also be made in cardboard and performs in a similar manner to the complete cross. It will spin about a vertical axis through its centre of gravity like the first model, and the arms will travel forwards and meet the air with a greater relative velocity on one side than on the other. The result will again be a couple tending to turn the plane of the projectile about its direction of flight, which will lead to a precessional rotation of the axis of spin which, in turn, will lift the front of the instrument and produce a climbing flight, as in Fig. XX (15). What is happening, however, becomes rather more clear when the complete, rather than the half cross, is considered.

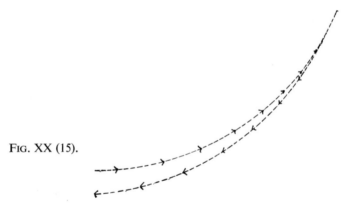

FIG. XX (15).

The rate at which a top precesses depends upon its initial angular velocity of spin and on the deflecting force—usually the top's weight. When the rate of spin is high, the angular velocity generated by the deflecting force will only be small in comparison, so that the angle turned through by the axis of spin in a given time will be small. As the rate of spin decreases, the velocity of precession increases. A gyroscope which spins very rapidly and which is mounted on gimbals so that only small deflecting forces can act upon it will continue to point in the direction in which it is first set spinning because the angular velocities generated by the residual frictional forces will be very small compared with the rate of spin. It is to keep the projectile pointing always in the direction in which it is fired that rifle barrels and the barrels of artillery pieces are given a helical groove to set the bullet or shell spinning as it is fired. If, as is usually the case, the thrust of the air does not pass through the centre of gravity of the projectile, the spin will cause it to precess and this leads to drift which has to be allowed for in aiming.

Spin imparted to a discus or javelin on launching can help it to keep from tumbling over and over in the air, so that advantage can be obtained from the lift which the air can provide. Also the resistance caused by the poor aerodynamic shape when travelling broadside on can be avoided. Precessional effects are to be expected in addition. With the discus these will lead to a rotation about the direction of flight, like the milk bottle top. The weight of a discus, however, is a good deal larger relative to the aerodynamic forces of lift, than is the case with the milk bottle top. The rotation of the discus about its direction of flight is therefore very much less.

It is similarly the spin which enables a top to remain upright, balanced upon its point, and provides the reason why a hoop being bowled along the ground does not fall over. In the case of the top, precession causes the axis of spin to trace out a conical surface. There is usually also an oscillation in the angle of inclination of the axis to the vertical, known as nutation or 'nodding'. When the hoop leans over, the precession causes it to follow a curved path, the radius of which decreases as the speed of the hoop diminishes. In the case of the front wheel of a bicycle, precession similarly causes the wheel to steer in the direction in which it is tilted. This enables a rider to control the machine without holding on to the handle-bars. As mentioned earlier, the spin of the wheels, though assisting balance, does not seem able to provide all the controlling force necessary to maintain it. Precession also provides the monocycle rider with a means whereby he can help his steering, for which, as we saw in Chapter XV, he has no wheel-base from which to obtain a purchase, but the effect will be very small, and to all intents and purposes, negligible.

CHAPTER XXI

The Biology of Athletics

WE have seen something of the mechanism of various parts of the bodies of animals, and of the laws of physics governing their motion. In conclusion we will try to link these to a few other factors, all of which control the final performance.

Every athlete knows that there is a lot more in his art than sheer muscle size. Brute physique with greatly developed muscles, especially in the shoulder region, is quite out of place in most events. Long-distance races are often won by the wiry type of figure. Fig. XXI (1) relates some of the interacting factors.

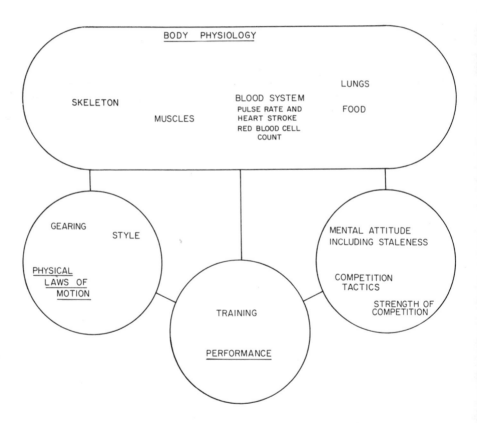

FIG. XXI (1). *Some of the factors affecting athletic performance.*

To make a choice of the most economical style involves the appreciation of the laws of motion together with body anatomy and muscle performance. Thus, for the high jump, we have traced the following development in style—

hurdling, scissors, Western roll, and the straddle. Similarly, the long jumper who can take off in a fairly upright, or even slightly forward position, but land with legs outstretched so that he only just avoids flopping into a sitting position, has potentially the best style. In swimming, the stroke which carries the swimmer steadily through the water is the ideal to be aimed at. Theoretically a style of rowing which enables a boat to proceed at an even velocity through the water would be more economical than one where the craft is almost brought to rest at a certain phase of the stroke. As we have seen in Chapter XI, the resistance of the water rises rapidly with increase in the velocity, so the jerks at high speed will waste more energy than can be saved in the slower part of the cycle. It would form an interesting experiment to design a boat permitting pairs of oarsmen to row a set angle out of phase with the next pair—i.e. a metachronal rhythm, like the legs of the centipede. A much steadier velocity should result. The method has indeed been tried, but so far the difficulty of co-ordinating the action of the crew has proved insuperable.

Once the style with its possibilities and limitations has been settled, improvement comes with practice. The development of the new skill, necessitating different co-ordinations, is the province of the central nervous system. In the early days of practice, conscious efforts are made to put parts of the body in the right place at the right time. As familiarity is gained, the action becomes less and less conscious, until it becomes a conditioned reflex. The mind is then free to concentrate on the finer points, and these, in turn, will also eventually become subject to conditioned reflexes. At this stage it is possible to recall any part of the action into consciousness in order to review it. After changing a high jumping style, for example, the new aerial lay-out takes some time to master; later, attention is paid to a more powerful take-off, and then the details of getting the parts of the body down as soon as they have crossed the bar are attended to. At first, the change in style is accompanied by a marked drop in performance, but if the new style is more economical, the former individual record will soon be surpassed. In motor racing, the skills of changing gear and steering are conditioned reflexes long before the driver starts competitive racing. Only when he changes car will he have to give some conscious effort to the slight differences in driving style to be adopted. In the race his attention is devoted to the position with respect to other cars, and to the one or two bends ahead. Similarly, in gliding, the actual flying control becomes conditioned, and the mind concentrates on the course and the weather.

With athletic events it is not easy to demonstrate improvements arising from changes in style, for they are normally made at the beginning of the season when bodily fitness is also improving. To illustrate the learning processes it is useful to undertake the learning of some simple skill which is new to the experimenter. In order to be able to record the results and the improvement with practice, one of the authors devised a number of such simple tasks. Though the examples chosen may appear at first sight to be somewhat pointless they were, in fact, chosen to involve purely mental skills divorced from the training of muscles. The results are set out in Fig. XXI (2).

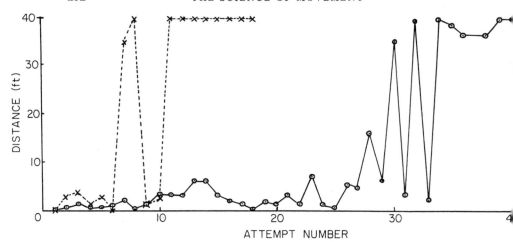

(A)

FIG. XXI (2) (A). *Performance of two boys learning to ride the bicycle with wheels set side by side (Plate III (xi) (B)) down a 40-foot track. The problem set by the machine was that of maintaining balance longitudinally.*

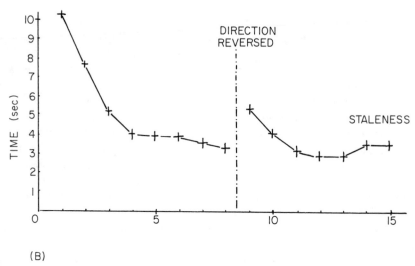

(B)

(B) *Improvement in the rate of transmission of a handshake along a chain of 24 boys. Eyes were closed.*

The first experiment was learning to ride the bicycle with wheels set side by side, described in Chapter III. The machine requires the development of an entirely new set of reflexes and the time required to master the machine by different individuals varies very greatly. Fig. XXI (2) (A) records the attempts made by two boys. For the second experiment a class of about twenty-four pupils were linked hand in hand, and the time it took to pass a handshake round the ring with eyes closed was measured. When this had become fairly constant the direction of the transmission was reversed and this involved the learning of some fresh technique. In this last experiment the results show a

reduced performance at attempt number fourteen, which coincided with a
general feeling that the best possible had been achieved and there was nothing
more to be gained. The change in direction of passing the shake is equivalent
to altering a style. Performance did not drop to the level of the first attempt,
for the skills have much in common. However, what might appear to be only
a slight change in technique did make a big difference, and three attempts
more were needed to regain the old standard. The last experiment involved
the running of a model of the Hampton Court maze by animals. The figure
records the learning of a particular rat, but many other animals were also
employed.

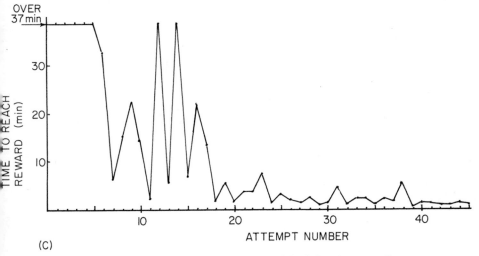

(C) *Performance of a rat running to food in a model of the Hampton Court maze.*

A common feature with early attempts is an erratic record where trial and
error play a part, and the more complex the action the more this is so. As
skill is learned, the performance becomes consistently better, and if there is
a will to break a record, concentration is intense enough for continuous
improvement to be possible. The complexity of the brain hides the learning
mechanism, but there are doubtless chains of circuits whose neurones become
associated with each other. Some sort of long-term facilitation of nerve pulse
transmission from each cell to the next must occur, so that once the action is
started, it proceeds automatically.

The problem of staleness, alluded to in the handshaking experiment, is
important in athletics. It is hard to imagine a physical decline in the muscles
being directly responsible, and staleness must also be classed as an accom-
paniment of one of the higher mental activities. A performer needs confidence
that his methods will bring improvements, and there should be a goal or
record to aim for.

Most people find their sport by a process of natural selection, so that they
concentrate on the things they do best. Within certain fairly wide limits,
people of certain physique are better suited for certain events than others. A

large number of measurements on Olympic athletes were taken by Tanner,[1] who compared them with a random sample of the population. He combined various measurements to give the compound factors plotted on his graphs. As is to be expected, athletes of international standing, upon whom he based his investigations, were better developed physically than the general run of the population as a whole, but nevertheless experts in certain events showed certain definite characteristics. Thus putters of the shot tended to be very tall and heavily built. Runners were more varied in height but more lightly built than the exponents of shot putting, sprinters tending to be more heavily built than the long-distance men. Thus considerations of build must play a large part in determining the type of event in which one is likely to be most successful.

The measurements tabulated in Fig. V (3) showed the lifting power of a number of people with arms of different sizes. It is possible to alter parts of the body by training, and one of the more plastic in this respect is muscle tissue. With exercise both the size of the muscle and its strength increase. However, there are limits to which such a process can be carried. It would be futile to attempt to develop, by training, powers for events for which one's build had not some initial suitability. To train for such events would be a very long and almost impossible process, for the factors are governed by the dimensions of the bones, which are far less plastic. Bones will, however, alter to a certain extent in response to prolonged forces. Sections of them often show stress lines, for the spongy material has been laid down in these directions. Another example is the skeleton of a coolie porter whose backbone tendons had ossified for short distances, thus increasing the strength of his platform for carrying loads—of course, at the expense of flexibility. Then, broken bones heal, which is a further way in which they show powers of response.

In most athletic events, however, absolute muscle strength does not count as much as the rate at which muscles can work. Although this was shown earlier to be related to their volume, it was also pointed out that the supply and disposal services must not be limiting factors. In short events, the reserves in the muscle itself are important, while in the long ones there is much more reliance on the blood system bringing oxygen and energy foods, and taking away excretory products, and also on the lungs and breathing system. The chemistry of these processes has been discussed earlier. It will be recalled that when resting, oxygen is used up at a certain rate, and if there has been no strenuous activity for some time previously, it is being supplied at that rate too. When strenuous exercise begins the oxygen used up is very much greater. Part of the extra supply comes from oxygen stored in the myoglobin, if the muscle is a red one, and the supply to the muscle is increased by a higher rate of beating of the heart and a deeper heart stroke. However, if the demand still outstrips the supply, the respiration in the muscle partly breaks down the sugars to lactic acid, a process needing no oxygen, but generating the poisonous lactic acid whose effect is to cause tiredness. All these processes lead to an oxygen debt which must be repaid when activity slackens.

[1] J. M. Tanner, *The Physique of the Olympic Athlete*, 1964.

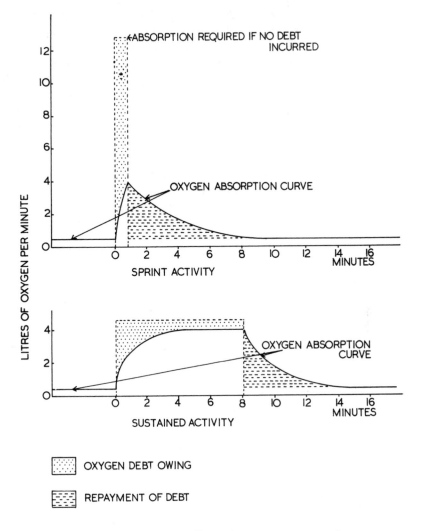

FIG. XXI (3). *Diagram illustrating oxygen consumption.*

Fig. XXI (3) illustrates typical curves for oxygen consumption during and after two spells of strenuous exertion lasting for four-fifths of a minutes to give the upper curve, and eight minutes to give the lower one. Such values are obtained by one of two methods. In one, samples of exhaled air are taken at intervals and analysed to discover how much less oxygen is present than in pure air. It is also necessary to know the total volume of air expired per unit of time. The second method, which is unsuitable for running subjects, involves breathing into a rigid airtight apparatus, the carbon dioxide in which is absorbed chemically. At constant pressure, the volume of enclosed air is continuously recorded by a device like a gasometer. The decrease in volume represents the oxygen absorbed. From time to time the original volume is restored by injecting pure oxygen. Body heating of the enclosed air demands corrections.

The importance of being able to run up an oxygen debt varies with the distance being run. It is probably of greatest importance in races up to about 440 yards. Sprints are run almost entirely on such overdrafts and the ability of the circulatory system to renew supplies is of less importance. The problem in the sprint is that of being able to move the legs fast enough to keep up with the body and prevent it falling forwards. The importance of being able to incur a large oxygen debt probably reaches a climax at about 440 yards because such races can be won by those who can treat them largely as a sprint and run them in the main on an overdraft. Very short distances can be covered by means of the 'savings' in the myoglobin. For long-distance running on the other hand, except for the final sprint if this is indulged in, ability to incur an oxygen debt is of no importance. The speed is determined by the ability of the heart and circulatory system to maintain supplies. The two types of race require different capabilities and it is unusual for a man to excel in both.

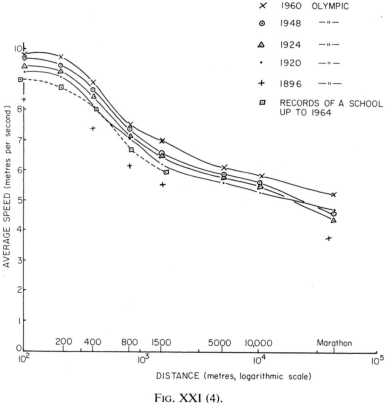

FIG. XXI (4).

The change in the processes involved leads to a drop in the average speed at which the race is run, as distance increases. This drop sets in markedly at about 220 yards and is clearly seen in the curves of Fig. XXI (4). For distances up to 220 yards, winning speeds are nearly the same—just over 21 miles per hour. On the other hand, mile races are won at speeds of about 15 miles per hour, and the winning speeds have only dropped to about 12·3 miles per hour for races up to 10 miles in length.

Different people, doing the same amount of work in the same time, use up different quantities of oxygen. That is, their efficiency varies. (Efficiency, it will be remembered, is the ratio of the work performed to the energy absorbed in the process.) Efficiency also varies with the speed of working. Most forms of resistance which absorb and waste energy, both those which are internal to the body, such as muscle viscosity, and those which are external, such as air resistance, increase as the speed increases. In general, viscous forces increase in proportion to the velocity but other resistances increase more rapidly. Thus it is always more economical not to be in a hurry. As with the boat being rowed through the water, it requires much more energy to restore the average speed by means of a spurt than can be saved by a corresponding period of easy going. That is to say, if one is out to break a record it is best to run at a uniform speed throughout the race, for a spell slower than the average must be made up by an equal increment above the average, and the latter will use more energy than was saved in the slow part. It was attention to this fact by the Finns that led to the improvement in the time for the mile that, at one time, was thought to be an impossibility. Practice with a stopwatch will enable a runner to determine the speed at which he can run a certain distance in order just to have exhausted himself by the end. It will be under such conditions that he will be able to accomplish his best time.

If the aim is to beat other competitors, rather than the clock, however, then different tactics are, of course, often employed. The competitor tries to exploit the weakness of the others. Thus a runner with a fast finish—the one able to incur a large oxygen debt—will not force the pace earlier in the race. If it is not a question of running a race, but of just getting somewhere, then there is a most economical speed at which to work, depending upon the internal gearing of the muscle and skeletal structures of the body. Inefficiency becomes of increasing importance when the limbs are forced to oscillate at a faster rate than they would swing naturally.

Sargent showed how close is the relation between oxygen debt and performance by comparing the expected performance of a runner with his actual times. (Figures published in *Proc. Roy. Soc. B*, vol. 100, p. 11.)

Distance	Calculated best time	Runner's actual best time
300 yds.	33·3 sec.	34 sec.
$\frac{1}{4}$ mile	51·5 sec.	51·4 sec.
$\frac{1}{3}$ mile	1 min. 12·5 sec.	1 min. 15 sec.
$\frac{1}{2}$ mile	2 min. 1 sec.	2 min. 2 sec.
1 mile	4 min. 41 sec.	4 min. 40 sec.
2 miles	10 min. 12 sec.	10 min. 10 sec.

It is extraordinary how closely the performance of a runner can be predicted from a knowledge of the oxygen debt which he is able to incur and the energy requirements for running at different speeds.

The calculated times came from a knowledge of the oxygen debt the performer could stand, plus the rate at which he absorbs oxygen. These give the total oxygen available for the duration of the race. This value is then inserted into a table of oxygen requirements at different speeds, previously prepared, allowing the resultant speed to be read off. He obtained very close agreement with the performance of expert athletes in this way. Such would not be expected from unpractised athletes for they would be likely to vary their speed during the race, and not tire themselves out completely by the end. The aim of the runner in running a race must be to use all his available resources and to exhaust himself completely in the process.

This straightforward dependence on oxygen shows the importance of the lungs and blood system. No doubt the heart will develop more muscle in response to the stresses of training, in just the same way that limb muscles do, but since these changes take a long time to come about, the need for a graded period of training is obvious. It is well known that athletes have very low resting pulse rates. This means that the heart is large and powerful and pumps a lot of blood on each pulse. Large hearts will not only deliver the oxygen during resting when they are beating slowly, but they will also be capable of delivering much more when their rate of beating does increase. The arteries are also involved in the process. They must not only be large to reduce resistance but more importantly they must be strong and elastic to cope with the pressure required to drive the blood rapidly through the capillaries.

In conclusion it is of interest to look at the history of athletic records, which indicate the improvements which have taken place since records have been kept and provide a pointer to future possibilities. Fig. XXI (5) gives the time for four races—the 100 metres, the 400 metres, the 1,500 metres, and the 10,000 metres—over the years from 1896 to 1960. All show an improvement of about 20 per cent over the period. In the case of the 100 metres race, half of this took place between 1896 and 1900 and progress since then has been much slower. The curve seems to be levelling off and the prospect of reducing the time for this event to any significant further extent seems small. The curve for the 400 metres race also shows some sign of levelling out, though the

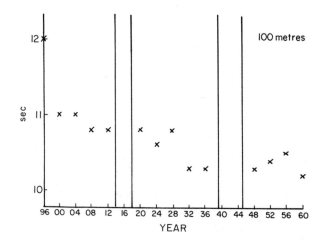

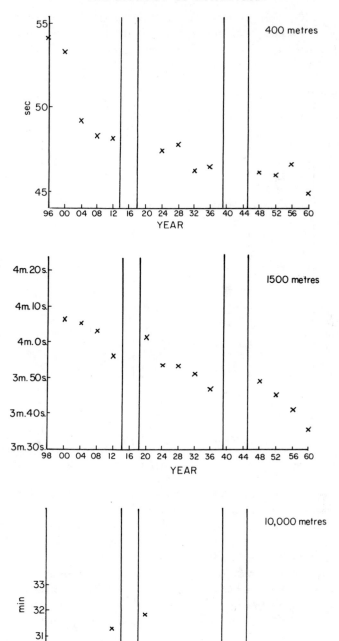

FIG. XXI (5). *Performance in some Olympic track events.*

tendency is still in the direction of shorter times. The longer distance races, however, indicate that steady improvement is still taking place. It is in these races that techniques have improved the most and it would seem likely that further improvement will be seen for some time yet.

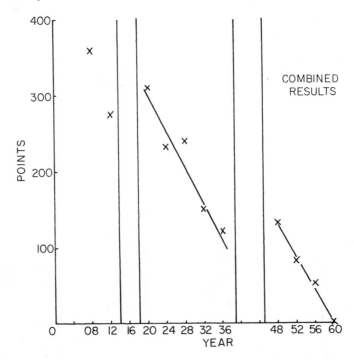

FIG. XXI (6). *Overall index of improvement 1908–60; Olympic track events.* (*The improvements in times for the 100 metres, 200 metres, 400 metres, 800 metres, 1,500 metres, and 10,000 metres were converted to the same scale and added up.*)

The curve drawn in Fig. XXI (6) is of some interest. In it the results of Olympic races from 100 to 10,000 metres have been integrated so as to provide an indication of the overall development in the running of races from 1908 to 1960. In this the changes in the times have been reduced to the same scale and added together, those for 1960 being taken for reference. This curve shows no sign of levelling off so that the end of the possibilities for further improvement in running has obviously not yet been approached. It is of interest also to note that the results are sufficiently sensitive to show very clearly the effect of the two periods of world war, during which there was no development at all.

The drawing of smooth curves through the points for each year raises the question of whether or not development in athletic achievement is a continuous process. When large numbers of events are added together, as in the last figure, smooth curves are, of course, likely to result from the summation of a number of improvements and averaging them out. On the other hand, with individual events there is much to be said for the view that such development as can take place must come about as the result of the invention of new techniques. As each new method is worked out the improvement which it enables to be achieved will be secured, and after that the results might be expected to show a stationary state of affairs. There is no reason to suppose that man is evolving sufficiently rapidly for changes in his physique to contribute significantly in such short periods as we have been considering. Improvement in nurture may well bring into the international classes a larger number of people who in earlier times might not have developed sufficiently physically to achieve that standard, and with the growth in the number of competitors some improvement in the achievements is to be expected, but in the future this seems likely to contribute only a small amount.

It seems much more likely that progress in athletics is a discontinuous process arising from new methods and improved skills, rather than changes in the human body. It is the new invention that produces the new leap forward. Of course, it takes time for the possibilities of each to be fully exploited and this tends to run the effects of one into those of the next, and so to give the impression of a continuous process. One conclusion, however, seems clear. It is that it has been the application of the intellect to the problems which athletes face that has been responsible for most of the advance in the records which has occurred in recent years.

Movement in a Circle

So far we have been able to discuss most of the important phenomena arising from movement without dealing with motion in a circle, which is usually included at an early stage in books on the subject. It is, nevertheless, an important topic, particularly in physics, and requires discussion before the book can be closed.

A moving body, left to itself, travels uniformly in a straight line. To make it move in a curved path, therefore, forces must be applied to it to make it leave the straight track which it would follow on its own. When a moving body follows a curved track the direction of its momentum is continually being altered. That is to say, momentum in one direction is destroyed and momentum in another direction created. This requires the action of forces. We will now investigate the forces which are required to do this. We will consider the case of a body acted on by a constant force, which is always at right angles to the direction in which the body is moving with a constant speed, v.

The force will generate momentum in the direction in which it acts and the rate at which momentum is generated is equal to the magnitude of the force.

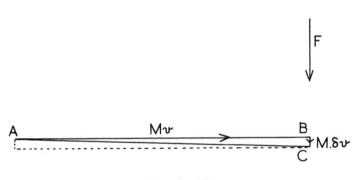

Fig. A.ı (1).

Suppose, in Fig. A.ı (1), AB represents the momentum of the body, Mv, at a certain instant. Let $BC = M . \delta v$ be the momentum generated at right angles to the direction of motion in a very small interval of time. Since momentum, being proportional to velocity, combines according to the usual parallelogram law, the momentum at the end of the small interval will be represented by AC, the diagonal of the parallelogram formed by AB and BC. The effect is thus to change the direction of the momentum of the body from AB to AC, without altering its magnitude.

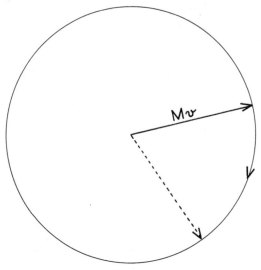

FIG. A.I (2).

As time goes on and the force continues to act at right angles to the momentum of the body, the line which represents the momentum will rotate uniformly and its end will trace out a circle. When the direction of the momentum has turned through 360° the arithmetical total of the momentum which has been generated by the applied force will be represented by the circumference of the circle, $2\pi Mv$.

During this time the body itself will travel round a path of constant curvature; that is, a circle. Suppose that the radius of this circle is r. The time taken by the body to go once round will be $\dfrac{2\pi r}{v}$. It will then be moving in the original direction once again.

Thus the force F generated momentum equal in magnitude to $2\pi Mv$ in a time $\dfrac{2\pi r}{v}$. The rate of generation of momentum throughout that time will be

$$2\pi Mv \div \frac{2\pi r}{v} = \frac{Mv^2}{r}.$$

Since the magnitude of the force is equal to the rate at which it generates momentum,

$$F = \frac{Mv^2}{r}.$$

Thus to make a body move round a circle at a constant speed v requires a force of $\dfrac{Mv^2}{r}$ always to act upon it. The force must also always act at right angles to the direction of movement and it is therefore always directed towards the centre of the circle. It is known as the centripetal, or centre-seeking force.

The centripetal force has to be applied to the body which moves in the circle by another body. This second body which applies the force will be acted on by an equal and opposite force. The force experienced by the second body is known as the centrifugal or centre-fleeing force. Thus the force which we feel when we whirl a stone round on the end of a string is the centrifugal force. The stone feels to us as though it was attempting to flee from the centre. The stone itself, on the other hand, is acted on by the string, which applies to it a force directed towards the centre—the centripetal force.

The experience of the centripetal force is a common one now that we move at comparatively high speeds. When a passenger in a motor-car is driven round a corner he often grabs the door handle, strap or seat, in order to apply the centripetal force to his body. If he does not do this then the force is applied by the seat.

The car, in its turn, gets its centripetal force to make it travel round the curved path through the tyres. When the car is stationary or travelling straight ahead, the reaction from the ground is directed vertically upwards and balances the weight of the vehicle. When the car turns a corner, however, the reaction becomes inclined, so that it possesses a component directed towards the centre of the circle. This horizontal component towards the centre is

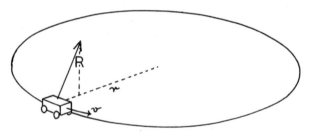

FIG. A.I (3).

provided by friction of the tyres with the ground. If the driver tries to turn in a very small circle, so that the radius r is small, the force required, $F = \dfrac{Mv^2}{r}$, becomes large. If it is greater than can be provided by friction, the car skids.

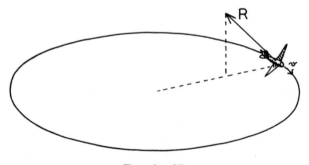

FIG. A.I (4).

In the case of an aeroplane, in which there can be very little lateral force like that provided by the tyres of the motor-car, the machine has to be banked over, and as the normal reaction of the air on the wings becomes inclined it possesses a horizontal component directed towards the centre of the circle.

For the same reason, racing tracks, railway lines, and roads are also banked on corners. When this is done the reaction between the wheels and the ground can be inclined inwards without friction having to supply the horizontal component, and the tendency to skid, or leave the rails, is removed.

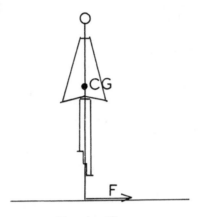

FIG. A.I (5).

There is also another consideration of some importance to be discussed. To make the body travel round a circle, the centripetal force has to be applied to its centre of gravity. In the case of the motor-car, however, the force is applied to the base of the wheels, well below the centre of gravity. In addition to making the vehicle turn in a circle, a force applied below the centre of gravity also tends to make it topple over outwards. For this reason the centre of gravity of a motor-car is placed as low as possible and the vehicle given a broad wheel-base.

In the case of a bicycle, the wheel-base is all lengthwise and it possesses no breadth at all. The only way, therefore, for a bicyclist to turn in a circle is for him to lean inwards, so that the reaction between the ground and the wheels continues to pass through the centre of gravity. For the same reason runners rounding a bend in the track, as in Plate IV (iv), also lean inwards. In both cases the feeling is that of balance in the inclined position. No conscious effort is required. The runner adjusts his inclination so that the reaction from his contact with the ground passes through his centre of gravity, just as was the case during the period of acceleration at the start of a race.

APPENDIX II

The Arrangement of Fibres in Muscles

IN Chapter V it was stated that the lifting strength of a muscle is proportional to its area of cross-section, and that the work it can do is proportional to the volume. These relations hold if the cross-section of the tissue has the same percentage of contractile material, and if the fibres run parallel to the direction of the muscle. In some muscles the fibres are arranged at an angle to the direction of action, inserting on to a tendon or connective tissue running into it. Such muscles, which are termed 'pennate', are, for example, the human rectus femoris which is part of the quadriceps femoris, the human gastro-cnemius, or calf muscle, and the large tibial extensor of the grasshopper, very important in its jumping.

Let x = the number of fibres per square centimetre, measured at right angles to the fibres,

f = the force per fibre
A = the total area of cross-section
L = the total length, and
l = the length of a fibre.

If the muscle is not pennate, the force exerted will be Afx.

In a pennate muscle, the pull each fibre exerts parallel to the tension is $f . \cos \theta$.

The number of fibres is $\dfrac{\text{total volume}}{\text{volume of one}}$

or

$$\frac{LA}{l/x} = \frac{LAx}{l}$$

and the force exerted, therefore, is

$$\frac{LAx}{l} . f \cos \theta.$$

Thus for pennate muscles of the same angle θ and area of cross-section, l will be constant, and the force exerted will be proportional to the total length, L, a dimension not present where all the fibres run parallel.

Considering the work capacity,

work = force × distance moved.

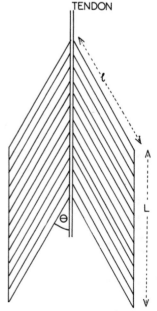

FIG. A.II (1).

Let $c =$ the fraction of a fibre's length through which it contracts. Where the fibres run parallel,

$$\text{work} = Afx \cdot cL.$$

If they are pennate, the contraction is cl parallel to the fibres, and $cl \cdot \cos \theta$ parallel to the whole muscle. Therefore in this case,

$$\text{work} = \frac{LAx}{l} \cdot f \cos \theta \cdot cl \cdot \cos \theta, \text{ or}$$

$$= Afxcl \cdot \cos^2 \theta,$$

in other words, as for parallel-fibred muscles $\times \cos^2 \theta$.

In the human rectus femoris, θ is about $18°$, although there is some variation from one part of the muscle to another; $\cos^2 18$ is about $0\cdot9$, so there is very little reduction in the working capacity compared with a muscle of equal size with parallel fibres. In this case L/l is roughly 2, so the force is increased by a factor slightly less than this.

The case of the grasshopper tibial extensor is much more striking, for although θ is much the same, and thus the work reduction about $0\cdot9$, the ratio L/l is about 11. In this case the force exerted, $\frac{L}{l} \cos \theta = 10$ times approximately that given by a parallel-fibred muscle of the same dimensions, a very considerable improvement.

The Effect of Stature on the Sprinter

THE calculation for the effect of height on the speed of an animal given in Chapter IX was worked out for a freely swinging leg, and so applies only to animals which are not exerting themselves. It was also implied that the legs are of similar shape, one being a scaled-up version of the other. Still keeping the idea of legs of the same shape but of different absolute sizes, let us calculate the advantage, if any, of being large, when the limb is being forced to oscillate faster than it would of its own accord.

The muscles will provide a restoring couple for the leg in addition to that supplied by gravity. The force a muscle exerts is proportional to the square of its dimensions. The couple provided by this force will vary as the magnitude of the force multiplied by a distance which will be proportional to the linear dimensions of the animal. In other words, the couple will be proportional to the cube of the linear dimensions of the animal. This couple is applied to the leg, the moment of inertia of which is proportional to its mass multiplied by the square of its radius of gyration, that is to say the moment of inertia of the leg will vary as the fifth power of the dimensions. Now the frequency of a rigid pendulum is given by

$$n = \frac{1}{2\pi}\sqrt{\frac{C}{I}}$$

where C is the couple applied per unit angular displacement (see Appendix IV).

The total restoring force is that given by the muscles plus that due to gravity. The couple arising from gravity will be proportional to the weight multiplied by a distance, i.e. to the fourth power of the dimensions. Hence we have:

$$\text{Total couple, } C = C_{\text{muscles}} + C_{\text{gravity}}$$
$$= K_1 L^3 + K_2 L^4.$$

Hence we shall have that the frequency will vary as

$$\sqrt{\frac{K_1 L^3 + K_2 L^4}{L^5}}.$$

The relative importance of the C_{muscles} couple depends upon how much the muscles are being exerted. If not at all, that part of the expression dies out, leaving the frequency varying as

$$\sqrt{\frac{1}{L}}$$

which is the result already arrived at in the case of free oscillation, where no muscular action is involved.

If, on the other hand, the utmost exertion is being made, much of the effort will be used in forcing the limbs to swing faster than they would naturally do. The effect of gravity will never be negligible, but missing it out will show how the muscle forces act when large compared with those of gravity.

Neglecting $C_{gravity}$ in comparison with $C_{muscles}$ would give the frequency to be proportional to

$$\frac{1}{L}.$$

Now, as before, the distance covered by the end of the limb in a given time will be proportional to the number of oscillations times the length, i.e. to nL.

If now n varies as $1/L$, it follows that the distance covered in a given time will be independent of the linear dimensions. Thus the speed of the animal will be independent of the length of its legs except in so far as gravity contributes to their swinging. Thus when the animal is exerting its full power, as when sprinting to escape a predator, long legs will confer little advantage.

The above result, that the top speeds of similar animals should be independent of their size, together with the similar relation that they should all be able to jump to the same height, was given by A. V. Hill ('Dimensions of Animals and Their Muscular Dynamics', *Science Progress* April 1950) on the basis of energy considerations. The simple calculation given here assumes, in effect, that muscles exert their forces like springs, the force being proportional to the displacement, so that motion is simple harmonic. It is not difficult to show, however, that the same result follows whatever may be the connection between the displacement and the force applied.

Suppose that besides being proportional to L^3 the couple exerted by the muscles on a limb varies as some function $f'(\theta)$ of the displacement, θ. The equation of motion of the limb will be

$$I\frac{d^2\theta}{dt^2} = K_1 L^3 f'(\theta).$$

Multiplying by $\frac{d\theta}{dt}$ and integrating, we have

$$\frac{1}{2}I\left(\frac{d\theta}{dt}\right)^2 = K_1 L^3 f(\theta)$$

where $f'(\theta) = \frac{d}{d\theta}f(\theta)$

or $$\frac{d\theta}{dt} = \frac{K}{L}\sqrt{f(\theta)}$$ since, as before, I varies as L^5.

Integrating a second time we have,

$$\frac{Kt}{L} = \int \frac{d\theta}{f(\theta)} = \varphi(\theta) \text{ say.}$$

If the animals we are considering are similarly built $\varphi(\theta)$ will be the same for all, and as before, the period T will be directly proportional to L, and the inversely proportional to frequency $\frac{1}{L}$.

The Period of Swing of a Pendulum

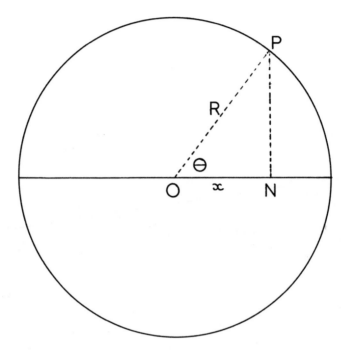

FIG. A.IV (1).

IF a point P moves uniformly round a circle of radius, R, with a speed, v, the foot of the perpendicular from P on to a diagonal of the circle will oscillate backwards and forwards. This oscillatory motion of N, the foot of the perpendicular, is known as simple harmonic motion.

The acceleration of N will be the component of the acceleration of P resolved in the direction ON (Fig. A.IV (1)). The acceleration of P is $\dfrac{v^2}{R}$, and is directed along PO. The acceleration of N is, therefore,

$$a = \frac{v^2}{R} \cos \theta = \frac{v^2}{R} \cdot \frac{x}{R} = \frac{v^2}{R^2} \cdot x.$$

It is therefore proportional to the displacement of N from the centre O, since v and R are both constant.

The time, t, taken by N to complete one oscillation backwards and forwards will be the same as the time taken by P to make one complete circuit of the circle.

Therefore,
$$t = \frac{2\pi R}{v}$$

and
$$a = \frac{4\pi^2}{t^2} x \qquad \qquad \text{. . . 1.}$$

The most important characteristic of simple harmonic motion is that the acceleration of the point describing it is proportional to its displacement from the centre. Any point or particle whose acceleration is always directed towards a fixed point and proportional to its distance from that point will describe simple harmonic motion.

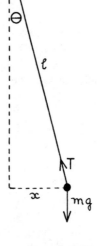

In the case of a pendulum swinging through a small angle, we have, if the tension in the string is T, the angle of displacement from the vertical is θ, and the mass of the bob is m,

$$T \cos \theta = mg$$
$$T \sin \theta = ma$$

where a is the horizontal acceleration of the bob.
By division we have,

$$\frac{a}{g} = \tan \theta$$

$$= \theta, \text{ if the displacement is small,}$$

$$= \frac{x}{l}$$

Thus,
$$a = \frac{g}{l} x \qquad \qquad \text{. . . 2.}$$

FIG. A.IV (2).

The acceleration is proportional to x, the displacement, the motion will be simple harmonic, and comparing equation 2 with equation 1 we see that,

$$\frac{4\pi^2}{t^2} = \frac{g}{l}$$

which gives,
$$t = 2\pi \sqrt{\frac{l}{g}}.$$

The time of swing of a pendulum is proportional, therefore, to the square root of its length, the result of which we made use in Chapter IX. It is also independent of the amplitude of swing so long as it is small, and also of the weight of the bob. Even if the total angle of swing is as large as 120° (i.e. 60° on either side of the vertical) the period is only increased by little more than one-sixteenth.

In the case of a rigid, as opposed to a simple pendulum, the couple acting will be,

$$mgh \sin \theta$$

when the axis which in equilibrium hangs vertically is displaced through an angle θ, and h is the distance of the centre of gravity below the point of support (Fig. A.IV (3)).

If the moment of inertia about the axis of support is I, the angular acceleration will be

$$\frac{mgh \sin \theta}{I}$$

$$= \frac{mgh}{I} \theta \quad \text{if } \theta \text{ is small.}$$

The angular acceleration is proportional to the angular displacement, so that the motion, in this case angular, follows the rules for simple harmonic motion. The period of the oscillation will be

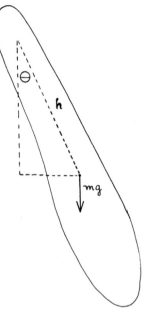

FIG. A.IV (3).

$$2\pi \sqrt{\frac{I}{mgh}}$$

and the frequency will be the reciprocal of this, namely,

$$n = \frac{1}{2\pi} \sqrt{\frac{mgh}{I}}.$$

Now mgh is the couple acting when the angle, θ, is unity and was called C in Appendix III. Thus,

$$n = \frac{1}{2\pi} \sqrt{\frac{C}{I}}$$

which is the expression on which the discussion in Appendix III was based.

The Combination of Angular Velocities

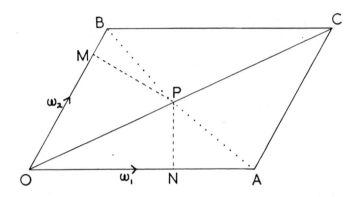

Fɪɢ. A.ᴠ (1).

SUPPOSE a body possesses an angular velocity ω_1 about OA and another, ω_2, about OB (Fig. A.v (1)) and let the lengths of OA and OB represent ω_1 and ω_2, respectively. Let us consider the motion of some particle in the body at a point P on the diagonal of the parallelogram $OACB$. Because of the angular velocity ω_1 it will be carried out from the paper a distance $\omega_1 PN.t$ in a very short interval of time t. (PN is the perpendicular from P on to OA.) In the same time the rotation ω_2 about OB will carry it into the paper a distance $\omega_2 PM.t$, where PM is at right angles to OB. Now

$$\tfrac{1}{2}\omega_1 PN = \frac{OA \cdot PN}{2} = \text{the area of the triangle } OPA,$$

and

$$\tfrac{1}{2}\omega_2 PM = \frac{OB \cdot PM}{2} = \text{the area of the triangle } OPB.$$

But the two triangles OPA and OPB are equal in area since they stand on the same base OP and possess the same vertical height. Thus the rotational velocity ω_1 about OA takes P as far into the paper as that of ω_2 about OB brings it out, and the two motions neutralise each other. P, therefore, does not move and it must thus lie on the axis of the resultant angular velocity.

Next consider the motion of the point A. It will not be moved by the angular velocity, ω_1, since it lies on the axis about which this rotation takes place. It will be moved only by the angular velocity ω_2 about OB. In the short time t, this rotation will shift the point A out from the paper a distance $\omega_2 AQ.t$ where AQ is drawn at right angles to OB.

273

Now

$$\tfrac{1}{2}\omega_2 AQ = \frac{OB.AQ}{2} = \text{the area of the triangle } OAB$$

$$= \text{the area of the triangle } OAC$$

$$= \frac{OC.LA}{2}$$

where LA is drawn at right angles to OC (Fig. A.v (2)).

Now $OC.LA.t$ is the distance that an angular velocity represented by OC would lift A out of the paper in time t. OC must, therefore, represent the resultant angular velocity both in magnitude and direction.

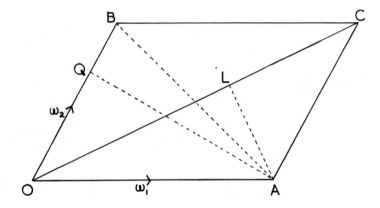

Fig. A.v (2).

Some Calculations on the Angle of Projection for Maximum Range

IN this Appendix two calculations dealing with this problem will be given. In order to bring it within bounds, however, a number of simplifying assumptions will still have to be made.

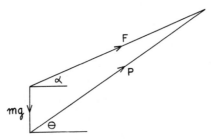

FIG. A.VI (1).

Suppose that the force applied to the missile is represented by P (Fig. A.VI (1)), at an angle θ to the horizontal. We will also take account of the weight, mg, of the missile itself acting downwards. The resultant force applied will be the force F, and projection will take place at the angle α. The problem will be to find the velocity of projection, V, as the angles θ and α are varied, and hence the range. The force F will accelerate the body being thrown over a certain distance, s, determined by the length of the arm of the thrower. We shall assume that the force, P, applied is the same at all angles. The throwing hand must move in the direction of F since it is along this line that the missile travels.

The component of the force P resolved along the path taken by the missile

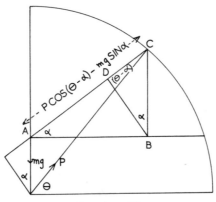

FIG. A.VI (2).

while in the hand will be $P \cos (\theta - a)$ and the work which it does in speeding it up will be $s.P \cos (\theta - a)$.

The work done against gravity will be $mg.s \sin a$ and this has to be subtracted from that done by the force P. The kinetic energy of the projectile will, therefore, be

$$\tfrac{1}{2}mV^2 = Ps \cos (\theta - a) - mgs \sin a.$$

The range of the projectile will be

$$R = \frac{2V^2 \sin a \cos a}{g} \qquad \text{(See p. 114.)}$$

$$= \frac{4s}{mg} \left(P \cos (\theta - a) - mg \sin a \right) \sin a \cos a.$$

Referring to Fig. A.vi (2) we see that

$$P \cos (\theta - a) - mg \sin a = AC$$

and that

$$\left(P \cos (\theta - a) - mg \sin a \right) \sin a = BC$$

and that

$$\left(P \cos (\theta - a) - mg \sin a \right) \sin a \cos a = BD.$$

Thus the range

$$R = \frac{4s}{mg} BD.$$

We have thus a simple geometrical construction for the range obtainable with a given angle of projection a. By drawing the triangle ABC for a number of different values of a, as in Fig. A.vi (3) we can measure the range for each, and hence determine the angle at which the range is a maximum.

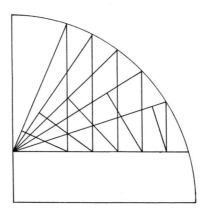

FIG. A.vi (3).

Curve I of Fig. A.vi (4) was obtained in this way and it shows that the optimum angle is always less than $45°$, and in cases where the force applied only slightly exceeds the weight of the projectile, it is markedly so.

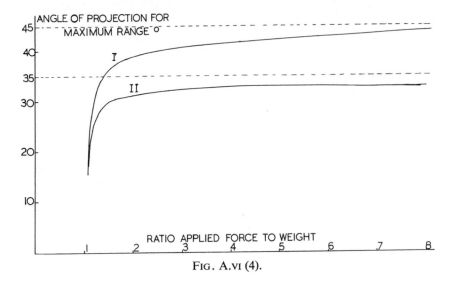

FIG. A.VI (4).

As a second example let us try to allow for the increased distance over which the throwing force can be exerted when the thrower runs forward from rest as he throws. Suppose that during the throw he moves through a distance d, and that his reach (i.e. roughly twice the length of his arm) is σ.

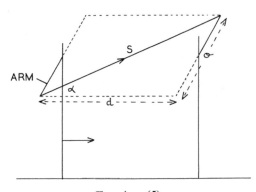

FIG. A.VI (5).

The distance, s, over which the force applied can be exerted is now greater than it was before when the thrower was stationary. Still lower trajectories will be favoured.

We have

$$\sigma^2 = d^2 + s^2 - 2d.s.\ \cos \alpha$$

giving,

$$s = d \cos \alpha \pm \sqrt{d^2 \cos^2 \alpha - d^2 + \sigma^2}.$$

Now during the throw the thrower will move through a distance about the same as his reach in many cases. In such a case we can put $d = \sigma$ and we find

$$s = 2d \cos \alpha$$

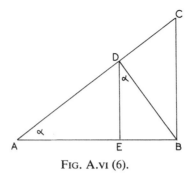

FIG. A.VI (6).

(the solution with the negative sign is of no interest since it corresponds to throwing backwards over the shoulder) and

$$R = \frac{8d}{mg} DB \cos \alpha.$$

In Fig. A.VI (6) we have

$$DB \cos \alpha = DE.$$

Maximum range will be attained for that value of α which makes DE a maximum. We have thus, again, a simple geometrical construction to determine it. Curve II of Fig. A.VI (4) corresponds to this case. As the force applied is increased, the angle for maximum range tends to the value of $35\frac{1}{4}°$, which is the value of α for which $\cos^2 \alpha \sin \alpha$ is a maximum.

These calculations are intended to serve as illustrations. Considerable simplifying assumptions have been introduced to render the problem amenable to discussion. In practice other factors will be concerned as well and the only approach which promises results of practical value is an experimental one. The calculations, however, do show that reliance cannot be placed on the 45° of the elementary textbooks.

Index

Also by R. A. R. Tricker

Bores, Breakers, Waves and Wakes

Most people enjoy looking at water—ask any travel agent—and part of its fascination lies in the fact that water surfaces are seldom completely still. Enjoyment could be increased by an understanding of what is going on, but hitherto the subject has been wrapped in abstruse mathematics beyond the reach of most people.

In this book Dr. Tricker gives an account of the tides, of river bores, of waves from Atlantic rollers to tiny ripples, of the wakes caused by ships and waterfowl, and of reflections, in terms that will be understandable to anyone who has done reasonably well at mathematics in ordinary school-leaving examinations. Explanations are often given in both mathematical and experimental terms so that the reader can take his choice, and are liberally supplemented by diagrams and photographs. A book on the one hand for the sailor, yachtsman, fisherman or simple beachcomber; on the other, for marine biologists, engineers, the university student of geography, etc., and all those experts concerned with the behaviour of water.

$8\frac{1}{4} \times 5\frac{1}{4}$ ins.; 20 colour plates; 63 black-and-white plates; 164 line drawings. 35s. net.

The Assessment of Scientific Speculation

The author—until recently H.M. Staff Inspector for Science—is concerned with the educational problem of seeing that science is more than 'a restricted diet of memorization of principles learnt dogmatically'. His book reminds us that much material which is taught as fact is really only opinion and theory; and it indicates four separate approaches to the challenge of discovering a satisfying intellectual basis for scientific activity. Examples are drawn from many fields, and the book could appeal equally to the student of pure or of applied science.

$8\frac{1}{4} \times 5\frac{1}{4}$ ins.; 198 pages; illustrated. 1st edition 1965. 30s net.

In preparation

The Paths of the Planets *(publication 1967)*

Astronomy, at the school level, is presented in a new and refreshing form and in simple, straightforward terms. School astronomical societies will find, in the suggestions of work to be done, valuable ideas for building up their programmes. Ancient problems, leading up to the modern situation, are discussed in an interesting way, and the book is fully illustrated with photographs and diagrams.